THE SCIENTISTS SPEAK

THE
SCIENTISTS
SPEAK

Edited by

WARREN WEAVER

BONI & GAER   ::   NEW YORK

PREFACE

THE SCIENTISTS speak! How did they come to tell these stories of modern science? What, in other words, is the origin of this book?

Beginning in May, 1943, Sunday afternoon concerts by the New York Philharmonic-Symphony were broadcast over a nation-wide chain of stations under the sponsorship of United States Rubber Company. Because the musical program was normally interrupted for ten or fifteen minutes near its midpoint, the men responsible for these broadcasts had the duty of furnishing a suitable and worthwhile intermission feature.

As it became clear that World War II was drawing to a close, those in charge of the Philharmonic broadcast felt that the time had come when it was less important to stress historical values, as had previously been the aim of the intermission program, and more important to look forward into the future.

What the future would be, no one could forecast. But one thing was sure: science would be a mighty and pervasive force in helping to shape that future. The time had clearly come when every man, woman, and child must recognize the role that science plays in modern society. The time had clearly come when everyone ought to have a broader and a more authentic understanding of what science is and how it operates.

Thus the officials of United States Rubber Company and of the Campbell-Ewald Company of New York, the advertising firm which managed the broadcast, were agreed in thinking that it would be a notable public service to devote the intermission program to a presentation of modern science. The officials of the two companies sought to interest a committee of scientists in the problem of planning and arranging the proposed new series of intermission broadcasts. The men approached were:

Dr. George W. Corner, anatomist and director of the Department of Embryology of the Carnegie Institution of Washington;

Dr. Douglas S. Freeman, historian and editor, who had the large duty of representing the viewpoint of the lay public on the scientific group;

Dr. Frank B. Jewett, former vice-president in charge of research of the American Telephone and Telegraph Company and president of the National Academy of Sciences;

Dr. Harlow Shapley, director of the Harvard College Observatory;

Dr. Wendell M. Stanley, chemist and virologist of the Rockefeller Institute for Medical Research;

Dr. Warren Weaver, director for the natural sciences of the Rockefeller Foundation.

There is surely no intent to be ungracious in remarking that no one of these men had the slightest interest in promoting the commercial welfare of United States Rubber Company, nor the advertising business of the Campbell-Ewald Company of New York. In fact, the initial response of the person first approached, the ultimate chairman of the science committee, was one of incredulous skepticism. Was it actually true that, on a commercially-sponsored broadcast, the responsibility for planning and arranging a series of science talks was to be turned over completely to such a committee? Was it actually true that this was to be real science, dignified and authentic, and not some jazzed-up radio version? Was the choice of speakers and the control of arrangements with the scientists really going to be left to the committee; or would the committee soon find itself receiving "suggestions" from the sponsors?

The assurances given in answer to these questions were complete. And it should be stated at once that these assurances were scrupulously observed. The committee planned this series with complete freedom.

With such a prospect before them, the men who were approached as committee members all considered this an opportunity which could not be passed by. For here was a vast national audience, brought together every Sunday afternoon by the glorious music of the New York Philharmonic-Symphony. A chance was offered to speak each week to this audience on some topic in basic science which would interest them, which would give them some direct awareness of what science is accomplishing and some appreciation of the ways in which scientific research is building a larger future for man.

This opportunity, moreover, had aspects which were broader and more significant than the proposed subject matter, however important that might be. For this was a large-scale experiment in adult education. What adult education could accomplish for man's welfare on this planet no one knows, for, like Christianity, it has as yet not been given a real trial. Mark Van Doren, in his *Liberal Education,* says: "It may be only adult education, conceived on a gigantic and liberal scale, that can bring the world commonwealth into being." Without accepting adult education as the sole major necessity, one can agree that its potentialities are great, and are as yet little developed.

After carefully considering many possibilities, the committee decided that the best way—especially in a program only eleven or twelve minutes long—to achieve some reasonable combination of interest, dignity, and authenticity would be to bring before the microphone the scientists themselves. The real, active, and creative leaders in American science should speak with their own voices, describe their own work, tell the stories that they themselves considered significant.

From the outset this program was designed primarily around men, rather than around subjects. Outstanding scientists were chosen and their topics were almost wholly self-selected, the committee never going beyond a tentative suggestion of theme. In some few instances, certain topics seemed of such particular interest that the committee looked about for scientists who would be specially qualified. The committee naturally tried to balance somewhat the time devoted to such broad fields as chemistry, biology, physics, etc. But in general it remained true that the range covered in these talks resulted from the choices of the outstanding men selected to speak. Science is so varied, there are so many topics of high interest, there are so many really first-class scientists in this country that all the committee could hope to do was to choose a reasonably representative sample.

The final form of each script was always under the complete control of the individual author. It was usual, however, for the scientists to prepare a somewhat extended first draft; on the basis of this draft a series of suggestions was made to the author by an editorial group. The main work of this group was done by the well-known writer on science topics, George W. Gray. Additional suggestions were made by Richard E. Hackenger of the Campbell-Ewald Company of New York who has special experience in the writing of material for radio presentation, and by the chairman of the science committee. The final form of the scripts was often arrived at only after many revisions. The members of the editorial group were deeply impressed with the skill and patience shown by the scientists, all of whom recognized the magnitude and character of this opportunity to interpret science to the people, and were entirely unselfish and co-operative in their efforts to achieve the utmost clarity while operating within the restrictions of a non-technical vocabulary and a short allotment of time.

In preparing the scripts, there was a sustained attempt to eliminate all unnecessary technical language, and to define clearly the few technical terms used. The style of the essays was frankly aimed at oral presentation. This criterion, for example, eliminated the use of sentences which, while powerful and condensed, require more than one reading to be clearly understood. And this criterion also made necessary a certain amount of repetition of key words and phrases.

In printing these essays, there has been no attempt to recast them, nor to add to them, although there have been a few entirely minor corrections. If specialists in the written word consider that there are some small inelegancies of style occasioned by the original purpose, it is hoped that these same specialists will agree that there are compensating gains in clearness and simplicity. For those who have a technical concern for style, it may be interesting to see what sort of statements, of this length and this kind of attempted general clarity, can be produced by top-notch scientists, working with minor collaboration and assistance of an editorial group which respected and understood the scientists' position. And the aim of the radio talks was, after all, to present aspects of modern science in a brief compass and in terms so clear and universal that the ideas could be grasped by everyone. A presentation which even approximately accomplishes this aim is worthy of dissemination by all available means.

How has the American public responded to these science talks? It was, of course, inevitably true that a very small minority of the devotees of symphonic music resented the intrusion, as they viewed it, of anything but silence as an interlude.

But the American public, it is a robust pleasure to report, did not agree. All in all, some quarter of a million requests were received for printed copies of the individual talks. The Columbia Broadcasting System produced on their own initiative an elegant and beautifully illustrated booklet, called "Crescendo," in which they dramatically told the story of the reception which the American public gave to this program of great music and great science. They focused their account on the fact—so human, so appealing, and after all so surprising—that a Chinese laundryman in Birmingham, Alabama, wrote in for copies of the talks on atomic energy. Believing that the total record "throws substantial light on the power of a program of that character to evoke response from many different kinds of people in many walks of life," their conclusions contained the remarks that "the testimony helps to scuttle a formidable body of superstition in the folklore of radio by establishing that a radio program can be sponsored and still be in the public interest, that the average American radio listener is capable of comprehending a program of substantial intellectual content. . . ."

There is surely a large gap between the reaction "That is really good and interesting," and the reaction "That is so good that I will write a letter about it." And there must be a still wider gap, for the majority of people, between the intention to write and the actual act of writing. When these gaps are considered, the number of thanks and of inquiries about these science talks which flowed in from the people of America becomes really overwhelming.

Most impressive of all has been the variety—geographically and socially—of the sources from which the letters of inquiry and appreciation have come. They were sent in by bank presidents and by filling station operators—by ministers and grocers and teachers and ambassadors and professors and inmates of penitentiaries—by ranchers and philosophers and housewives and business executives and school children. They came from New England and the back country of Arkansas and Tennessee; they came from the plains of Mon-

tana, from the cornfields of Iowa, from the hills of the Carolinas;
they came from the city, the desert, the farm, the factory, and the
village. They came from America.

GEORGE W. CORNER
DOUGLAS S. FREEMAN
FRANK B. JEWETT
HARLOW SHAPLEY
WENDELL M. STANLEY
WARREN WEAVER, Chairman

> Advisory Committee,
> Intermission Science Series,
> New York Philharmonic-Symphony Broadcasts

New York
May, 1947

CONTENTS

CHAPTER 1

SCIENCE AND COMPLEXITY

By Warren Weaver

Dr. Warren Weaver is director for the Natural Sciences at The Rocke-feller Foundation.

Science has led to a multitude of results that affect men's lives. Some of these results are mere conveniences of a relatively trivial sort. Many, based on science and developed through technology, are essential to the machinery of modern life. Many others—and one thinks specially of the biological and medical sciences—are of unquestioned benefit and comfort. Certain aspects of science have profoundly influenced men's ideas, and even their ideals. Still other aspects of science are thoroughly awesome.

How can we get a view of the role that science should play in the developing future of man? How can we appreciate what science really is, and—equally important—what it is not?

It is, of course, possible to discuss the nature of science in general philosophical terms. For some purposes this is important and necessary, and there are some remarks of this sort which we will wish to make later; but for the present, let us make a more direct approach. Let us, as a very realistic politician used to like to say— let us look at the record.

We will not have time, although that is a pity, to examine the older history of science. We will go back only three and a half centuries; and we will necessarily have to take a broad view that tries to see the main features and omits all details.

Let us begin with the physical, rather than the biological sciences. The place of the life sciences in the descriptive scheme will become evident as we proceed.

Speaking roughly, one may say that the seventeenth, eighteenth, and nineteenth centuries formed the period in which physical science learned how to analyze two-variable problems. Thus during that three hundred years, science developed the experimental and analytical techniques for handling problems in which one quantity

1

—say, a gas pressure—depends primarily upon a second quantity—
say, the volume of the gas. The essential character of these problems
rests in the fact that, at least under a significant range of circumstances, the first quantity depends wholly upon the second quantity,
and not upon a large number of other factors. Or in any event, and
to be somewhat more precise, the behavior of the first quantity can
be described with a useful degree of accuracy by taking into account
only its dependence upon the second quantity, and by neglecting
the minor influence of other factors.

These two-variable problems are essentially simple in structure,
and precisely for the reason that the theories or the experiments
related to them need deal with only two quantities, changes in one
of which cause changes in the other. The restriction to two variables meant simplicity in theory, and simplicity in experiment: and
simplicity was a necessary condition for progress at that stage of
development of science. It turned out, moreover, that vast progress
could be made in the physical sciences by theories and experiments
of this essentially simple character. The great scientists of this
period could analyze how the intensity of light varies with the distance from the source; how the strength of a beam depends upon
its dimensions or upon the physical properties of its material; how
electric current is related to voltage; how gravitational attraction
depends upon distance; how steam pressure is related to steam
temperature; and hundreds of other such things. The resulting
knowledge made possible great advance in our understanding and
control of nature, great practical advances in technology. It was
this kind of two-variable science which laid, over the period up to
1900, the foundations for our theories of light, of sound, of heat,
and of electricity. It was this kind of two-variable science—or minor
extensions of it to handle three or four variables—which brought
us the telephone and the radio, the automobile and the airplane, the
phonograph and the moving pictures, the turbine and the Diesel
engine and the modern hydroelectric power plant.

The concurrent progress in biology and medicine was also impressive, but was of a different character. The significant problems
of living organisms are seldom those in which one can rigidly
maintain constant all but two variables. Living things are more
likely to present situations in which a half-dozen, or even several

dozen, quantities are all varying simultaneously, and in subtly interconnected ways. And often they present situations in which the essentially important quantities are either non-quantitative, or have at any rate eluded identification or measurement up to the moment. Thus these biological and medical problems often involve the consideration of a most complicatedly organized whole. It is not surprising that up to 1900 the life sciences were largely concerned with the necessary preliminary stages in the application of the scientific method—preliminary stages which chiefly involve collection, description, classification, and the observation of concurrent and apparently correlated effects. They had only made the brave beginnings of quantitative theories, and hardly even begun detailed explanations of the physical and chemical mechanisms underlying or making up biological events.

To sum up, physical science before 1900 was largely concerned with two-variable *problems of simplicity;* while the life sciences, in which these problems of simplicity are not so often significant, had not yet become highly quantitative or analytical in character.

Subsequent to 1900—and actually earlier, if we remember heroic pioneers such as Josiah Willard Gibbs—the physical sciences developed an attack on nature of an essentially and dramatically new kind. Rather than study problems which involved two variables or at most three or four, some imaginative minds went to the other extreme, and said: "Let us develop analytical methods which can deal with two billion variables." That is to say, the physical scientists (with the mathematicians often in the vanguard) developed powerful techniques of probability theory and of statistical mechanics which can deal with what we may call problems of *disorganized complexity.*

This last phrase calls for explanation. Consider first a simple illustration in order to get the flavor of the idea. The classical dynamics of the nineteenth century was well suited for analyzing and predicting the motion of a single ivory ball as it moves about on a billiard table. In fact, the relationship between positions of the ball and the times at which it reaches these positions forms a typical nineteenth-century problem of simplicity. One can, but with a surprising increase in difficulty, analyze the motion of two or even of three balls on a billiard table. There has been, in fact, considerable

study of the mechanics of the standard game of billiards. But as
soon as one tries to analyze the motion of ten or fifteen balls on
the table at once, as in pool, the problem becomes unmanageable,
not because there is any theoretical difficulty, but just because the
actual labor of dealing in specific detail with so many variables
turns out to be impracticable.

Imagine, however, a large billiard table with millions of balls
flying about on its surface, colliding with one another and with the
side rails. The great surprise is that the problem now becomes
easier: now the methods of statistical mechanics are applicable.
One cannot trace the detailed history of one special ball, to be sure;
but there can be answered with useful precision such important
questions as: On the average how many balls per second hit a
given stretch of rail? On the average how far does a ball move
before it is hit by some other ball? On the average how many im-
pacts per second does a ball experience?

Two paragraphs back it was stated that the new statistical
methods were applicable to problems of disorganized complexity.
How does the word "disorganized" apply to the large billiard table
with the many balls? It applies because the methods of statistical
mechanics are valid only when the balls are distributed, in their
positions and motions, in a helter-skelter—that is to say, a disorganized—way. For example, the statistical methods would not
apply if someone were to arrange the balls in a row parallel to one
side-rail of the table, and then start them all moving in precisely
parallel paths perpendicular to the row in which they stand. Then
the balls would never collide with each other nor with two of the
rails, and one would not have a situation of disorganized complexity.

We can see, from this illustration, what is meant by a problem of
disorganized complexity. It is a problem in which the number of
variables is very large, and one in which each of the many variables
has a behavior which is individually erratic, or perhaps totally
unknown. But in spite of this helter-skelter or unknown behavior
of all the individual variables, the system as a whole possesses
certain orderly and analyzable average properties.

A wide range of experience comes under this label of disorganized complexity. The method applies with increasing precision

when the number of variables increases. It applies with entirely useful precision to the experience of a large telephone exchange, predicting the average frequency of calls, the probability of overlapping calls of the same number, etc. It makes possible the financial stability of a life insurance company. Although the company can have no knowledge whatsoever concerning the approaching death of any one individual, it has dependable knowledge of the average frequency with which deaths will occur.

This last point is interesting and important. Statistical techniques are not restricted to situations where the scientific theory of the individual events is very well known—as in the billiard example where there is a beautifully precise theory for the impact of one ball on another. This technique can also be applied to situations—like the insurance example—where the individual event is as shrouded in mystery as is the chain of complicated and unpredictable events which leads to the accidental death of a healthy man.

The examples of the telephone and insurance companies will suggest a whole array of practical applications of such statistical techniques. But they are in a sense unfortunate examples, for they tend to draw attention away from the more fundamental use which science makes of these new techniques. The motions of the atoms which form all matter, as well as the motions of the stars which form the universe, all come under the range of these new techniques. The fundamental laws of heredity are analyzed by them. The laws of thermodynamics, which describe basic and inevitable tendencies of all physical systems, are derived from statistical considerations. The whole structure of modern physics, our present concept of the nature of the physical universe and of the accessible experimental facts concerning it, rest on these statistical concepts. Indeed, the whole question of evidence, and the way in which knowledge can be inferred from evidence, is now recognized to depend on these same statistical ideas; so that probability notions are essential to any theory of knowledge itself.

And yet this new method of dealing with disorganized complexity, so powerful an advance over the earlier two-variable methods, leaves a great field untouched. One is tempted to oversimplify, and say that scientific methodology went from one extreme to the other—from two variables to an astronomical number—and left untouched a great middle region. The importance of this middle region, moreover, does not depend primarily on the fact that the number of variables involved is moderate—large compared to two, but small compared to the number of atoms in a pinch of salt. The problems in this middle region, in fact, will often involve a considerable number of variables. The really important characteristic of the problems of this middle region which science has as yet little explored or conquered lies in the fact that these problems, as contrasted with the disorganized situations with which statistics can cope, show the essential feature of *organization*. In fact, we will refer to this group of problems as those of *organized complexity*.

What makes an evening primrose open when it does? Why does salt water fail to satisfy thirst? Why can one particular genetic strain of micro-organism synthesize within its tiny self certain organic compounds that another strain of the same organism cannot manufacture? Why is one chemical substance a poison when another, whose molecules have just the same atoms but assembled into a mirror-image pattern, is completely non-toxic? Why does the amount of manganese in the diet affect the maternal instinct of an animal? What is the description of aging in biochemical terms? What meaning is to be assigned to the question: Is a virus a living organism? What is a gene, and how does the original genetic constitution of a living organism express itself in the developed characteristics of the adult? Do complex protein molecules "know how" to reduplicate their patterns; and is this an essential clue to the problem of reproduction of living creatures? All these are certainly complex problems. But they are not problems of disorganized complexity, to which statistical methods hold the key. They are all problems which involve dealing simultaneously with a *sizeable number of factors which are interrelated into an organic whole*. They are all, in the language here proposed, problems of *organized complexity*.

On what does the price of wheat depend? This too is a problem of organized complexity. A very substantial number of relevant variables is involved here, and they are all interrelated in complicated, but nevertheless not in helter-skelter fashion.

How can currency be wisely and effectively stabilized? To what extent is it safe to depend on the free interplay of such economic

forces as supply and demand? Or to what extent must we employ
systems of economic control to prevent the wide swings from pros-
perity to depression? These are also obviously complex problems,
and they too involve analyzing systems which are organic wholes,
with their parts all in close interrelation.

How can we explain the behavior pattern of an organized group
of persons such as a labor union, or a group of manufacturers, or a
racial minority? There are clearly many factors involved here, but
it is equally obvious that here also we need something more than
the mathematics of averages. With a given total of national resources that can be brought to bear, what tactics and strategy will
most promptly win a war? Or better—what sacrifices of present
selfish interest will most effectively contribute to a stable, decent,
and peaceful world?

These problems—and a wide range of similar problems in the
biological, the medical, the psychological, the economic, and the
political sciences—are just too complicated to yield to the old nineteenth-century techniques which were so dramatically successful
on two-, three-, or four-variable problems of simplicity. These new
problems, moreover, cannot be handled with the statistical techniques which are so effective for describing average behavior in
problems of disorganized complexity.

These new problems—and the future of the world depends on
many of them—require science to make a third great advance, an
advance which must be even greater than the nineteenth-century
conquest of problems of simplicity or the twentieth-century victory
over problems of disorganized complexity. Science must, over the
next fifty years, learn to deal with these problems of organized
complexity.

Is there any promise on the horizon that this new advance can
really be accomplished? There is much general evidence, and there
are two recent instances of specially promising evidence. The general
evidence consists in the fact that, in the minds of hundreds of
scholars all over the world, important though necessarily minor
progress is already being made on such problems. As never before,
the quantitative experimental methods and the mathematical analytical methods of the physical sciences are being applied to the
biological, the medical, and even the social sciences. The results are

as yet scattered, but they are highly promising. A good illustration
from the life sciences can be seen in a comparison of the present
situation in cancer research with what it was twenty-five years ago.
It is doubtless true that we are at present only scratching the surface of the cancer problem, but at least we have some tools to dig
with and we have located some spots beneath which there is almost
surely pay-dirt. We know that certain types of cancer can be induced by certain pure chemicals. We know something of the inheritance of susceptibility to certain types of cancer. We have
million-volt X rays, and the still more intense radiations made
possible by atomic physics. We have radioactive isotopes, both for
basic studies and for treatment. We are tackling the almost incredibly complicated story of the biochemistry of the aging organism.
We are beginning to have that base of knowledge concerning the
normal cell which makes it possible to recognize and analyze the
pathological cell. However distant the goal, we are now at last on
the road to a successful solution of this great problem.

In addition to the general growing evidence that problems of
organized complexity can be successfully treated, there are at least
two specially promising bits of evidence. Out of the wickedness of
war have come two new developments which may well be of major
importance in helping science to solve these complex twentieth-
century problems.

The first piece of evidence is the wartime development of new
types of electronic computing devices. These devices are, in flexibility and capacity, more like a human brain than like the traditional
mechanical computing device of the past. They have "memories"
in which can be stored vast amounts of information. They can be
"told" to carry out computations of very intricate complexity, and
can be left unattended while they go forward automatically with
their task. The astounding speed with which they proceed is illustrated by the fact that one small part of such a machine, if set to
multiplying two ten-digit numbers, can perform such multiplica-
tions some forty thousand times faster than a human operator can
say "Jack Robinson."

This combination of flexibility, capacity, and speed makes it seem
likely that such devices will have a tremendous impact on science.
They will make it possible to deal with problems which previously

were simply too complicated. And, more importantly, they will justify and inspire the development of new methods of analysis which are applicable to these new problems of organized complexity.

The second of the wartime advances is the "mixed-team" approach of operations analysis. These terms require explanation, although they are very familiar to those who were concerned with the application of mathematical methods to military affairs.

As an illustration, consider the over-all problem of convoying troops and supplies across the Atlantic. Take into account the number and effectiveness of the naval vessels available, the character of submarine attacks, and a multitude of other factors, including such an imponderable as the dependability of visual watch when men are tired or sick or bored. Considering a whole mass of factors, some measurable and some elusive, what procedure would lead to the best over-all plan—best from the combined point of view of speed, safety, cost, and so on? Should the convoys be large or small, fast or slow? Should they zigzag and expose themselves longer to possible attack, or dash in a speedy straight line? How are they to be organized, what defenses are best, and what organization and instruments should be used for watch and attack?

The attempt to answer such broad problems of tactics, or even broader problems of strategy, was the job during the war of certain groups known as operations analysis groups. Inaugurated with brilliance by the British, the procedure was taken over by this country, and applied with special success in the Navy's anti-submarine campaign and in the Army Air Forces. These operations analysis groups were moreover—specially in England—what may be called mixed teams. Although mathematicians, physicists, and engineers were essential, the best of the groups also contained physiologists, biochemists, psychologists, and a variety of representatives of other fields of the biochemical and social sciences. Among the outstanding members of English mixed teams, for example, were an endocrinologist and an X-ray crystallographer. Under the pressure of war, these mixed teams pooled their resources and focused all their different insights on the common problems. They found, in spite of the modern tendencies toward intense scientific specialization, that such diverse groups could work together and could form a whole which was much greater than the mere sum of its parts. They found that they could tackle certain problems of organized complexity, and get useful answers.

It is tempting to forecast that the great advances that science can and must achieve in the next fifty years will be largely contributed to by voluntary mixed teams, somewhat similar to the operations analysis groups of war days, their activities made effective by the use of large, flexible, and highspeed computing machines. But we cannot assume that this will be the exclusive pattern for future scientific work. For the atmosphere of complete intellectual freedom is essential to science. There will always, and properly, remain those scientists for whom intellectual freedom is necessarily a private affair. Such men must, and should, work alone. Certain deep and imaginative achievements are probably won only in such a way. Variety is, moreover, a proud characteristic of the American way of doing things. Competition between all sorts of methods is good. So there is no intention here to picture a future in which scientists are, as a whole, organized into set patterns of activity. Not at all. It is merely suggested that some scientists will seek and develop for themselves new kinds of collaborative arrangements; that these groups will have members drawn from essentially all fields of science; and that these new ways of working, effectively instrumented by huge computers, will contribute greatly to the advance which the next half century will surely achieve in handling the complex, but essentially organic, problems of the biological and social sciences.

Let us return now to our original question. What is science? What is it not? What may we hope from it?

Science clearly is a way of solving problems—not all problems, but a large class of important and practical ones. The problems with which it can deal are those in which the predominant factors are subject to the basic laws of logic, and are for the most part measurable. Science is a way of organizing reproducible knowledge about such problems, of focusing and disciplining imagination, of weighing evidence, of deciding what is relevant and what is not; of impartially testing hypotheses, of ruthlessly discarding what proves to be inaccurate or inadequate, of finding, interpreting, and facing facts, and of making the facts of nature the servants of man.

The essence of science, just like anything else, is not to be found in its outward appearance, in its physical manifestations: it is to be found in its inner spirit. That austere but exciting technique of inquiry known as the scientific method is what is important about science. This scientific method requires of its practitioners high standards of personal honesty, open-mindedness, focused vision, and love of the truth. These are solid virtues, but science has no exclusive lien on them. The poet has these virtues also, and often turns them to higher uses.

Science has made notable progress in its great task of solving logical and quantitative problems. Indeed, the successes have been so numerous and striking, and the failures have been so seldom publicized, that the average man has inevitably come to believe that science is just about the most spectacularly successful enterprise man ever launched. The fact is, of course, that this conclusion is justified.

But impressive as the progress has been, we have seen that science has by no means worked itself out of a job. In fact, it is soberly true that science has, to date, succeeded in solving a bewildering number of relatively easy problems; whereas the hard problems, and the ones which perhaps promise most for man's future, lie ahead.

We must, therefore, stop thinking of science in terms of its spectacular successes in problems of simplicity. This means, among other things, that we must stop thinking of science in terms of gadgetry. Above all, we must not think of science as a modern improved black magic which can accomplish anything and everything.

Every informed scientist, I think, is confident that his work is capable of tremendous further contributions to human welfare. Not only can science go forward in its triumphant march against physical nature, learning new laws, acquiring new power of forecast and control, making new material things for man to use and enjoy; but science can also make further brilliant contributions to our understanding of animate nature, giving us new health and vigor, longer and more effective lives, and a wiser understanding of human behavior. Indeed, I think most informed scientists go still further in their hopes, and expect the precise, objective, and analytical techniques of science to find useful application in limited areas of the social and political disciplines.

There are even broader claims which can be made for science and the scientific method. As an essential part of his characteristic procedure, the scientist insists on precise definition of terms and clear characterization of his problem. It is easier, of course, to define terms accurately in scientific fields than in many other areas. It remains true, however, that science is an almost overwhelming illustration of the effectiveness of a well-defined and accepted language, a common set of ideas, a common tradition. The way in which this universality has succeeded in cutting across barriers of time and space, across political and cultural boundaries, is significant indeed. Perhaps better than in any other intellectual enterprise of man, science has solved the problem of communicating ideas, and has demonstrated that world-wide co-operation and communion of interest which then inevitably results.

Yes, science is a powerful tool, and it has an impressive record. But the humble and wise scientist does not expect or hope that science can do everything. He remembers that science teaches respect for special competence, and he does not believe that every social, economic, or political emergency would be automatically met if "the scientists" were only put into control. He does not—with a few aberrant exceptions—expect science to furnish a code of morals, or a basis for esthetics. He does not expect science to furnish the yardstick for measuring, nor the motor for controlling, man's love of beauty and truth or his sense of value or his convictions of faith. There are rich and essential parts of life which are at bottom alogical, which are immaterial and non-quantitative in character, and which cannot be seen under the microscope, nor weighed with the balance, nor caught by the most sensitive microphone.

If science deals with quantitative problems of a purely logical character, if science has no recognition of or concern for value or purpose, how can modern scientific man achieve a balanced good life, in which logic is the companion of beauty, and efficiency the partner of virtue?

In one sense the answer is very simple: our morals must catch up with our machinery. To state the necessity, however, is not to achieve it. The great gap which lies so forebodingly between our power and our capacity to use power wisely can only be bridged by a vast combination of efforts. Our knowledge of individual and group behavior must be improved. Communication must be improved between peoples of different languages and cultures, as well as between all the varied interests which use the same language, but often with such dangerously differing connotations. A revolutionary advance must be made in our understanding of economic and political factors. We must develop a willingness to sacrifice selfish short-term interests, either personal or national, in order to bring about long-term improvement for all.

All of these advances, however, must be accomplished in a world in which modern science is an inescapable, ever-expanding influence. None of these advances can be won unless men understand what science really is.

With such issues at stake, it is the duty of every thoughtful citizen to bring to these problems his own personal maximum of reliable knowledge. It is not merely desirable or interesting, but rather imperative, that all citizens be informed about the methods and accomplishments of the solid core of basic science. It has been this feeling of compulsion which has made it seem so important to make available to a large audience the following essays by great scientists. Science is, after all, the activity of scientists. In these essays the scientists speak. They describe, first-hand, what they have done and are doing. You have here a chance to learn and to judge science for yourself.

CHAPTER 2

THE SCIENCE OF THE EARTH

A FISH, someone has said, is the most unlikely of all creatures to be aware of the ocean. Man, in the same way, is apt to take for granted the earth on which he lives.

The earth is not only the home of man: it is his chief storehouse of treasure. Man must have energy at his disposal, both to sustain life and to provide for its varied activities. Until scientists learned to control nuclear fission, the chief source of our energy had always been the sun. The earth, in various ways, serves as the bank from which man draws out the energy previously deposited there by the sun. Since we have not yet worked out very good methods of utilizing directly the sun's energy, we have had to depend largely on the complex cycle whereby the sun's radiant energy is absorbed into chemical compounds of living plants. This energy may then be stored for vast periods of time as coal or oil; or it may be more promptly utilized through direct consumption of the plants by animals or by man himself. The energy of the winds and of the high-level water which operates hydro-power plants—these again are sun energy which the earth holds in trust for us. The energy of the tides, which man might make use of some day, is still another instance of energy stored in the earth. Tidal energy is associated with the earth's rotation, and is hence of ancient cosmic origin.

The earth is also the storehouse for all our reserve stock of minerals; and since this wealth is hidden beneath the surface, the exploration geologist and the geophysicist have had to develop ingenious methods of discovery. The distribution, the availability, and the mode of use of all of this mineral wealth are matters of central economic and political importance.

The earth is the great natural laboratory of the geologist; and it being the one accessible planet, the history which the geologist reads from the rocks forms a most intimate and dependable part of the larger story of the evolution of the universe. Even though this planet home of ours has already had millions of years of development, the geomorphic and historical geologists can see that its external features continue to change slightly and slowly. In addition to these exceedingly slow changes, occasional sudden readjustments in the earth's crust still occur. The resulting earthquakes are microscopic events on the cosmic scale, but from our point of view, they may nevertheless cause major disturbance.

The meteorologist and the oceanographer are concerned not with the solid earth, but with the vast seas of air and of water. A considerable fraction of mankind lives near the shores of those lower seas of water which were his ancient home; and man depends upon those seas in many ways, some obvious and some hidden. We all live at or near the bottom of the omnipresent upper sea of air, and our lives are so steadily influenced by its behavior that we are glad to learn that the meteorologists are hard at work improving their techniques of weather forecast, and that there is even talk, at last, of influencing weather as well as merely describing it.

The geographic exploration of the earth has been largely completed, but the deeper scientific exploration of the earth has just begun. After a period in which earth science has sometimes been viewed as being a little old-fashioned, there is now a revival of interest. The physicist, the chemist, and the mathematician, not to recite the list of many specialists, are now deeply concerned with the science of the earth. Indeed the biologist should by no means be omitted, for the earth does, after all, furnish the environmental stage on which the whole drama of life is played.

W. W.

The Face of Our Continent

By Eliot Blackwelder

Dr. Eliot Blackwelder is professor emeritus and was formerly head
of the Department of Geology at Stanford University.

THE best way to survey the face of our continent is from an airplane. Suppose we take off from Washington for a nonstop flight to San Francisco.

Soon after leaving the nation's capital we shall be looking down upon a long dark ridge—the Blue Ridge Mountains. Beyond the first ridge we shall see other mountains much like it, and between the parallel ridges the valleys, each with a river winding through it. These ridges and valleys are all that now remain of a great mountain system that was once higher and more rugged, like the Andes today.

We call this existing system of mountains the Appalachians. By carefully examining the ground both of the mountains and the valleys, taking advantage of quarries and road cuts, geologists have learned something of the past. They find that the rocks are all in layers. Once these layers consisted of sand and various kinds of mud, but now they are hardened into stone. The original materials were such as could only have been deposited as horizontal beds on plains or sea bottoms. But the layers now stand sharply folded like corrugated paper, the effect of pressure from the southeast toward the northwest squeezing the rocky strata as though in the jaws of a gigantic vise.

It is significant that only the lower sections of these rock folds remain—the upper parts, the tops of the arches, are gone.

For strange as it may seem to those who are used to thinking in terms of what happens in a few weeks, or months, or years, these rock folds have been worn down thousands of feet by the action of streams during the millions of years since the folds were made.

There is also a significant difference in the various materials which form the Appalachian ranges. The ridges consist of hard rock such as sandstone, while under every valley there is only soft rock, such as shale or limestone. These differences induce differences

16

in the rate of erosion and decay. Shale decays and is eroded away faster than the sandstone. Hence the edges of the harder upturned sandstone layers are left standing out in relief while the softer shale beds are worn down almost to sea level. Thus, although the Appalachian mountain system was produced originally by the folding, it owes its present features to difference in hardness of its rocks.

As our airplane flies westward, the mountains give way to hills, and the hills to a vast plain, interrupted only by the shallow valleys of the rivers. No longer are the features parallel in long bands, and again the explanation is to be found in the underlying rocks. For below the soil of this rich farming country, one usually finds beds of shale and limestone lying nearly horizontal, as they were originally deposited. Evidently the ancient compression which folded the Appalachians did not extend so far to the west. Here there are no tilted layers of hard rocks to resist erosion and stand out as mountains. So the whole region from Ohio to Colorado is substantially a plain, drained by the Mississippi River and its tributaries. The slopes of this plain coincide closely with the least slope on which a river can flow and continue to do its work of erosion. Apparently, then, enough time has elapsed to permit the streams to wear down and slice off the entire region to that very slope—in other words to what the geologist calls a plain of erosion.

How old is this great central plain? No appreciable change has been noted in it in the century or two in which the white man has occupied it, nor has any considerable change been observed in the thousands of years during which he has dwelt on similar plains in Europe and Asia.

There is abundant evidence that this central plain has been in process of formation for at least fifty million years.

That long history has not been without minor events. Hence we find that the plain is not uniformly smooth. Occasional slight uplifts of the land have stimulated the streams to entrench themselves in the plain as they seek a new and slightly lower slope of equilibrium. Hence now we find in most places a gently hilly surface—flat-bottomed valleys bordered by bluffs and separated by uplands, like those near St. Louis and Kansas City.

As we approach Denver we see the Front Range of the Rocky Mountains, rising like a wall. Study of the ground reveals the reason. The thick beds of soft shale that underlie the plain were long ago bent up sharply, and from beneath them now emerges a broad mass of older and harder rock, mostly granite. Hence, while the shale has been worn down to a plain, the granite has been merely carved into ravines and canyons, leaving the maze of rugged mountains which now occupies much of Colorado. The same principle—that of survival of the hardest material—applies to the many other ranges of the Rocky Mountain system extending from Mexico to Alaska.

Flying westward across the sage-brush steppes and mountains of Utah and Nevada, we reach California. There the Sierra Nevada rises above timberline with the sharp rocky peaks that indicate the former presence of glaciers upon their sides. Farther west these mountains gradually sink into a smooth plain, beyond which lie the Coast Ranges—the last barrier before the Pacific.

This plain between the Sierra Nevada and the Coast Ranges is quite unlike the plains of Kansas and Illinois. It slopes gently from both sides toward an axis that is parallel to the Coast Ranges. The plain is deeply underlain by sand and silt deposited by the streams which descend from the bordering ranges. In fact the plain is now being built by these streams out of the debris of the wasting mountains. Only one or two million years ago (and thus very recently in the geological history of the continent), this region was a gulf of the Pacific Ocean; but the washing in of sediment has built it above sea level, except for the last remnant which is now called San Francisco Bay.

Far to the north, if the day is clear, we may see the snow-covered peaks of Mount Shasta and Mount Lassen. Both are volcanic cones, and like other scattered volcanoes of the western states are either dead or dormant, although Mount Lassen suffered a short but violent eruption in 1915.

The Coast Ranges, though not imposing for height or rugged scenery, are unlike any of the mountains farther east. Many of these mountain ridges consist largely of soft rock such as shale.

In fact, there is little relation here between the kinds of rock and the arrangement of mountains and valleys, such as prevails in all of our eastern states. Like the eastern mountains, however, this Pacific coastal belt has been compressed from the sea toward the land, so that the beds of rocks are now bent up, folded, and badly cracked.

The continuing presence of soft shales in mountain ridges means that the erosive processes have not yet had time to wear down the rising folds and blocks. Evidence indicates that the compression began only a few million years ago, that it has continued to the present time, and that these mountains are still rising faster than erosion can destroy them. In fact, the occasional earthquakes that affect the Coast Ranges are clear evidence of the continued grinding of the earth blocks against one another as they are compressed and bulged upward. Unlike many of the other geological processes, this one is proceeding at a rate fast enough for us to measure, at least roughly. It amounts to inches per century. Here then, on the very border of the Pacific Ocean, we find a young mountain system still growing. It is in striking contrast with the mountains of the eastern states, which have been left almost undisturbed for scores of millions of years, and are now largely demolished by erosion.

Although necessarily brief, this survey of the face of our continent will serve as a sample of the recent histories of the other continents, although each has its distinctive features.

Unraveling the histories of all of them is one of the tasks undertaken by the geologists of the world.

The Science of the Atmosphere

By Francis W. Reichelderfer

Dr. Francis W. Reichelderfer, for many years an aviator and aerologist in the Navy, is the director of the United States Weather Bureau.

Man is no longer earthbound. He can rise above both land and sea and cruise through the air to the farthermost corners of the earth, but there is one environment that man cannot leave. He cannot leave the atmosphere which sustains not only his flying machines but also his very breath of life.

The science of the atmosphere, usually called meteorology, and its characteristics at any particular time and place, which we commonly call weather, are the subjects to be viewed briefly here.

In this science of the weather progress is difficult. Only during the last few years have we had the means to measure with some accuracy the elements far above the ground where our weather destiny is written from day to day. In earlier days, only a decade or two ago, the best we could do was to observe the conditions from the ground and wonder what went on in the clouds and the invisible air beyond our reach.

The thin slice of atmosphere within which we dwell on the ground is barely one-hundredth the thickness of the atmosphere as a whole. We live at the very bottom of this vast and deep ocean of air, and the thin layer near the ground holds only a small part of the story behind the weather. But the airplanes and the miracle of modern electronics are opening up the frontiers of our weather knowledge. Now, by meteorological observations made in aircraft and by radio sounding devices, the significant features of the atmosphere over many regions of the globe are revealed each day. Concise reports are telegraphed to the principal meteorological centers and there within an hour or two, after the hundreds of observations of weather near and far, the reports are charted, analyzed, and processed as upper level maps and cross section diagrams, which piece together the structure of the atmosphere and its air masses at the moment. Comparison of successive charts indicates the trends and thus determines the forecast.

The organization that performs this service is in part an outgrowth of World War II—a development that otherwise would still be years in the future. The military need for up-to-the-minute weather information for strategic and tactical planning led the Army and Navy to send their meteorological units into regions where observations have never before been made. Nor was the enemy idle in this field. We may recall his many attempts to establish and maintain weather observers in Greenland because of the value of their reports in planning his warfare on the continent of Europe. When D-Day approached, enemy meteorologists in France spent many worried hours over their incomplete weather charts in the effort to anticipate invasion weather. We are told by news reporters who subsequently obtained the facts that the enemy weather forecasters were correct in their predictions that June 5 and 6, 1944, would be stormy and unfavorable for invasion, but their tacticians were wrong when they underestimated the determination and implements of invasion of the Allies. The invasion was made despite stormy weather, and its success was due in part to the element of surprise in attempting and accomplishing what the enemy thought impossible.

Have you ever wondered why the weather is so changeable? Why a ring around the moon sometimes portends rain: or why the weather can ever be "too cold to snow"? The answers are surprisingly entertaining. Stated simply, the weather in the temperate zones is a succession of huge masses of air from the Arctic, very cold in winter, and sometimes only slightly cool in summer, separated in all seasons by currents of warm air from the tropics. The warm currents are sometimes very broad and last for days; sometimes narrow and transitory; at other times lifted above the ground by the cold air so that they are not felt by surface dwellers. Whenever we pass through the boundary between one of these cold air masses and its adjacent warm current we experience a change in weather; usually, we remain in one place and the weather changes whenever the boundary moves across our locality. The cold wave that brings freezing temperature in winter is often less than 48 hours away from its point of origin in the natural refrigerator of the Arctic. Radio sounding balloons reveal its structure and show that it is several thousand feet deep. Above it the air over the Arctic is warmer, and usually very much warmer, than the air at the same height over the equator. At great heights the temperature regime that we know on the ground is reversed and cold waves come from the direction of the equator, not from the poles.

The clouds and rain or snow that we normally consider bad weather are the result of condensation of warm moist air from the Tropics as it moves upward over its boundary with a cold air mass. Our upper air soundings show that sometimes these boundaries become very complex in structure and their associated weather is difficult to understand and predict. Sometimes, on the ground, we are engulfed in air fresh from the North Pole, while the sounding balloons show a warm current of air only a few thousand feet above our heads. Three or four days previous this warm air current had moved as a gentle breeze over the surface of the warm Caribbean. Still higher, a few hundred feet above the upper boundary of this warm air, there is often another relatively warm current which, only a week previous, absorbed heat and moisture from the far waters of the Pacific, many thousand miles beyond our coast line. These several boundaries between air masses from different regions give rise to various forms of cloud layers, some associated with rainy weather. When the moon is seen through the ice or water particles making up these high cloud forms, its light is refracted to form a halo or ring around the moon. Because such clouds often are part of a formation of bad weather, the halo is an indication of storm, an observation woven by Longfellow into the tragedy, "The Wreck of the Hesperus." Anyone who has followed this sign knows that it is definitely not an infallible indication of bad weather.

And why is it ever too cold to snow? In fact, it never is! But when we are deep within one of the cold air masses we are likely to be far distant from its boundary between air masses where conflict between warm and cold air is active and where rain and snow usually are formed. With no supply of relatively moist air nearby, there is no moisture to condense into snow, and therefore we conclude it is "too cold to snow."

One of the most important of the results of our intensive war-time research is the great reservoir of young scientists who have been trained in meteorology. Today there are one hundred times as many graduate meteorologists as there were ten years ago. Many will continue to pursue research in this field and the science will move forward more rapidly with their help. Others are likely to aid in a relatively new profession—the private practice of meteorology. Although the meteorologist cannot as yet produce weather to order, he can, like the physician and the lawyer, advise how to make the best use of conditions as they occur, now and in the future: and recent experiments in precipitating rain or snow by artificial means have indicated that some day we may to some extent produce weather as well as predict it.

In times of peace the world-wide weather organization operates something like an international news service to flash the latest observations of ever-changing weather from all parts of the earth. Collected at the respective national meteorological centers these reports should be freely exchanged among the nations to serve in the preparation of daily weather charts and forecasts for use of aeronautics, agriculture, commerce, and industry.

Whether in fundamental research in the expansive laboratory of the atmosphere, or in teaching the science in high school, college, or graduate school; whether in private enterprise as consultant for industries whose weather problems are special and continuous, or in the public service of the national Weather Bureau, there will be willing and competent workers. They will have many opportunities to promote progress and human benefit in this inexhaustible field of the Science of the Atmosphere.

Oceanography

By Columbus O'Donnell Iselin

Mr. Columbus O'Donnell Iselin is the director of the Oceanographic Institution at Woods Hole, Massachusetts.

Some three-fourths of the earth's surface is ocean, and the science of oceanography is the study of this vast domain and all that it contains. Men have gone down to the sea in ships since early Biblical days, but it is only in comparatively recent times that significant progress has been made in finding out how oceans work.

The early students of oceanography were chiefly concerned with learning the extent of the oceans. Merely to map the boundaries was a long and adventurous task, beset with great difficulties.

More recently science has moved from the ocean surface down into the ocean depths. About seventy-five years ago biologists began systematic efforts to find out what lives in the ocean. Expeditions were sent out to collect sea plants and sea animals, and to learn about their distribution. In the course of these biological surveys it became apparent that the fundamental subject in oceanography was the circulation problem—that is to say, the problem of understanding the movement of the ocean waters.

Almost any serious investigation of what goes on in the sea must take into account the movements of the waters. Whether one is concerned with a problem of ocean biology, ocean chemistry, sedimentation, or some other aspect of the sea, in the end it will be found that ocean currents play a primary role. There are great major movements—such as the Gulf Stream in the North Atlantic and the Japan Current in the North Pacific—and there are also numerous smaller-scale superimposed circulations. A large part of the efforts of oceanographers in recent years has gone into the study of these currents, both the large ones and the small ones.

Perhaps the simplest approach to an understanding of ocean currents is through the analogy of wind movements in the atmosphere. The fact that the oceanographer is studying the movement of a liquid and the weather man is concerned with that of a gas makes surprisingly little difference.

Both water and air are fluids and are governed in many instances by the same laws.

In both cases we are dealing with large-scale eddy-type movements in which most of the motion is in horizontal directions. There can be no actual beginning or end to an ocean current, no more than there can be to a wind system. The velocity may vary along different parts of the circuit, but in any given region inflow must nearly equal outflow. For the most part, in both the air and the water circulation the density increases as you go downward, so that vertical stability prevails—that is to say, there is no inherent tendency for up-and-down currents to get started. Another common property of both wind and water currents is that in each case the internal distribution of the density is very much influenced by the effect of the earth's rotation. It is generally characteristic of fluids that motion takes place in the direction in which pressure changes rapidly. But weather maps have acquainted many of us with the fact which apparently contradicts the general law—that winds usually flow nearly parallel with the lines of equal pressure. Mathematicians have been able to explain that this apparently anomalous direction of winds is due in large part to the rotation of the earth; and their calculations indicate that water currents in the ocean should, again because of the earth's rotation, show similar peculiarities in their direction.

Meteorologists use the barometer to measure air pressure, but the oceanographer has no such convenient instrument to give a direct measure of the pressure distribution in the sea. Moreover, the weather man can easily observe the direction and strength of the wind at ground level, and by watching the movements of clouds or sending up a balloon he can gain a measure of the winds aloft. By setting up a network of observing stations he can chart both the winds and pressures over considerable areas and learn how they are interrelated.

In contrast with these comparatively simple techniques of the meteorologist, the oceanographer is at a disadvantage. In the deep ocean it is most difficult to measure directly the surface current, let alone the currents at considerable depths. So the oceanographer has had to fall back on indirect methods. He measures the distribution of temperature and salinity at different levels below the surface of the sea. From these primary measurements he is able to calculate how the density and pressure of the sea water vary from one place to another. Theory then tells him what currents must prevail to establish such a distribution of density and pressure.

The oceanographer's procedure is more indirect than that of the meteorologist, but in one limited sense it is easier. The oceanographer deals with slow, relatively steady movements which are confined by the shape of the ocean basins; whereas the air currents which the meteorologist must follow are often strong and variable winds which soon move off the continent out over the ocean where the observers are too few and scattered to yield satisfactory information.

The atmospheric circulation is primarily caused by heating of air masses in low latitudes and cooling in high latitudes; but this thermal process is only partly responsible for ocean currents. The ocean currents gain most of their energy from the winds. Over each ocean in the northern hemisphere the winds move in a general clockwise direction, and in the southern hemisphere the circulation is anticlockwise. Only in high southern latitudes do the prevailing westerly winds drive the water round and round the earth.

In the tropics and particularly near the equator, the surface waters of the sea are warmed by the tropic sun, and this warming expands the water and makes it less dense. In the Arctic and Antarctic just the opposite is occurring. Cooling makes the water more dense, consequently this colder, heavier water sinks and starts moving slowly along the bottom toward the equator.

It is a major question of oceanography how much of the ocean circulation is caused by horizontal density differences maintained by the climate and how much is due to the frictional force exerted by winds moving over the ocean surface. In general, winds seem to be mainly responsible for the large-scale circulation pattern—such as the Gulf Stream—while convection, caused by local heating and cooling seems to determine the small-scale movements.

What we have learned of the circulation of the ocean has been won at great effort, through the patient painstaking work of many men of different nations. It has been expensive and time-consuming, and one may well ask: "What is the good of all this research? What are the practical applications of such knowledge?"

In the early days of oceanography it would have been difficult to give a satisfactory answer. Before science gained some understanding of the ocean circulation it seemed that the details of such studies could have only academic interest. Fortunately, however, some men have a curiosity to know, and they push ahead without caring whether or not the result will have practical application. As has often happened in science, so it turned out in the case of oceanography; once the basic research got under way and began to yield new knowledge, it soon became clear that many uses could be made of the knowledge.

For one thing, oceanography has contributed directly to the solution of many naval and maritime problems. It has contributed to our knowledge of climatic influence and conditions. The tremendous capacity of the oceans for absorbing the solar heat makes ocean circulation an important regulator of climate. If long range climatological forecasts are ever to be attained, they will depend in part at least on results achieved in studies of the variability of ocean currents. Oil geology also stands to benefit from oceanographic studies, for petroleum is a product of marine sediments. Our ability to find new deposits of oil and to exploit known reserves depends on knowing more about the conditions under which oil-bearing sediments are laid down.

In other words, none of the earth sciences stop at the beach. The more dependent man becomes on the successful exploitation of his environment, the more necessary it will be for him to have detailed knowledge concerning what is going on in the waters which cover roughly three-quarters of the globe.

Forecasting Earthquakes

By James Bernard Macelwane

The Reverend James Bernard Macelwane is professor of geophysics and dean of the Institute of Geophysical Technology at St. Louis University.

It was twelve minutes after five in San Francisco on the fateful morning of April 18, 1906. Most of the city's inhabitants were still in bed when the earthquake struck and the Great San Francisco fire was started. Why was the public not warned of the coming catastrophe? Why were the people of San Francisco not told of the imminent danger of the earthquake so that they could save themselves and their movable possessions? Why were the city officials not alerted so that the gas and electricity could be cut off? We may ask similar questions about our other destructive earthquakes—about New Madrid and Charleston, about Santa Barbara and Long Beach, about Helena and El Centro.

Why do we not have an earthquake forecasting service to parallel the United States Weather Bureau? Storms are forecasted; why not earthquakes? From time to time articles have appeared in the newspapers about men who claimed to have arrived at a complete solution of the problem of earthquake forecasting. They give you long lists of supposed verifications to prove the success of their predictions. Some forecasters base their predictions on the influence of the moon, others on the relative position of certain planets, others on sunspot activity, and no doubt there are persons entirely sincere who are allured and deceived by a specious theory and by a series of apparent verifications, but who lack sufficient scientific background to make a critical appraisal of the factors involved. No doubt, too, there are charlatans and notoriety seekers. But seismology, the study of earthquakes, is a highly technical science, and it must be pursued by the patient, objective, fact-finding method of scientific research.

If the earthquake prediction is made general enough, it will not be difficult to find some earthquake that would seem to verify it. Therefore, it is essential, before we proceed further in the discussion, that we clarify our ideas. We must be sure that we are all talking about the same thing.

It is not enough to predict that earthquakes will continue to occur in the future. To a person with any knowledge of earth science, that is an obvious truth. Actually more than one million earthquakes occur every year. Would I be forecasting in any true sense if I told you an earthquake will occur in Japan next week? Any experienced seismologist knows that, on the average, two dozen earthquakes occur in Japan every week. My prediction of an earthquake in Japan next week would be a statement of a moral certainty; but it would be too vague to be of any help as a forecast. What then is a forecast?

A forecast, in the modern sense, is not a mere guess. Neither is it a prophecy.

A forecast is a definite statement in regard to the sequence of future events based on a balancing of probabilities derived from experience, observation, and the laws which are known to govern such happenings. I think we can agree, from the analogy of weather forecasting, that an earthquake prediction would not be called an earthquake forecast unless it were sufficiently probable and specific to serve a useful purpose. A public prediction of an earthquake will be useful if it serves to protect life and property without arousing undue panic.

An earthquake forecast must be *specific*. This means that the forecaster must predict three things about the earthquake. In the first place, the forecast must announce the *time* of the earthquake, at least within a few hours. Secondly, the forecast must specify the *intensity* of the coming earthquake or the extent of the damage to be expected from it. Thirdly, the forecast must state in just what *place* or places the destruction of property is going to occur.

Besides being specific, the forecast must also be *reliable*. That is, a predicted disaster must be sufficiently probable to justify public authorities in removing the threatened populations, cutting off the gas supply and the electricity, and otherwise disrupting the normal life of the people. The mere heralding of a disastrous earthquake would create a panic and might drive many people insane.

Is it possible, in the present state of scientific knowledge, to predict earthquakes in this definite and positive sense which alone deserves the name of forecasting? Unfortunately, no! All reputable seismologists agree that we have no means at the present time of arriving at a reliable forecast of any earthquake anywhere.

The problem of earthquake forecasting has been under intensive investigation in California and elsewhere for some forty years; and we seem to be no nearer a solution of the problem than we were in the beginning. In fact the outlook is much less hopeful.

In the California earthquake of 1906 the earth was torn by a crack or fault which extended more than 150 miles in a north-northwest south-southwest direction. All structures, roads, fences, rows of trees, which crossed this fault were rent apart and offset. The portion on the west side of the crack was permanently shifted toward the north relative to that on the east side of the fault. The horizontal offset, or shift, between the two parts originally continuous across the fault amounted in one case to as much as twenty-one feet.

Immediately after the earthquake, the United States Coast and Geodetic Survey made a resurvey of the area, and found that points many miles west of the fault had been displaced northward and points east of the fault had displaced southward. These scientists also found that the regional shifts were made up of two parts. There was a smaller shift which had occurred sometime between the years 1866 and 1874, and a larger shift that had taken place between 1892 and July 1906. In the first of these intervals the earthquake of 1868 had occurred with relative movements on the Haywards fault east of San Francisco Bay. In the second interval was the earthquake of 1906 which involved the relative displacements we have described along the San Andres fault west of the San Francisco Bay.

To explain these distinct sets of movements a well-known seismologist proposed the theory of a slow northward creep of the coastal region, which creep gradually distorted the rocks in that portion of the earth's crust until they were strained beyond their capacity to resist. When this limit was reached, fracture occurred along the weakest zone, and the rocks on both sides of the fault rebounded elastically to new positions of equilibrium. It was as if the Pacific Coast started on a vacation trip to Alaska and the rest

of California refused to go along and held back until their rock
mantle tore.

"Ah!" said the seismologists, "here is a means of forecasting
earthquakes. Measure the gradual creep. When the shear approaches
the ultimate strength of the rocks there will soon be an earthquake."
So concrete pillars were placed on both sides of the San Andres
fault and their relative positions were determined very accurately
with surveying instruments. The relative positions have been rede-
termined again and again in succeeding years but no trace of creep
has been observed.

"The pillars were placed too close together," said the seismologists. "Let us set up a precise network of triangulation stations and
lines of leveling and let us repeat the measurements after a few
years." The United States Coast Guard and Geodetic Survey repeated its survey of California. This was done in the early twenties.
No sure sign of regional creep was found. Then a very dense network of triangulation and leveling stations was laid across the faults
in southern California and another in central California. So far,
no evidence of regional creep has appeared.

The Japanese claimed to have observed a tilting of the ground
before an earthquake. American seismologists eagerly seized on
this as a possible means of forecasting earthquakes and set up
tiltmeters at Berkeley, California. Tilts were observed and so were
earthquakes of very near origin. But unfortunately there was no
correlation between the tilts and the earthquakes.

Do earthquakes come in cycles? Can they be triggered by weather
or tidal action? If so, they might be forecasted. Many statistical
studies were made; but the conclusions were all negative or very
uncertain.

Every lead that was suggested has been followed and all of them
so far have led up blind alleys. Of course, earthquake prediction in
a wider sense is possible. We know from history and from the
records of modern seismographs that many more earthquakes occur
in certain parts of the world than in others. The rim of the Pacific
Ocean is particularly active. No year passes without a strong earthquake somewhere in the lands that border the Pacific Ocean. The
same is true of most of the larger groups of islands in the Pacific.
Hence one needs only to make his prediction broad enough in space

and time and it is sure to be verified. But this is not earthquake forecasting as we have defined it and as forecasting is usually understood.

Minerals in Relation to War and Peace

By C. K. Leith

Previous to his retirement, Dr. C. K. Leith was for many years the head of the Department of Geology at the University of Wisconsin. In both world wars he was the leading minerals adviser to our government.

WHAT are minerals? To some, I think, they are only dusty museum specimens with unpronounceable names, or one of the well-known trio of "animal, vegetable or mineral" in a childhood game. Others think of them as precious stones or precious metals like gold and silver, or as ores of iron and copper and zinc, or as coal, oil, or gas. To the geologist or mineralogist they all are the substances of the earth, including its solids, liquids, and gases. There are thousands of mineral varieties, both metallic and non-metallic.

I propose to mention here only the few score that man has learned to use in building and driving the machines of this machine age. These include the implements of war—guns, ships, planes, tanks, transportation, and communication. The scale of use of minerals is mounting at a startling rate both in peace and war. New end products of minerals are multiplying, and advancing technology is constantly requiring minerals not heretofore used. In World War II we used at least thirty more varieties of minerals than in the previous war. Some of them were rare and needed in very small amounts, but they were vital to new critical gadgets both for war and peace. Mineral reserves which formerly seemed adequate for the long future now look small when seen against the new horizon.

To meet modern demands in both scale and variety, as well as to conserve resources, an immense range of scientific effort is involved. Hardly a month passes without some new and spectacular advance in discovery, extraction, and conversion of minerals into usable forms.

First, as to discovery—each mineral has its own geologic environment. The geologist is busy mapping the world, in length and
breadth and depth, to discover favorable locations for exploration.
He must literally see into the earth. Today he has powerful aid
from geophysical methods, using sound waves and electrical devices,
to enable him to tell what is below the surface. This is the modern
version of the witch hazel divining rod. Although geologists still
work in the laboratory, it is no exaggeration to say that the geologist's real laboratory is the world itself. The surface of the earth
has now been fairly explored. The future job involves knowledge
of what is beneath the surface and any forecast of reserves or of
future possibilities depends mainly upon geologic science.

The next stage after discovery of the location of minerals is their
recovery from the raw material by various methods of concentration, physical and chemical—that is, by getting rid of what we do
not need and saving what we do need. New processes are now
making available low grade ores which were formerly not used
because they contained too little of value to pay their way.

Next comes the smelting and refining to convert the mineral
products into usable condition. This includes the mixing of minerals to make the new alloys so necessary to meet the exacting
requirements of modern industry.

Because of the impossibility of securing enough of all the raw
materials, it was necessary also in the recent war to make technical
studies of substitution and of conservation of critical materials. The
results have greatly widened the range of possibilities and have
materially lessened our dependence on certain minerals formerly
regarded as indispensable.

Just a few illustrations of these activities taken from our recent
war effort:

The new science of radar calls for the use of the comparatively
rare element, tantalum, in electronic tubes, and for special varieties
of quartz crystals to control the radio frequency. The United States
has neither one in sufficient quantity. The finding and the preparation of these minerals require new technology. One spectacular
incident is the discovery that the molecular structure of quartz can
be changed by radiation, bringing inferior grades up to standard.

The vast expansion in the use of light metals, magnesium and aluminum, has required literally hundreds of new processes to get the raw materials out of the earth, to convert them into metals, to find out how to work and weld these metals. A great plant in Texas is now extracting magnesium from ocean water. We have learned how to recover alumina from low-grade bauxite, which is the ore of aluminum, and are well on our way to recovery of aluminum from clay and other low-grade sources.

You are probably familiar with the vast technical effort involved in the finding and processing of oil, but perhaps you are not so familiar with the fact that useful derivatives of oil, such as synthetic rubber and a host of chemical products, are becoming so numerous and important that the time may come when the value of these derivatives will approach the primary value of the oil for heating and transportation purposes.

War implements require the use of alloys on a scale never before known, and have also required new alloys or super-alloys to meet specially strenuous requirements—as, for instance, the high temperatures of the jet engine. Because of the limited supplies of alloying minerals, it has been necessary to use them in new combinations, like the so-called National Emergency steels, representing a wide departure from old formulae. In this way it has been possible to make nearly three times as much alloy steel as formerly without a proportional increase in the use of alloying metals. Early in World War II, when tungsten was tight, molybdenum was substituted. Later, when tungsten became more plentiful, it was reinstated. Still later the shift was again reversed because of the need for tungsten carbide as a core for more powerful armour-piercing shells. New technology of these kinds has almost revolutionary possibilities for improvement of metallurgy.

In the war days of shortage, it was not necessary to remind you of the compelling necessity for conservation and substitution. The saving of tin in the manufacture of a tin can, or the substitution of lead or plastic coatings for tin, calls for the most elaborate tests under all conditions to make sure of the usefulness and safety of the can.

In conclusion, weight of metals and minerals, as expected, proved a decisive factor in winning a mechanized war. The job of war mobilization of mineral supplies was excellently done. Scientists and technologists are now looking for ways and means to continue the impetus of their part of this effort into the future, for the sake of industrial advancement and future security.

But their interest does not stop there. Because of their knowledge of the physical background and potentialities, they are also keenly concerned with another phase of the mineral problem having to do with world peace.

Minerals are irreplaceable assets which are being depleted at an alarming rate. No nation has enough of all commercial minerals. The United States is better supplied than any other nation, but during the war it had to import about seventy varieties of minerals. Interdependence of nations as to minerals is a physical fact, not theory. Since World War I, as nations have waked up to the overwhelming importance of mineral supplies both for their future industry and for their security, there has been a world-wide scramble to control them, resulting in growing international friction. The degree of success in acquiring mineral supplies measures war-making power in a mechanized war. There now looms before us the problem of equal access to the world's minerals.

This is the very heart of the problem of world peace. Shall we adhere to the methods of procurement of the past with their ever more threatening consequences, or shall we attempt to devise some wise administration to insure equal access by peaceful nations and to withhold these war-making potentials from nations threatening peace? An adequate answer to these questions will require not only international co-operation based on goodwill and pious hopes, but a very high order of scientific fact-finding and analysis.

CHAPTER 3

THE SCIENCE OF THE SKY

FROM THOSE ancient days when herd boys, watching their flocks, first looked up into the night of stars, the heavens have always filled men with wonder and awe, wonder as to the nature and laws of those twinkling points of light, awe at the beauty and grandeur of the universe.

The common identification in men's minds of the stars with beauty, of astronomy with religion, of cosmology with philosophy, is compactly indicated by our use of the word "heaven." We regularly take this word to mean not only the great dome of space over the earth, but also the dwelling place of the Deity and the celestial abode of the dead.

Astronomy is perhaps the oldest branch of science. At least four thousand years before the telescope was invented, Chinese astronomers were able to determine equinoxes and solstices from the stars, and the face of the sky had doubtless served man as a clock and as an almanac from still more ancient times. At the beginning of the seventeenth century came the telescope, and late in that same century Newton's great discovery of the universal law of gravitation, a law which describes the forces between all heavenly bodies. There followed some two centuries of steady and brilliant progress in knowledge of the stars. Over the last hundred years, however, two other great scientific instruments, the camera and the spectroscope, have essentially remade astronomy.

Indeed, the modern astronomer spends little or no time looking through a telescope with his own eyes. Instead he photographs. Not usually does he photograph the position of the stars, although the geometric pattern of the universe continues to be of basic importance. Most of his photographs are taken with light gathered by his telescope, but then spread out by the spectroscope into wavelength bands.

From this spectrum the astronomer identifies the elements which make up the stars, determines their velocities in space, and infers many facts about the physical conditions which obtain in stars.

To the astrophysicist, the spread-out spectrum from a star is as much more interesting and revealing, as compared with the original spot of light, as a symphony is more interesting and beautiful than would be all these same sounds played in one single simultaneous burst. The spreading out is accomplished relative to space in the optical instance, and relative to time in the musical instance; but in each case it is the detailed pattern of frequencies which is essential.

The astronomer has become, in much of his modern work, a physicist whose laboratory is the universe. His central problem is nothing less than the detailed description of those vast fleets of stars which form, in ascending order, our solar system, our galactic system, the other galaxies such as the nebulae, multiple galaxies, clusters of galaxies, and finally the total universe itself.

W. W.

The Exploration of Space

By Edwin P. Hubble

Dr. Edwin P. Hubble, an astronomer of the Mount Wilson Observatory in Southern California, has been specially concerned with
studying nebulae—their types and their distribution in space.

ASTRONOMY is the study of the universe—the study of its structure
and its behavior. From our home on the earth we look out into
the dim distances, and we strive to imagine the sort of world into
which we are born. We are confined to the earth. Our knowledge
of outer space is derived from light waves and other radiations
which come flooding in from all directions.

From time immemorial men studied the heavens with the unaided eyes. Finally, about three centuries ago, the telescope was
invented. With the growth and development of these giant eyes,
the exploration of space has swept outward in great waves. Today
we explore with a telescope 100 inches—more than 8 feet—in
diameter. It has the light gathering power of more than 200,000
human eyes. We observe a volume of space so vast that it may be
a fair sample of the universe itself. Men are already attempting to
infer the nature of the universe from a study of this sample.

The explorations fall into three phases. The first phase led long
ago to a picture of the solar system—the sun with its family of
planets, including the earth, isolated and lonely in space.

Then, after several centuries had passed, a picture of a stellar
system began to emerge. This was the second phase. The sun was
found to be merely a star, one of several thousand million stars
which, together, form our stellar system—a swarm of stars drifting
through space as a swarm of bees drifts through the air.

From our position within the system, we look out through the
swarm of stars, past the boundaries, into the universe beyond. The
conquest of this outer space is the third, and most recent, phase
of the explorations.

The outer regions are empty for the most part. But, here and
there, scattered at immense intervals, we now recognize other
stellar systems, comparable with our own. These stellar systems,

these lonely drifting swarms of stars, are the true inhabitants of the universe.

They are so remote that, in general, we cannot distinguish their individual stars; the swarms appear merely as vague, cloudy patches of light, and were called by the name "nebulae," the Latin word for "clouds."

A few of the nebulae appear large and bright; these are the nearest swarms. Then we find them smaller and fainter, in constantly increasing numbers, and we know that we are reaching out into space farther and ever farther until, with the faintest nebulae that can be detected with the greatest telescope, we reach the frontiers of the Observable Region.

This glimpse of space, thinly populated by drifting swarms of stars, has been revealed by great telescopes, and in particular by the greatest of all those in actual operation, the 100-inch reflector of the Mount Wilson Observatory. It was the 100-inch that first detected individual stars in a few of the nearest nebulae, and identified among them several types of stars that are well known in our own system. Since the real brightness, or candle-power, of such stars had already been measured in our own system, their apparent faintness indicated their distances and, consequently, the distances of the nebulae in which they lay.

Once the essential clue of the distances was found, the mystery of the nebulae was quickly solved. They are, in fact, huge stellar systems, like our own system, and they appear small and faint only because they are vastly remote.

Some nebulae are giant systems and some are dwarf systems, but the range in candle-power is not great. For statistical purposes, they can all be considered as equally luminous. Therefore, their distances are correctly indicated by their apparent faintness. This property has been used to survey accurately the whole of the Observable Region out as far as telescopes can reach.

The scale of the survey is so immense that a special unit of distance is employed in the reports. This unit is the *light year*— namely, the distance light travels in a year going at the rate of 186,000 miles each second. The number of miles in a light year is six million million—in other words, six followed by 12 ciphers. Light reaches the earth from the moon in about one and one-third seconds, from the sun in about eight minutes, and from the nearest star in about four and one-half years. This last figure is typical. The average distance between neighboring stars in our system is several light years. The diameter of our system (which is one of the giant nebulae) is about 100,000 light years.

The faintest nebulae that can be detected with the greatest telescope are, on the average, about 500 million light years away. We intercept and photograph today the light which left these stellar systems far back in a remote geological age. This light has been sweeping through space for millions of centuries at the speed of 186,000 miles each second. Truly, as we look out into space, we look back into time.

With the largest telescope, we can look out into space about 500 million light years in all directions. Thus, the Observable Region is a vast sphere, about 1000 million light years in diameter, with the observer at the center. Throughout this sphere are scattered about 100 million nebulae, each a stellar system at some stage of its evolutional history. These nebulae average about 10,000 light years in diameter and about 100 million times the brightness of the sun. The average distance between neighboring nebulae is about two million light years.

A rough model of the Observable Region might be represented as follows. Assume that the sphere, 1000 million light years across, is reduced to a sphere with a diameter of one mile and a half. Then the 100 million nebulae are reduced to the size of golf balls. And they are scattered through the sphere at average intervals of about 30 feet. On this scale, the earth could not be seen with a microscope, not even with an electron microscope.

The nebulae are scattered singly, in groups, and even in clusters, but this irregularity is a minor detail. When very large volumes of space are compared, they are found to be remarkably alike. On the grand scale, the Observable Region is very much the same everywhere and in all directions—in other words, it is homogeneous.

This feature could not be predicted. It is the first characteristic definitely established for our sample of the universe.

Only one other general feature has been found. Light reaching us from the nebulae has lost energy in proportion to the distance it has traveled. The fact is established but the explanation is still uncertain.

The problem, thus posed, which involves the possibility of an expanding universe, makes an exciting story in itself. It is mentioned now merely to complete the description of the Observable Region as known today.

To summarize: the explorations of space have swept outward in three waves—through the system of the planets, through the stellar system, into the realm of the nebulae. In the first phase, the earth was found to be one of the family of planets which circle the sun. In the second phase, the sun was found to be one of the millions of stars which make up our stellar system. In the third phase, our stellar system was found to be one of the millions of nebulae which are scattered rather evenly through the region of space that can be observed with telescopes.

The next step involves some guesswork. We suppose that the region we have explored is like any other large region of space —that the Observable Region is a fair sample of the universe. With the aid of this assumption, we may discuss the universe on the basis of factual knowledge. Men are already assembling the types of possible universes which are consistent with the known facts. As more facts are discovered, the number of such universes will steadily decrease. Thus, step by step, we may hope to whittle down the possibilities, and finally recognize the universe we actually inhabit.

The venture stirs the imagination profoundly. It has become feasible only in our generation. With the aid of great telescopes we have at last won our way beyond the stars of our own system, out into the very depths of space.

The explorations will continue. Still greater telescopes will be put into operation. And slowly, as the darkness recedes, the universe will loom forth.

The 200-Inch Camera

By Ira Sprague Bowen

Dr. Ira Sprague Bowen is research associate at the California Institute of Technology, and director of the group of astronomical observatories which includes the Mount Wilson Observatory of the Carnegie Institution of Washington, and which will include on its completion the Palomar Mountain Observatory of the California Institute of Technology.

TODAY a great astronomical instrument is nearing completion on Palomar Mountain in Southern California. It is commonly called the 200-inch telescope, but more accurately it should be named the 200-inch camera. Let me explain why I make this distinction.

The human eye has a limited sensitivity. No matter how long and intently we gaze at a faint object on a dark night we cannot bring to view any fainter details than were seen at first glance. In contrast, the photographic plate is quite different. It can build up an image through prolonged exposure. If you should try to photograph the starry heavens, for example, a few seconds exposure would get images of only a few stars. You could see more with the unaided eye. But prolong the exposure, and the photograph will record fainter and fainter stars, and in a few minutes its plate will have reached the sensitivity of the eye. By extending the exposure to many hours we may push far beyond anything the eye can see and record objects of almost any degree of faintness.

Because of this greater sensitivity of the photographic plate all large astronomical instruments are used almost exclusively as cameras rather than as visual telescopes. It is only by the use of the photographic plate that we have been able to obtain most of the knowledge we have of nebulae and other faint objects. No human eye has ever seen their details directly.

Let us therefore consider the Palomar Mountain instrument as a camera. The heart of any camera is its lens. The function of the lens is to collect the light coming from the object and bring it to a focus on the photographic plate. The quality of the photographs obtained depends to a large extent on the accuracy of design and perfection of workmanship of this vital part of every camera.

In the Palomar Mountain camera the role of the lens is taken by a great mirror. This mirror is in the form of a slightly concave disk 200 inches in diameter. It has been necessary to shape the surface of the mirror with the most extraordinary accuracy, for an error of more than a few millionths of an inch at any point on the surface would distort the image. This work of grinding and polishing is now in its final stages, and when completed some seven years will have been spent giving this surface the necessary perfection.

The mirror must not only have the right curvature, but it must be sufficiently stiff to maintain this accuracy of shape as the camera is pointed in various directions. To provide the necessary rigidity, the mirror is made of a huge ribbed block of pyrex glass. The glass is nearly 17 feet in diameter, 30 inches thick, and weighs nearly 15 tons.

The next essential, after the lens or mirror, is the camera body. The purpose of this structure is to support the lens and the photographic plate in their proper relative positions. Since the 200-inch mirror has a focal length of 55 feet, the mirror and photographic plate must be separated by this distance. To hold the mirror and plate with sufficient rigidity during the long exposures, requires a considerable structure. Actually, the body of the 200-inch camera is a framework of steel girders, weighing 125 tons.

The camera body is mounted in a huge steel cradle which permits the camera to be pointed at any point in the sky. The complete assembly—mirror, body, and cradle—weighs a total of over 500 tons, and the huge mechanism is precisely mounted on bearings and so adjusted that it can turn about an axis parallel to that of the earth. Its motion is controlled by a very precise clock. This arrangement is necessary since the camera must be kept pointed at a given star as the star moves from east to west in the sky.

A steel dome 135 feet in diameter and 135 feet high houses the telescope. To permit the camera to look out through a slot at any desired point in the sky, the dome can be rotated about a vertical axis, and it moves with great ease despite its weight of 1,000 tons.

In the construction of the 200-inch camera, the builders were faced, on the one hand, with most of the problems of heavy structural engineering. On the other hand, was the necessity of attaining high instrumental accuracy and smoothness of operation in these huge and massive mechanisms. It is no wonder that fifteen years have been required to build this instrument. The 200-inch camera on Palomar Mountain has probably cost more in both time and money than any other single instrument that has ever been constructed for peacetime scientific research.

At once a question presents itself. What is the justification for this huge expenditure of effort?

In answering, let us compare the 200-inch camera with the largest now in operation: namely, the 100-inch instrument on Mount Wilson. The mirror of the new camera has twice the diameter; therefore it has four times the area and, accordingly, four times the light-gathering power of the old one. Hence, the new camera should be able to photograph faint objects twice as far distant from our earth as was hitherto possible. But increasing the observable distance by a factor of two increases the volume of observable space by a factor of eight. In general, therefore, the Palomar Mountain camera should allow us to explore eight times as large a volume of the universe as has been possible in the past.

And now for some specific problems.

One of the outstanding accomplishments of the older 100-inch camera was the definite identification of the spiral nebulae as great systems of stars similar to our Milky Way. This was followed by measurements of the dimensions, the distances, and the velocities of these nebulae. For the first time we had a true picture of the structure and dimensions of the universe out to very distant limits.

However, despite this gain, many fundamental questions have remained unanswered. For example, are the stellar systems distributed through space uniformly and do they extend on indefinitely, or is a boundary finally reached beyond which there are fewer and fewer nebulae? Science also wants to know what is the true interpretation of the huge velocities with which all the stellar systems appear to be receding. Are these true velocities?

If so, are we to conclude that these stellar systems were thrown out by an enormous explosion involving the whole universe some billions of years ago? Or can these apparent velocities be interpreted as some strange pseudo-velocity caused by a curvature of space or by some little understood property of light? It is hoped that the answers to these questions will be found when we can observe a larger sample of our universe, such as the 200-inch camera will bring to view.

The possibility of changing one chemical element into another, with the release of enormous quantities of energy, was dramatically demonstrated at Hiroshima and Nagasaki. It had previously been shown that the energy which causes the sun and most of the stars to shine comes from a somewhat similar transformation in their substance, changing hydrogen into helium. We have reason to believe the chemical elements now on the earth and in the stars were formed from hydrogen by such a reaction in the past. Therefore, a study of the present chemical composition of these stars should provide important clues of conditions that existed in the earlier history of the universe—and we believe the 200-inch camera can assist those studies. With its fourfold increase in light-gathering power, the big mirror should open up many doors to this type of investigation—doors that were hitherto closed because of lack of light.

These are all important cosmic problems; the 200-inch camera on Palomar Mountain is a uniquely powerful instrument, and we have every reason to believe that it will make possible many major steps forward in our knowledge of the structure and history of the universe in which we live.

The Utility of Meteors

By Harlow Shapley

Dr. Harlow Shapley is Paine professor of Astronomy at Harvard University, and the director of the Harvard College Observatory.

I ADMIT that meteors do not look useful when you see them as quick flashes in the night sky. They certainly seem to be utterly impractical. Even when the astronomer patiently tells you again that meteors are not falling stars, or shooting stars, or stars of any kind whatever; and tells you also that they are, on the average, only forty to eighty miles above the earth's surface, that they are mostly tiny specks of dust burning up through friction with our rare upper atmosphere, and that they are related to comets and to the cosmic dust clouds of the Milky Way, even then they do not seem to be particularly useful.

But that is where you are mistaken. For meteors have, of a sudden, high practical importance. They have entered the affairs of men, and that is what we rather foolishly praise as practical. On the pure science side meteors have for a long time been regarded highly. To me they appear to be so important, as clues to the origin of the universe, and as evidence of how the universe works, that we give them high priority on the research programs of the Harvard Observatory.

Before I tell you how war and technology suddenly made meteors of practical importance, I should like to build up a little background. Many of my readers will be familiar with meteors in two forms—as the flashes in the sky, and as the bits of iron and rock of odd shapes found occasionally on the surface of the earth. Some meteors are large and move so slowly, relative to the earth, that they are not completely burned up in passing through its atmosphere.

Those meteors that reach the surface of the earth we call meteorites, and the most conspicuous meteorites are collected into our museums. But only the occasional meteor reaches the earth, while literally billions of ordinary meteors strike the earth's atmosphere daily. They are tiny. Some are iron fragments, but many are mere pebbles or dust grains, so small that a thousand of them would scarcely weigh one ounce. Although they come from outer space, they are made of the same stuff as the rocks of the earth's crust.

How can such tiny particles make those bright flashes we see forty to eighty miles above the earth's surface? It is the speed that does it. When a dust grain from interplanetary space dashes into our upper air it may be moving twenty-five miles a second or even faster. There is so little atmosphere above one hundred miles that the onrushing meteor rarely gets hot enough to shine in those altitudes, but when it falls to about eighty miles altitude it encounters denser air, and the farther it falls the denser and more resistant the air becomes. The atmospheric friction not only generates temperatures of thousands of degrees Fahrenheit and burns the particle, but also slows it down.

Meteors are difficult to observe with precision. Any clear moonless night you can see several every hour, usually more of them after midnight than before. But they appear without warning and move so rapidly across the sky that estimates of their positions and speeds are very uncertain. Photographic observations, however, can be highly accurate, but the meteors are so swift that only the brightest ones can be recorded photographically with the fastest plates and the most suitable telescopes.

Astronomers have developed an ingenious but simple photographic way of measuring the paths of meteors, their altitudes, and speeds. Of still more importance, they can measure the slowing down, the deceleration, we call it. The principal instrument in this work is the telescopic patrol camera, which covers a large segment of sky and photographs everything that happens within a given period of time.

We get the altitude by using the surveyor's method—triangulation. The meteor is photographed from two stations, simultaneously, of course, stations separated by some twenty to twenty-five miles. As it moves across the sky, the meteor leaves a trail on each photographic plate. Careful measuring of the plates gives the angles, and simple computing gives the height above the two observing stations.

We get the speed by use of a rotating interruptor whose blades whirl between the camera and the sky. These uniformly rotating blades interrupt the exposure twenty times a second, and transform the long meteor trail into a broken line. The distance between breaks varies along the trail, getting less as the times goes on, and thus giving a measure of the slowing down. The total duration of the average meteor flash is less than a second and for that reason the rotating interruptor must cut off the light at least twenty times a second to get enough breaks for a satisfactory measure.

The slowing down of the moving meteor gives a very important result; namely, a measure of the density of the atmosphere at these great heights. It tells us also about the temperature of the upper air and how much the thin atmosphere drags on the particle. Some very surprising facts have been discovered about the temperatures and densities. For instance, it is much hotter forty miles up than at the earth's surface.

Despite important contributions, the science of meteor deceleration is still young and much remains to be done. The Harvard Observatory is now setting up a powerful set of meteor cameras of new design at its station in Colorado, high in the Rocky Mountains, above the dustiest part of our troublesome atmosphere.

The new equipment should be about one hundred times as fast and effective as any that we have used heretofore. When these cameras are operating, instead of having to fish photographically for a hundred hours or so to get one satisfactory meteor, we hope to land a brilliant trail every fifteen minutes.

This new program should add greatly to our knowledge of the nature of the upper atmosphere and the nature of the meteors themselves. We shall find out some more about comets, too, because meteors and comets are related. In fact, comets are made of clouds of meteoric material. Some of the orbits of comets around the sun pass near the orbit which the earth travels. Many of the comets have meteoric particles tagging along behind, scattered all along their elliptical paths from one end to the other. As a result, when the earth, in its yearly trip around the sun, comes nearest to the path of a comet, it may encounter some of these straggling meteors. If there are many of them, we have what we call a meteor shower. That's what happened on October 9, 1946. Dozens of meteors were seen every minute for two or three hours, all appearing to come from the same point in the sky, the constellation Draco.

Every August there is a fairly rich meteor shower called the Perseids. The parent comet of that meteor stream last visited the vicinity of the earth in 1866.

Other meteor streams are associated with the famous Halley's Comet, which comes in near the earth every seventy-six years. Halley's comet will not be here again for about forty years, since it is now in the outermost part of its orbit, quite invisible, out beyond the planet Neptune. If you are not patient enough to wait to see Halley's Comet when it comes back in 1986, I can help you out with a simple experiment. On May 4 and October 22 of each year the earth passes near the orbit of Halley's Comet. I suggest that you watch for meteors on these nights. If on May 4 of any year you see some meteors coming from the constellation Aquarius, or on October 22 coming from the constellation Orion, the chances are good that you have seen parts of Halley's Comet. Several thousands of years ago those tiny flashing fragments were a part of the comet itself. In the meantime the gravitational pulls by the various planets have relentlessly proceeded with the slow dismemberment of the once much greater Halley's Comet. In a million years there may be no Halley's Comet left; then only the memorial meteors in the earth's atmosphere in May and October will bring us visual reminders of the most famous comet of human history.

But how about the highly practical value of the new studies of meteors? Well, I thought perhaps you would guess.

The new studies, as I have said, are going to give us accurate information on the temperatures, densities, and other properties of the earth's atmosphere at forty to eighty miles above the earth's surface. And precise information on this region of the atmosphere is exactly what we anxiously need for the development of high altitude jet-propelled airplanes, as well as for the rocket ships of the near future, and alas! for rocket bombs. The part of the earth's gaseous envelope that was formerly reserved wholly for the shooting stars has now become a region invaded by ambitious man, who no longer finds himself confined to the earth's surface and to the thick cloud-traveled lower atmosphere. He wants high-altitude wings and the meteors can help in their design and use.

Are the Planets Habitable?

By Henry Norris Russell

Dr. Henry Norris Russell, a research associate of the Mount Wilson Observatory and official adviser of the Harvard Observatory, was until his retirement in 1947 research professor of astronomy and director of the Observatory at Princeton University.

EVER since it was known that the planets were bodies more or less like the earth, people have asked: "Are there living things on them too?" This is a hard question, but by pooling the resources of most of the sciences, we can make a pretty good answer.

First, let us consider life on our earth for a bit. Our world would not be habitable if it did not have water on it. All living things are absolutely dependent on water. We digest our food, for example, only when it is dissolved in water in our stomachs. Moreover, this water must be liquid—neither ice nor gaseous water vapor, but ordinary liquid water. Many living things—such as the inner bark of trees—can survive being frozen and thawed out again; but nothing grows while it is frozen. And no living thing can stand having the water boiled out of it. Hence the temperature on a habitable planet must be above freezing part of the time, and below the boiling point all the time.

Light is necessary too. Practically all the food in the world is produced by green plants. These are the most marvelous laboratories in the world. Plants take in simple raw materials, carbon dioxide gas from the air and water with some things dissolved in it from the ground, and build up out of these, as they grow, all the complex substances of which they themselves are made, and some of which serve as food for animals. The plants get the energy required for this process from sunlight.

The waste product of the green-leaf laboratories is oxygen gas, which is turned back into the atmosphere. There is good reason to believe that the vast store of oxygen in the air has all been put in by plant life during the long course of geological time. Without plants, there would be no food for us animals to eat, nor oxygen-containing air for us to breathe.

There is, however, another geological process which takes oxygen out of the air. Most of the igneous rocks, which, like lava, have come up melted from below, contain a good deal of incompletely oxidized iron. As these rocks are "weathered," that is, broken down and carried off by rain and streams, the iron in them combines with more oxygen, taken from the air, and the originally black or gray rocks give rise to red or yellow sand, mud or clay.

This is a one-way process, and one might fear that there might ultimately be no oxygen left in the air. But it works so slowly that there is no cause for alarm for a great many hundred million years to come.

If we inquire whether other planets are habitable, we must then try to find out whether their temperatures are suitable for life, whether they have water and atmospheres on them, and, if so, whether oxygen and carbon dioxide are present in these.

As for the composition of the atmospheres, certain gases, if present in them, absorb light of particular wave lengths. We therefore study the planet's light with a spectroscope—an instrument which can tune out and separate different wave lengths of light many hundreds of times more powerfully than your radio can separate two stations of nearly the same wave length. And with this sensitive device we can find whether or not oxygen, carbon dioxide and water vapor are present in any considerable quantity, and, if so, can estimate their amounts.

Electrical heat-measuring devices can be made so sensitive that, when attached to a great telescope, they could measure the heat from a single candle 400 miles away. By measuring the heat from a planet with such equipment, it is possible after a good deal of calculation, to get a pretty close estimate of the temperature of its visible surface.

Measures of planetary heat show that Mercury, which is the nearest planet to the sun, has a noonday temperature of about 600 degrees, as measured on the Fahrenheit scale used in ordinary thermometers. For the remoter planets, Jupiter, Saturn, Uranus, Neptune and Pluto, the temperatures range from 180 degrees to 300 degrees below zero. All these planets are evidently uninhabitable by any form of life known to science. The moon, which we can observe in great detail, shows no trace of atmosphere or water, and must therefore also be a dead world.

This leaves for consideration only Venus and Mars. Venus is the least satisfactory planet to observe. She is surrounded by an atmosphere so hazy that it hides her solid surface. There is a large quantity of carbon dioxide in her atmosphere, but too little oxygen or water vapor to measure. The maximum surface temperature is probably about that of boiling water. This indicates strongly that there is no life on Venus. It is, however, very interesting to note that, except for the higher temperatures, conditions on Venus are decidedly similar to the theoretical picture of what our earth was like before life started on it.

Turning finally to the one remaining possibility, we find that Mars has a thin atmosphere, so that we can see the surface clearly. The planet has seasons like our own, and the heat measures indicate that, in the tropics, the temperature rises above freezing (to about 50 degrees) every day and falls below freezing every night. At the poles, the maximum temperature in summer is also about 50 degrees; the winters must be very cold.

White caps form at the poles of Mars every winter, and shrink almost to nothing in summer. This immediately suggests snow, and the temperatures confirm this beyond reasonable doubt. Hence there is water on Mars. The polar snows are, however, probably only a few inches thick, for spectroscopic observations show that there is little water vapor in the atmosphere. They indicate, too, that there is at present very little oxygen on Mars—not over a thousandth part of the amount above an equal area on earth. But there is strong reason to believe that there once was oxygen there, for most of the surface has the characteristic yellow-red color of weathered, oxidized material. There is nothing like this color on any other of the planets. The moon, for example, which has no atmosphere, does not have a single red or yellow patch on it.

Mars, then, matches closely the theoretical picture of a planet in a late stage, when rock weathering has used up almost all the oxygen of the atmosphere. The darker parts of its surface show seasonal changes and are larger and greener in summer than in winter. They probably represent surviving vegetation; but it has not been proved that some other explanation may not be possible. Whether animal life ever existed on Mars and whether it has been able to survive is at present beyond our finding out.

Outside the system composed of our sun and its circulating planets, there was no evidence for the existence of other planets till within the last three years. Recent precise photographic observations, however, show that several of the nearest stars have invisible companions, revolving about them, which can be detected because their attraction causes the bright stars to move in slightly wavy curves. The smallest of these companions are certainly dark bodies, and may fairly be called planets. We can find small companions of this sort only if they belong to some one of the few hundred stars which lie nearest to the sun. Among the many millions of remoter stars, there are very likely great numbers of them. Though the conditions for habitability are fairly stringent, there may well be thousands or more of habitable worlds among them.

Thus, in our own sun-planet system, there are only three possibly habitable bodies—Venus, the earth and Mars. Life is in full blast on the earth; and has probably existed, and may still exist, on Mars. That is, life has scored twice out of three tries. It is therefore reasonable to suppose that, within the vast expanse of the universe, there may be very many other bodies which are actually the abodes of life.

With Mars at its nearest, a spot about eight miles in diameter would just be visible with a 100-inch telescope under ideal conditions, and a spot one-half as big with a 200-inch. There is obviously no hope of seeing individual animals. Inhabitants could be detected only if they were intelligent enough to construct large-scale engineering works.

Unfortunately we have to observe Mars through the ocean of air above our heads. This is always turbulent, and so the rays of light which fall on different parts of the telescope mirror are slightly but irregularly deviated, blurring the image, and it is not possible to see the finest details clearly enough to be certain what they are like.

A larger telescope collects more of this trouble, and the 200-inch is likely to be too big to give the best view of Mars. It was built for other purposes.

Even if we could observe with it often, under perfect conditions, it would be very hard to find out whether any queer things we saw on Mars were artificial, and the problem appears to be practically insoluble.

It is hardly reasonable to suppose that on all habitable worlds, life is in the same stage of evolution as on earth today. On some there may be only primitive forms; on others there may be living creatures far surpassing mankind in intelligence and character. What these forms of life, high or low, may be we have no way at all of finding out. The variety of living things, past and present, on our planet is vast. The material possibilities of life probably outrun the human imagination. Our race has possessed intellectual and moral capacities for something like a thousandth part of the time in which life has existed on earth, and the possibilities in this field presumably transcend our present powers of thought.

We may hope at least that the desperate struggle in which mankind is engaged may represent a critical, rather than a widespread feature in the history of life. This may be at present one of the least pleasant worlds in which to live, but if so, we are on the moral firing line of the universe. We can make it a better world if we acquit ourselves like men.

CHAPTER 4

THE SCIENCE OF NEW MATERIALS
AND IMPROVED PROCESSES

IN THE first stages of his cultural development, man presumably used only those objects which nature furnished to him directly. His weapon was a tree branch; his scraping knife was the edge of a sharp stone; his easy chair was a ledge in a cave.

Later man began to fashion to his own use the objects furnished by nature, and a stone was chipped into a more useful shape. Much later he learned to grind and polish stone implements, developed the beginnings of the ceramic and textile arts, and began to join natural objects together in useful combination, so that a piece of sinew and a flexible stick became a hunting bow.

Still later men learned to separate out and use a vast number of materials which nature provided, but ordinarily not in forms which could be used directly: cement, the metals, and many more. This stage presumably began with the ancient forging of iron and has continued right up to the present day.

Great advances in science and technology have now again shifted the emphasis in this long story of development. For now science and technology are engaged in beating nature at its own game. Rather than purifying and using the material which nature furnishes, we are now frequently finding it possible—and preferable—to make new and improved materials of our own.

There is a constant interplay, moreover, between this progress toward new materials and progress toward improved processes. A new substance may be better because it has a longer life or is more attractive, but often it is also better because it has new or improved properties which make possible new uses. Thus new materials often mean improved processes, just as new processes mean improved materials.

Sometimes, as in the case of synthetic rubber or nylon, we have learned how to start with basic chemicals and synthesize a product which both imitates and improves on the original. Sometimes, as in the case of light alloys, we have used the mineral or other elements furnished by nature to make combinations which are different from any natural material and which are better for many purposes. Sometimes, as in the case of modern glass and high octane gasoline, we have taken familiar natural products and used science to improve them vastly. And sometimes new improved products and methods, developed by modern science, are combined to make possible a great process such as photography.

It is this interaction between new process and new product which has developed some of the most useful of the contributions of modern science to our daily life.

W. W.

Lightweight Metals

By Zay Jeffries

Dr. Zay Jeffries, vice-president of General Electric Company in charge of its Chemical Department, has worked on aluminum and magnesium for about twenty years and helped to develop many of the alloys now in use.

A SHOVELFUL of common clay-dirt may contain a pound of aluminum. A tubful of seawater will yield a pound of magnesium. These two metals, which are among the most abundant contained in the earth's crust, came into large production during World War II. The peak was reached in 1943 when over 4,000 million pounds of aluminum and over 500 million pounds of magnesium were produced. There is another light metal which is also suitable as a structural material—the element berylium. But thus far berylium has been produced only in limited quantity and its industrial applications are for the most part, still in the future. Aluminum weighs only about one-third as much as iron, while magnesium is still lighter, weighing about two-thirds as much as aluminum. Berylium is slightly heavier than magnesium but lighter than aluminum.

Aluminum is almost twice as abundant as iron in the earth's crust, and it may seem strange that this metal should have been so long coming to industrial application. The reason, however, is not hard to find. The production of iron is relatively easy and inexpensive. Iron ore can be reduced at red heat—literally at the blacksmith's forge—whereas aluminum ore requires high temperatures and special techniques.

It was not until electric power became available that the industrial development of aluminum was feasible.

The year 1886 really marks the birth of the aluminum industry. In that year an American chemist, Charles Martin Hall of Oberlin College, and a French chemist, Paul Heroult, working independently, invented the electrolytic process that made a large industrial development of aluminum practicable. This process is still in almost universal use by aluminum manufacturers throughout the world.

Someone has said that nature made aluminum light but it required research to make it strong.

The first noteworthy result in this development came in 1911. In that year a German metallurgist, Dr. Alfred Wilm, announced an interesting experiment with aluminum. He had melted up a mixture of four per cent copper, one-half of one per cent magnesium, and 95½ per cent aluminum. He made a rolled sheet of this alloy, quenched it from 932 degrees Fahrenheit and on testing found that the alloy had a tensile strength of 35,000 to 40,000 pounds per square inch. That was regarded as high strength for aluminum, but four days later Dr. Wilm tested the material again and found that its strength had increased to 55,000 pounds per square inch. Nor was that all.

Other tests showed that the metal had also increased in hardness during the four days. Dr. Wilm named his new alloy "duralumin," and it came into wide use as an air craft structural material.

It was clear that the lapse of time had allowed some process to operate which gave strength and hardness to the duralumin, but what was this process? The secret eluded everybody for eight years. Then, at last, Dr. Paul D. Merica, a metallurgist at the National Bureau of Standards in Washington, fathomed the mystery. He pointed out that the atoms of copper and magnesium which were dispersed among the more numerous atoms of aluminum were in a state of motion even at ordinary room temperature. And as the relatively few copper and magnesium atoms moved about among the numerous aluminum atoms, there were gradually formed new patterns, new crystalline arrangements, and it was these eventual rearrangements of the atoms of copper, magnesium, and aluminum that accounted for the stronger harder texture of the four-day-old alloy. The process is technically known as precipitation hardening, which in recent years has been widely developed and applied.

Today there are dozens of different types of precipitation-hardened alloys of aluminum. While some of these undergo precipitation hardening at room temperature, others exhibit the hardening effect only when moderately heated. Still others show part of the hardening effect at room temperature, and elevated temperatures are required to produce maximum hardening. In some alloys precipitation can be stopped at any desired stage, making possible a wide range in the combinations of properties that are attainable from a given alloy.

Duralumin was the first of a large group of strong light alloys.

One of the most remarkable of the new alloys is 75S which was introduced during World War II. This material is not only stronger than many other alloys, but of lighter weight. For example, in the B-29 Superfortress the new and improved 75S alloy was substituted for the usual 24S alloy in the upper wing-spar and stiffener structure and, as a result, the weight of the big bomber was reduced by 400 pounds. This 75S alloy is the present top achievement of researches extending back fifty years. In some of its forms and treatments 75S has a strength of 80,000 pounds to the square inch, and that's a third more than the strength of mild steel. 75S is quite a combination of metals.

It contains, in parts per hundred, about 5.5 zinc, 2.5 magnesium, 1.6 copper, 0.2 manganese, 0.25 chromium, in addition to small amounts of silicon, iron, and titanium, all added of course to aluminum. This alloy requires very carefully controlled heat treatment to develop maximum properties and to keep it free of metal diseases.

It is possible to put surfaces harder than glass on most of the aluminum products. These so-called anodic coatings, so thin that they cannot be seen by the unaided eye, are formed by electrically dissolving some of the aluminum. The coatings can be varied in thickness, hardness, and porosity, and can be given any desired color.

The uses of aluminum are multitudinous, and are growing. Aluminum alloys are the foundation of the aircraft industry. Trucks, buses, and tank cars use large quantities. The lives of bridges are increased as much as 25 years by replacing steel floors with aluminum alloy. A skyscraper is proposed for Park Avenue in New York to be built with structural shapes of aluminum instead of the usual steel. Millions of aluminum screws, aluminum nails, and other hardware are going to market. Lawn mowers, canoes, out-board motors, and handtrucks are made lighter with aluminum.

Massive parts for Diesel engines have been in use for years.

In commercial applications today, aluminum and its alloys account for about 90 per cent of the lightweight metal industry. The remaining 10 per cent is almost all magnesium. Magnesium costs about the same per cubic inch as aluminum. There are peculiar chemical and physical properties which make magnesium superior for many uses and competitive for many others. New and better alloys of magnesium have been developed, and these are becoming important in aircraft construction and in other industries.

Magnesium has entered the kitchen in cooking utensils. It is going into piano frames, wheelbarrows, and bicycles. I am told that a baby bathinet with magnesium frame is soon to appear. The automobile has not been neglected by the magnesium advance. One make of automobile alone has used 5 million magnesium die castings in the generators. It has been found that a strip of magnesium planted in the ground near an iron pipe protects the iron from rust. The magnesium is gradually consumed and disintegrates, and in doing so it slows down the rusting process in the iron pipe.

Before World War II, iron, copper, lead, and zinc each surpassed the light metals in tonnage production. In 1943 only iron and copper were produced in greater weight, and only iron in greater bulk—that is, in cubic inches. In that peak year aluminum alone accounted for two and a half times as many cubic inches as copper. Thus, in terms of cubic volume, aluminum was second to iron.

The future of the light metals will not be limited by ore supply, for both aluminum and magnesium are available in ultimately usable concentrations and in unlimited quantities in various parts of the world. With the passage of time, aluminum and magnesium will become cheaper in comparison with other metals. Add these factors together, consider the modern tempo of technological advance, and it becomes clear that in the not distant future the light metals will, in both weight and bulk production, be second only to iron.

Today's Glass

By George V. McCauley

Dr. George V. McCauley is research physicist of the Corning Glass
Works, Corning, New York.

Glass is an ancient material. Its historical origins go back more
than 5,000 years to early Egypt, but I shall confine myself only
to very recent developments in glass technology—to those modern
products of the research chemist's crucible which we may appro-
priately call *today's glass*.

Today's glass is as different from the glass of fifty years ago as
the radar is different from the wig-wag signaling of the nineteenth
century. The uses of yesterday's glass were limited because the
glass maker did not know the secret of controlling its color, its
strength, its resistance to the passage of electricity, and its other
properties. Today practically every characteristic of glass is alter-
able at will by the research chemist. Glass is no longer just a substance for windows, lamp chimneys, beakers and tumblers, and
other traditional uses. It has become a widely versatile material,
an essential material, on which we depend to give safety, ease,
convenience, and comfort to our way of living.

Because its applications are so many and so varied, today's glass
is, in reality, thousands of glasses, each with one or more of its
properties enhanced to adapt it for a specific use.

Today's glass in all its infinite variety and uses is determined by
the chemicals that are melted together to make it, by the forms
into which it is shaped, and by the temperature changes these
forms are subsequently made to undergo.

In fact, today's glass is whatever the glass research chemist and
his co-workers in physics and engineering will it to be.

It is well known of course, that ordinary white light, such as
sunlight, is a blend of all the colors of the rainbow, ranging from
red to violet. Certain types of modern glass will select particular
radiations specified by the chemist, and transmit only these. For
example, if our chemist wishes objects to appear a pure red, today's
glass will eliminate the orange, yellow, green, blue, indigo, and

THE SCIENCE OF NEW MATERIALS 61

violet, and pass undiluted red. If a wholly yellow world is wanted, or a green world, or a blue world, today's glass will halt the unwanted colors and give the pure tint that is desired. The chemist has made this modern colored glass serve wherever color is desired. It furnishes effective traffic signals on land and sea and in the air and provides the color by night for the "Broadways" and "Main Streets" of our world.

Another modern glass will halt all radiations which are visible to the eye, and pass only the heat rays. This infra-red glass will send and receive a beacon ray that can neither be seen by the eye nor intercepted by radio. Still another glass is opaque to both light and heat but transparent to those high-frequency vibrations which we designate as ultra-violet. This ultra-violet glass transmits radiation to sterilize our food, to produce suntan, and to make visible to the airplane pilot at night the luminous dials of his instrument board.

Enclosed within a shield of glass, the X-ray tubes of our hospitals cannot send forth their rays except through the small uncovered window of another type of glass that forms the tube itself. Glass thus confines the searching and healing X rays to the path desired by the operator without danger of excessive exposure to himself.

Because of its high resistance to the passage of electricity and its lower power loss, glass is a vital part of every radio, television set, and radar installation. This modern glass, endowed by science with enhanced electrical properties, insures the fidelity of music and speech as transmitted by telephone and radio.

Sometimes the prime requirement, after transparency, is strength. We desire that the windshields of our automobiles, the goggles for our eyes, the windows for our fighting tanks, and the crystals for our watches, be capable of standing hard knocks. By a process similar to that by which steel is hardened, glass is tempered and made resistant even against bullets.

Sometimes weakness is desired. A device used during the war to attach extra fuel tanks to the fighter airplanes was a sharp elbow of glass tubing. The glass was purposely made weak so that it would break at the first tug and thus relieve the plane of the now empty and useless receptacle.

Today's glass expands with heat and contracts with cold, little or much, according to the formula of the glass research chemist. The manufacturer wants a pipe line to carry hot and cold chemicals, brines, or juices through some industrial process. The housewife desires utensils in which she can prepare food and at the same time witness pies or bread in process of baking, potatoes boiling, coffee percolating, eggs or meat frying. One type of glass, with low expansion on heating, satisfies these desires. Another type of glass goes to the opposite extreme, and with an expansion equal to that of iron, meets the requirements of the vacuum tube in which glass and iron must be tightly sealed together.

One form of modern glass has the texture of angel-food cake. It starts out as quite ordinary glass, is then ground to a flour-like consistency, and after being mixed with carbon soot the glass dough is baked at a high temperature. As it bakes, the glass rises under the influence of millions of tiny gas bubbles, and as it cools the glass hardens into a texture so light that it will float on water. This angel-food glass is used as a heat-insulating material for refrigerator cars and cold storage rooms.

Glass is being spun into fibers finer than the thread of the silk worm's cocoon, these fibers are being twisted into yarns, and woven into cloth. The resulting glass textiles are used to make fireproof curtains, insulation for electrical transmission wires, and even comforters, quilts, and sleeping bags.

Today's most remarkable glass, a monument to the ingenuity and skill of the glass research chemist, is of pure silica. Like the beautiful luna moth which emerges from the lowly caterpillar, this glass is an end result of evolution, a creation brought into being by the chemist as an otherwise useless member of the glass family is destroyed.

The glass begins as any normal glass—a mixture of molten oxides including sand. Sand, I may add, is the oxide of silicon. In this molten stage of the mixture the glassmaker can fabricate any vessel, beaker, flask, tube, or other useful article of glass for the laboratory, the home, or industry. Let us assume that the thing being made is a beaker, a simple glass vessel of a sort which the chemist uses constantly. As the beaker cools and becomes rigid, the chemist arrests the cooling at a chosen temperature. Gradually, under this temperature control, the oxide of silicon separates from the mixture and forms the walls for a labyrinth of invisible connecting tunnels leading through the entire thickness of the beaker, from outer surface to inner surface. The tiny tunnels are not empty, however—the mixture of remaining oxides fills them. Fortunately, these remaining oxides are removable, for by nature they are soluble in dilute acids and water. So now, by the simple process of immersing the beaker in a bath of weak acid and washing it with water, the contents of the tunnels are removed.

The beaker, its shape maintained by the silica tunnel walls, is now reheated to a high temperature. Under this extreme heat the silica walls of the labyrinth shrink and coalesce to form a beaker only two-thirds the size of the object which began the evolutionary process.

This new glass is very extraordinary. It is clear and transparent, and readily transmits heat rays and ultra-violet radiations as well as light. It possesses strong resistance to the passage of electricity, and withstands rapid heating and cooling to a greater degree than any other glass. It can be heated red hot and then plunged into ice water. The severest temperature shock will not break or even crack it.

It has been possible in this brief article to review only a few of the developments and applications of today's glass. Strange and fanciful as they may appear, already in the glass-research laboratories they are being supplemented by stranger and more fanciful substances that will become the glass of tomorrow.

Bouncing Molecules

By Willis A. Gibbons

Dr. Willis A. Gibbons is associate director of research and technical development of United States Rubber Company. During the recent war he and his associates played a vital role in connection with the development of the synthetic rubber industry.

THE CONTROLLED release of atomic energy is the greatest scientific development of our time. But in our preoccupation with this great achievement let us not forget other aspects of atoms which have

more intimate relation to our daily life and well-being. Think of
the vast and useful array of properties which characterize the matter
forming our bodies and all animate nature—the air we breathe,
the water we drink, the materials we use in our work or play.
How can we explain all these forms of matter? The properties
of all these different forms of matter are largely the properties of
their molecules, and these properties are in turn determined by
the nature and arrangement of the atoms which compose the molecules. Many different kinds of molecules occur naturally and man
has made many new kinds.

Of all the various known materials, rubber is one of the most
remarkable. It has a unique assortment of physical properties—
great elasticity, stretchability, and toughness. Rubber has contributed directly to many modern inventions such as the motorcar.
So vital is rubber to our civilization that it was a near catastrophe
when the supply of natural rubber was cut off by the war. Fortunately we were able to produce synthetic rubber promptly enough
so that our war effort was not retarded.

The peculiar properties of rubber have excited the curiosity of
scientists. As a result of their efforts we now have a good idea
of the structure of the molecules of rubber, both natural and synthetic.

Let us assume that we are wearing extraordinary spectacles,
so powerful that we can see the molecules of matter and the atoms
of which they are composed. The rubber molecule is exceedingly
complicated, so suppose we look first at something comparatively
simple: for example, a molecule of ordinary paraffin wax. We
would see that the paraffin wax is made up of two kinds of atoms
—carbon and hydrogen. The carbon atoms are linked together
in a chainlike arrangement and the separate hydrogen atoms are
attached directly to the carbon atoms.

There may be from 25 to 50 carbon atoms in the chain. That
is paraffin wax. Now let us look at a molecule of rubber. It too
consists of carbon and hydrogen, and most of the carbon atoms
are again fixed together to form a chain. However, we have some
difficulty in seeing the rubber molecule as a whole, for two reasons. First, it is very long; if we have the patience to count the
carbon atoms we shall find that there are several thousand of them

in the chain. The second difficulty in looking at the entire rubber molecule is that it, like all its fellow molecules, is kinked, twisted, and in a general state of disorder. If our spectacles are so powerful that the paraffin or rubber molecules appear to have the thickness of a good sized rope, say one inch in diameter, the paraffin molecule will appear to be about 15 inches long. Rubber molecules under the same conditions would appear to be some 30 to 150 feet in length, provided of course we could untangle them so as to see the entire molecule at a glance.

As would be expected, these giant chainlike molecules of rubber behave very differently from the short molecules of paraffin wax. If a large assemblage of rubber molecules—in other words, a piece of rubber—is stretched, the long chains are brought into alignment one with another. In fact, the aligning operation is the stretching operation. As you hold the piece of rubber in your hand, the kinked and twisted molecules are in a state of constant movement. Individual atoms vibrate without losing their relative positions in the molecule. Whole sections of the molecule also oscillate. This motion increases as the temperature rises; actually the warmth in the substance which we feel with our hands is the movement of the atoms and groups of atoms. When we stretch the rubber, we enforce some semblance of order. We thus restrict some of the motions of the molecules as though they were confined in a smaller space, and accordingly the remaining movements become more rapid; that is, the temperature rises.

The molecules tend to resist this straightening out. When the stretched rubber is released, matters revert to about their original state—the rubber contracts and the molecules resume their unruly ways. Likewise, if we suddenly compress the rubber it will resist; in other words it bounces.

We have seen that the paraffin wax and rubber both consist of chains of carbon atoms, although of very different length. This chainlike arrangement permits the molecules to slip past one another when force is applied to them. In other words, both materials are plastic. Plasticity is important because it permits convenient manufacturing processes such as molding.

The giant threadlike molecules of rubber can be fastened together by cross links. When it is thus cross-linked, rubber ceases to be plastic. This process is called vulcanization, and sulfur is the usual cross-linking material. The properties of the vulcanized rubber vary with the number of the cross-links. If there are relatively few, the rubber is soft and flexible, and will stretch easily. With a greater number of cross-links the rubber becomes stiffer and harder and more force is required to stretch it.

Seen through our magic spectacles, the cross-linked or vulcanized rubber seems more complicated than the unvulcanized material. Adjoining chains are linked together at irregular intervals by atoms of sulfur, but the linking is not merely a matter of joining two chains together in a structure similar to a tire chain. The linking extends to three dimensions and probably is not at all regular. The process of vulcanization was discovered a hundred years ago but our knowledge of it is still incomplete.

The plastic properties of rubber permit us to put it into any desired shape; the cross-linking or vulcanization operation sets the material in that shape. These changes of state are all-important to the utilization of rubber as a structural material.

What we have said thus far applies to both the natural and synthetic rubber molecules. However, there are some differences which can be observed. If the chainlike molecule is built in a regular fashion, that is, if the atoms of carbon and hydrogen are so arranged that a regular repeating order exists, the stretched rubber will show certain peculiar properties. For example, when stretched natural rubber is examined in an X-ray spectrograph it gives a regular pattern similar to the one we see when an ordinary crystalline structure is examined in the X-ray. This means that stretched rubber molecules have an orderly repeating arrangement, like a crystal. The orderly pattern is not apparent when the tension of the rubber is released, and the molecule is no longer straight. In somewhat the same way the pattern of a plaid necktie is not evident when the tie is crushed into a shapeless mass, but becomes evident when the tie is pulled out straight.

Some of the synthetic rubbers, however, do not show this effect when they are examined by the X ray. There is no regular pattern, and we believe that this is a consequence of the molecular structure. We believe that the atoms in the chain of synthetic rubber are not so orderly in their arrangement as is the case with natural rubber. This difference is particularly in evidence when natural rubber is compared with the type of synthetic rubber known as GR-S—a variety produced from butadiene and styrene. GR-S is the synthetic rubber that was manufactured in large amounts during the recent war, which provided tires and other articles used in the war effort. Despite its lack of orderly arrangement of atoms, this synthetic rubber has proved to be highly satisfactory for most of the important uses.

A task which remains for the rubber technologists to solve is that of producing synthetic molecules having a more orderly arrangement of atoms in the chain. When that is attained, we shall have a man-made rubber which should more closely resemble the natural product.

Science has made rapid advances in recent years in its ability to explain the physical properties of substances in terms of the arrangement of the atoms in their molecules, and these advances are a tribute to the work done by the chemists and the physicists. The success which has attended these efforts to explain the nature of the material world prompts us to believe that still greater discoveries lie ahead, for there are yet many mysteries that await understanding. Many of these discoveries will be made by the young people of America who in increasing numbers are devoting themselves to careers of science.

The Story of 100 Octane Gas

By Robert E. Wilson

Dr. Robert E. Wilson, formerly a professor of chemical engineering and a research director, is now chairman of the Board of the Standard Oil Company (Indiana).

THE REMARKABLE product I want to tell you about is known as 100 octane aviation gasoline, but the term "gasoline" applied to this fuel is almost as obsolete as the term "horseless carriage" when applied to the modern automobile. Even the term "100 octane" no longer states adequately the quality built into today's fuel for military aviation engines.

Crude petroleum consists of thousands of different compounds of carbon and hydrogen, known as hydrocarbons. All of them have high fuel value, but they differ in many respects depending on the size and structure of the individual molecules. Those having the smaller molecules constitute gas and gasoline, while the larger and heavier molecules may be progressively separated into kerosene, heavier fuel oils, lubricating oils, and asphalt.

The term "gasoline" originally described the very inflammable light ends which, if not removed from kerosene, made it likely to explode. It was largely a waste product until a use was found for it in early automobiles.

For many years gasoline consisted solely of these lighter hydrocarbons recovered from crude oil by simple distillation. Thirty-odd years ago, when the demand began to exceed this supply, Dr. W. M. Burton discovered a practical way to double the amount of gasoline obtainable from crude oil by heating some of its heavier portions under pressure until the large molecules were split apart or cracked, as we call it, to form smaller and more volatile hydrocarbons. Without cracking, our country could never have operated its 30,000,000 cars or fought a motorized war. While gasoline was steadily improved, most prewar motor fuel was still not far from a 50-50 mixture of gasoline distilled out of crude and similar hydrocarbon molecules produced by cracking.

100 octane aviation gasoline, born of war needs, is a very different thing. More than three quarters of it consists of molecules specially made by new chemical processes to do a particular job—namely, to operate smoothly in supercharged, high-output, aviation engines.

Basically it is the offspring of research started during World War I. It was already known that, as the compression of an internal combustion engine was increased, greater efficiency and more power could be obtained from a given size and weight of engine. However, attempts to apply this fact ran into a serious obstacle. It was found that fuels tended to knock as compression ratios increased. At first this behavior was thought to be due to preignition of the gasoline ahead of the spark, but the late Thomas Midgley showed that the knock was not due to preignition but to a form of excessively rapid burning, or detonation, of the air-fuel mixture when it was subjected to high pressure. He also found that cracked gasoline had less tendency to knock than straight run gasoline, which until then had been considered superior.

Publication of these results started a whole era of competition between automobile companies in designing engines and spark plugs to reduce knocking tendencies, and between oil companies to produce fuels which would stand higher compressions and higher temperatures without knocking. Midgley and his associates also developed antiknock agents, like tetraethyl lead, and the constituents of gasoline itself were gradually improved by improved cracking processes. But there were endless arguments as to which fuels were best. It became evident that to make real progress an accurate measuring scale was needed to determine the knocking tendency of fuels.

A knock rating scale was eventually developed by Dr. Graham Edgar, using mixtures of a hydrocarbon called normal heptane, which knocked very badly, and another called iso-octane, which had about the least knocking tendency of any known hydrocarbon. Thus, a fuel which knocked just as badly as a mixture of 60 per cent iso-octane and 40 per cent normal heptane in a given test engine was said to have an "octane number" of 60.

An *immediate* result was that progress in the development of better automobile fuels was speeded up. In the next 15 years the average rose from about 55 to about 72 octane number. An *indirect* result was that this unusual kind of iso-octane became the star to which research workers could hitch their wagon. Strangely enough, it has never been found among the thousands of hydrocarbons present in crude petroleum, but could only be made by a complicated chemical process at a cost of about ten dollars per gallon. Too costly to be used even in knock-*testing* as a regular practice, it was like the platinum meter stick in the Bureau of Standards— something to use in standardizing other and less costly comparison fuels.

However, some scientists could not forget that there was one hydrocarbon, however expensive, which was the last word in antiknock perfection; and kept diligently at work attempting to find some way of producing this iso-octane or similar hydrocarbons at lower cost. In the early thirties it was found possible to make a fairly pure iso-octane by first combining two gaseous hydrocarbon molecules, which were by-products of cracking, and then adding hydrogen in the presence of a catalyst. This was a fairly simple two-step synthetic process. Its product initially cost around a dollar per gallon and still seemed too expensive to have any practical value.

In spite of this, some farsighted men in the National Advisory Committee for Aeronautics and in the Army reached the conclusion that for military purposes the value of really high octane gasoline would be so great that even a dollar per gallon was not prohibitive, at least as a starting point. Accordingly, about a dozen years ago, they ordered a whole tank car of 100 octane to be painstakingly made up in small-scale apparatus, and started developing really high-compression aviation engines to take advantage of this super-fuel. So promising were the results, and the progress of the petroleum laboratories in making similar synthetic fuels at lower cost, that well before the recent war began, our Army and Navy decided to build their engines to operate on 100 octane fuel, of which we then had the only known supply. However, when the few British fliers "to whom so many owe so much" shot down hundreds of German planes in the Battle of Britain, they had 100 octane gasoline in their Spitfires, giving them that vital extra margin of speed and altitude over German fliers using inferior fuel. Ten to thirteen octane numbers may well have shaped the history of the world in that battle!

But that was only the beginning. In the summer of 1940 the total military demand for 100 octane was less than ten thousand barrels a day. The petroleum industry, spurred by competition and confidence in future demand, had developed capacity to make about thirty-five thousand barrels per day, which was beyond the then estimated requirements of the military for two years ahead.

Soon the estimates of requirements began to soar. In the midst of frenzied war-time construction of all kinds of war plants the demand for 100 octane for the insatiable war machines climbed to 100,000—200,000—300,000—400,000 and finally 500,000 barrels for every day. New constituents were found—new processes developed and put into commercial operation without waiting for the usual small-scale tryouts. Thousands of chemists and engineers and refinery workers toiled day and night to get the plants into successful operation. The petroleum industry spent over nine hundred million dollars of its own money in plants to make hydrocarbons fit for our modern aviation engines. By the beginning of 1945, we were producing that 500,000 barrels per day of superfuel—about 75 per cent of it consisting of tailor-made molecules—by processes not dreamed of a dozen years ago. The average refinery cost is now around 14¢ per gallon (not including taxes of course), and the war-time quantities dwarfed all other synthetic chemicals put together.

And that was not all—for as soon as the end of the European war eased the demand for peak production we found that we could leave out some of the less valuable constituents and produce a *real* all-synthetic superfuel for the special benefit of the B-29's operating out of the Marianas.

Best of all, our research workers now have before them some other "unattainable" goals. There are two or three new stars on the horizon—new hydrocarbons which are in some respects as much better than iso-octane as iso-octane was better than any previous gasoline. Again, we do not know how to make them at reasonable cost. The work of science, like that of women, is never done, and a new generation of young scientists is just itching to show us oldsters how far they can excel our achievements. I have supreme confidence that they will do as much for us in peace as the Spitfire pilots, aided by 100 octane gasoline, did for us in war.

Cows, Movies and Color-Photography

By C. E. K. Mees

Dr. C. E. K. Mees was for many years the director of the Research Laboratory of the Eastman Kodak Company. He is now a vice-president of that Company, and its director of research and development.

ALL of us are interested in photography. Even if we don't take photographs ourselves, we like to look at them, and movies are photographs, you know.

But what has photography to do with science? Perhaps you remember what movies used to be like. If old pictures are projected nowadays, the news pictures of the last war, for instance, they are in startling contrast to the pictures made today. That difference is chiefly due to the work of the men who study the science of photography. Twenty years ago we found out that if cows didn't like mustard there wouldn't be any movies at all. This is the story:

Film is made of tiny crystals of a chemical called silver bromide imbedded in gelatin. Gelatin is made by boiling clippings from calves' hides in water and then the liquid is chilled to set it to a jelly and the jelly is dried.

Twenty years ago, some batches of gelatin gave light-sensitive film and some gave insensitive film. We who made the film didn't know why. So we were forced to select our gelatin by trial, using only the lots of gelatin which by test gave sensitive film. Chemical analysis didn't show any difference between the batches of gelatin which gave good film and those which didn't. Dr. S. E. Sheppard in our laboratory decided to study samples taken from all stages of gelatin manufacture. In making the gelatin, the calf skin is first soaked with lime for many weeks. Then the lime is washed out with acid and with water before the gelatin can be cooked out. Sheppard found, after hundreds of tests, that this acid wash liquor contained something which made a gelatin give sensitive films. Then the liquors were concentrated, and a substance was extracted which contained a concentrated form of the unknown sensitizer. Still Sheppard couldn't identify it. But the extracted substance reminded him of materials that can be extracted from some plants. So he made plant extracts of the chemical type indicated. When he made them from wild mustard, he found that the extract had a most energetic sensitizing effect. This clue enabled him to identify the sensitizer. It was mustard oil. The chemical composition of mustard oil is well known. Synthetic mustard oil proved to be as effective as natural mustard oil in sensitizing gelatin, from which highly sensitive film can be made.

But this discovery didn't enable us to make better film at once. The best combination of artificial sensitizers wouldn't give more sensitive film than the best natural gelatins. But from our research we learned much about the nature of sensitizing. What we got was not an immediately applicable discovery but knowledge, the systematic knowledge we call science. The main purpose of a research laboratory is not to make inventions but to create knowledge.

Photographic film can be made more sensitive by making the crystals of silver bromide larger. However, when these large crystals of silver bromide turn into silver in development, little clumps of silver become visible on the screen and the pictures look grainy. Our understanding of the nature of sensitizing has enabled us to make film more sensitive without increasing the graininess.

In the improvement of movie films another piece of work in a different field of chemistry has played a great part. Because silver bromide is sensitive only to blue, violet, and ultraviolet light, the movies of twenty years ago were taken by daylight or by arc lights. The ultraviolet rays produced by the powerful arc lights hurt the eyes of the actors and made colors and complexions seem pasty.

Fortunately, science was ready with a solution of this problem. Many years before, photographic scientists had found that film could be made sensitive to yellow light by adding a dye to the silver bromide. But only a few dyes were known to work and the use of them had practical disadvantages. Before 1914 these dyes came from Germany. However, the German chemists had contented themselves with finding a few useful dyes and had not identified their structure. When the supply of German dyes ceased in 1914, English and American chemists started to produce them. The chemists of Cambridge University were not satisfied simply to make the dyes; they also investigated the composition of each dye. They found out how the molecules were put together.

As a result of this scientific research, it became possible to make a great many new dyes—thousands of them—and some of these dyes were much better sensitizers for silver bromide than any of the German dyes. With these new dyes, film could be made more sensitive to yellow light than to blue. Also, these dyes sensitize fine-grain film so much better than they sensitize film of coarser grain that fine-grain film could be made very sensitive either to daylight or to artificial light from tungsten lamps.

This new panchromatic film, as it was called, had an influence in two directions in photography: It made possible the use of miniature cameras to take small pictures which could be enlarged without showing graininess, and it made possible the replacement of arc lamps on movie sets by the more convenient and noiseless tungsten lamps. This development came just in time for use in sound pictures, in the making of which the new lamps were a great advantage. But notice again that these practical advantages didn't come from looking for them. They came from looking for knowledge, a knowledge of the chemical molecular structure of the sensitizing dyes.

The development of the new sensitizing dyes and, thus, of panchromatic film made possible the realization of the photographer's dream—photography in color. The principles of color photography were established about eighty years ago by a very clever and farseeing Frenchman, Duces du Hauron, long before there was any possibility of realizing his plans. More than thirty years ago, a patent was granted for making a color photograph by coating on a single film three layers of photo-sensitive material, one layer sensitive to red light, one to green, and one to blue light and then, after exposure, producing in each layer dye images complementary to the light to which the layer was sensitive; that is, a blue-green image in the red-sensitive layer, a magenta image in the green-sensitive layer, and a yellow image in the blue-sensitive layer.

Unfortunately, this could not be done because neither the sensitizing dyes nor the chemicals which produced the dye images would stay in their own places; instead, when the three layers were coated they wandered into the wrong layers. It was not until so many excellent sensitizing dyes were found that it was possible to choose dyes which would not wander and to overcome the other difficulties.

It will be of particular interest to learn that the first successful color film was made by two young musicians, Leo Godowsky, Jr., and Leopold Mannes, who were trained in chemistry and were enthusiastic experimenters in color photography.

They deserted their music for a time, came to our laboratory, and there with the aid of the new sensitizing dyes and our knowledge of photographic science perfected a practical process of color photography. From this have come many developments, so that almost all the home movies are now made in color while the ordinary snapshots can be made in color as easily, though not yet as cheaply, as in black and white.

While all this has been going on, our knowledge of the science of photography has been growing steadily. Forty years ago, when all this work on photography was starting, there was no thought of new film, of better movies, or of pictures in color. We wanted to understand how a photographic image was produced, how silver bromide came to be so sensitive to light, what happened when it was exposed, and how it turned into silver during development. Step by step the nature of these mysteries has become clearer. Today our aim in the research laboratory is still a better understanding of the science of photography.

CHAPTER 5

NEW INSTRUMENTAL TECHNIQUES—
NEW CHEMICALS

THE INTRODUCTION to the last chapter pointed out that new materials and new processes go hand in hand as technology moves forward. In much the same way, new instrumental techniques are essential to advancement in the fields of basic science. With this latter progress have come such new substances as the wonder chemicals we hear so much about these days.

In the following chapter two of these chemicals—DDT and streptomycin—are discussed. There are many more that deserve mention: penicillin, the sulfa drugs, the synthetic vitamins and hormones, and so on. The readers may wonder why these new chemicals are described in this chapter, while the new materials produced by modern technology were dealt with in the last one. The honest answer is that this division is largely an arbitrary one.

For the microbiologist in a university laboratory, the biochemist in a pharmaceutical laboratory, the organic chemist synthesizing a new plastic—these modern scientists are all producing new chemicals, new substances, new materials for man to use. In referring to some of their results as "materials" and to others as "chemicals" there is no intent to infer that the latter are any less practical or the former any less scientific.

In fact, modern technology and modern basic science are inextricably interlocked. The distinction between applied science and basic science (the latter of which is sometimes rather unfortunately referred to as "pure" science, just as though applied science were somehow impure) is to be found in motivation and organization, but not in knowledge, intellectual capacity, or imagination.

There will also be found in this chapter a discussion of two powerful instrumental techniques. The first involves a microscope which uses electrons instead of light beams. This is a new instrument which is proving of the greatest value. The second involves the spectroscope, an instrument which is by no means new, since it was devised over a hundred years ago. Recently, however, the spectroscope has undergone great technical improvement, and only recently has it been really widely exploited by science. Originally a somewhat clumsy and specialized instrument of the physicist and the astronomer, it has now become an essential tool for the biologist and the medical researcher.

Should another volume similar to this one be written later, there are many other new scientific instruments which ought to be described and explained. The ultracentrifuge, the phase microscope, the mass spectroscope, the Tiselius apparatus, the vacuum still, the modern vacuum tube, the cyclotron, the synchrotron—actually the list is so long and so interesting that an entire book would be needed to begin to do justice to the story of the instrumentation of modern science.

W. W.

The Story of the Electron Microscope

By James Hillier

Although Dr. James Hillier is a young man, he has been a pioneer in the development of the electron microscope. He is a research engineer at the RCA Laboratories.

OUR story concerns one of the latest developments of modern science, but its beginnings go back some two hundred and fifty years. At that time there was a certain merchant in the city of Delft, Holland, who had a curious hobby. This man, Anton Leeuwenhoek, was possessed with the idea of making a perfect optical lens, and after his store closed for the day he used to spend his nights patiently grinding small bits of glass and shaping them into carefully curved surfaces. This inspired amateur became an expert. He made for himself a microscope and was fascinated by the world of little things which it brought into his view.

For centuries, scientists had speculated on the nature and structure of the invisible world that lies beyond the range of the unaided eye. It was for Leeuwenhoek to open the door and take a look. What he saw was enough to show the possibilities of microscopy. Gradually the microscope was accepted as a regular tool of science. In the nineteenth century Pasteur, Koch, and others made spectacular advances in biology and medicine through the use of the relatively crude microscopes of their time.

In the early days it was assumed that there was no theoretical limit to the magnifying power of microscopes. It was supposed that as lenses became improved, one could see continuously smaller and smaller objects. A rude awakening came, however, about seventy years ago. At that time the German physicist, Ernest Abbe, pointed out that it would never be possible to observe directly an object which was considerably smaller than the wave length of the light used to illuminate it.

In effect, what Abbe said was this: That no microscope using ordinary light could usefully magnify an object by more than about 1000 diameters, no matter how perfect its lenses. He showed by optical theory why this must be so.

But, as so often happens in science, the theory which sets a limit to what can be accomplished with existing methods at the same time points out the way in which those methods can be improved and the limit thus removed. If ordinary light is too coarse, reasoned the scientists, why not use ultraviolet light since its wave lengths are only about one-half that of ordinary blue light? This stratagem was tried and it worked. By making their lenses of special materials which are transparent to ultraviolet light, the optical experts were able to construct an ultraviolet microscope with a magnification of 2500 diameters. This was more than double the power of the ordinary microscope.

Of course it was natural to think of further extending the method and using still shorter wave lengths, for there are many rays beyond the ultraviolet. But this time the physical properties of the rays put a stop to progress. For either the waves were absorbed by the lenses, as was the case with the extremely short ultraviolet rays; or else the waves were so penetrating that they passed through the lenses without being affected and focusing became impossible, as was the case with X rays, for example.

Thus we have the situation in the 1920's. Research scientists were becoming more and more aware of the existence of many small structures that could best be studied through a microscope, if only a microscope powerful enough could be devised. Probably no one was more surprised than the microscopists themselves when the solution came not from students of optics, but from the atomic physicists studying electrons.

Electrons are the particles of negative electricity whose flow through wires and vacuum tubes constitutes an electric current. In 1924 the French physicist, Louis DeBroglie, presented a thesis in which he suggested that a beam of electrons had what we may call a dual personality. He pointed out that such a beam was not just a stream of particles but that it also had associated with it something in the nature of a wave.

Later, when the truth of DeBroglie's theory was demonstrated, the wave length associated with an electron beam was found to be almost inconceivably small. Actually, the electron wave length is one hundred thousand times as short as that of visible light. The conclusion was obvious. If a microscope could be devised to use a beam of electrons in place of the usual beam of light, it should bring to visibility objects far, far smaller than anything previously seen. It was an exciting idea, but there was one forbidding detail. Nobody knew a way of focusing electrons, and until the electron beam could be focused there was no prospect of constructing an electron microscope.

Meanwhile, and quite apart from these desires and speculations, a certain Dr. Busch in a physical laboratory in Germany was having difficulties with an experiment in electronics. Busch decided to calculate the magnitude of his errors. History doesn't tell whether he was successful in tracking down the degree of those errors, for in the course of his computations he noticed something that set him on another trail. He noticed that the equations he was getting for the behavior of the electrons moving through a special type of magnetic field were exactly the same as the well-known equations defining the behavior of light rays when traveling through a lens. In other words, electronics could be focused by certain kinds of magnets just as light is focused by certain kinds of lenses. And if electrons could be focused, then an electron microscope could be built.

That chance discovery marked the birth of the new science of electron optics. It provided the basic idea for the electron microscope. The idea was easier to put into words than into practice, however. Six years of heart-breaking frustration had to pass before an electron microscope was built that even approached the capabilities of an ordinary optical microscope. Research workers had to learn a lot of new techniques. They had to become familiar with the peculiarities of a fickle substitute for light. By 1938 these researches were bearing fruit. In that year instruments with magnifications up to 30,000 diameters were put in operation both here and abroad. By 1940 electron microscopes with a useful magnification of 100,000 diameters were in use. Today in my own laboratory we have an experimental instrument which has attained useful magnifications of more than 200,000 diameters. And the end is not yet in sight—for still greater powers are possible theoretically.

It is difficult for the mind to visualize what is meant by a magnification of 200,000 diameters. At that magnification an inch-long cockroach would appear more than three miles long; a gnat would seem larger than a B-29 Superfortress. Of course, objects the size of cockroaches and gnats cannot be viewed through the electron microscope—one can examine only a microscopic area of each insect's leg or other minute part. The objects to be seen in their entirety are such otherwise invisible things as the bacillus of tuberculosis, the virus of influenza, and smaller structures ranging down to protein molecules. Indeed, the world of the electron microscopist is a very extensive one. If I were to start now it would take all the remainder of my life and part of the next to explore a single square inch of my garden.

More than 100 electron microscopes are in use today in industrial, medical, and university laboratories of this country. They bring to view the fine structure of every conceivable material that concerns our everyday life: from food products to synthetic rubber, from the structure of steel to that of nylon, from ordinary bacteria to the smaller viruses. We are already enjoying many benefits that have come from scientific study of those things of nature which cannot be observed through our normal sense of vision. When we remember that those advances have been made by devious and indirect methods, we see the significance of the electron microscope. It is an incomparable tool in the hands of scientists who are interested in the structure of material, a weapon in the hands of those who study the microorganisms of disease, a source of "light" to illumine the hidden world beyond the veil of the visible.

Fingerprints in Medicine

BY CORNELIUS P. RHOADS

Dr. Cornelius P. Rhoads is the director of the Memorial Hospital, New York City, the largest institution in the world devoted to the care and cure of patients with cancer.

THE human eye is our most useful scientific instrument. It works on the principle of the photographic camera, converting into pictures on its back wall the light which comes to it by reflection from the objects at which we look. Unfortunately, however, the eye is not sensitive enough to photograph the details of distant objects, like stars, or small objects, like blood cells. So we have arrangements of lenses in the form of telescopes and microscopes to gather and concentrate the light and enlarge the image. Such magnifications enable us to see the shape and physical form of structures which to the unaided eye are invisible. But microscopes and telescopes bring only a physical picture—they are not able to peer into the inner nature of things and reveal the stuff of which an object is made. For this function science has another instrument, known as the spectroscope. A spectroscope is an apparatus of prisms and lenses which is able to identify the presence of hidden chemical elements by a technique that I may liken to fingerprinting.

The invention of the spectroscope had its origin in the experiments of Isaac Newton in 1670. Newton was deeply interested in the behavior of light, and one day he drilled a tiny hole in the wall of a closed room, and the sunlight passing through this hole formed a bright spot on the opposite wall. Then Newton placed a prism, a triangular piece of glass, over the hole and the spot of light became a band of colors, the familiar pattern of the rainbow.

Thus Newton showed that white light is a mixture of many colors, ranging from red to violet. This sequence of colors is called a spectrum, and the spectroscope is a device for sorting light out into its spectral components, and studying the colors in detail.

The spectroscope operates on the basic principle that the color of an object depends upon its absorption or reflection of light. A red blood cell is red because it absorbs the other colors but rejects and therefore reflects red light. A piece of charcoal is black because it absorbs all colors. A Japanese woman wearing a black-and-white striped dress was exposed to the terrible light from the atomic blast. Her skin was burned through the dress, but only under the black stripes. The black absorbed the light, whereas the white reflected it. The black stripes had been made by adding a black dye to the originally white fabric, and the molecules of this dye were able to absorb all the colors composing the light. Hence the skin burn under the black stripes.

The spectroscope is more versatile than our eyes; for we can see light of only a narrow range of colors, from violet at one end of the spectrum to red at the other, but the spectroscope is sensitive to light beyond the violet, the ultraviolet, and to rays beyond the red, the infrared.

Although human vision has never seen these invisible colors, the spectroscope unveils them, sorts them out, and by photography brings their effects to view.

One of the spectral effects that was discovered many years after Newton's historic experiment is the absorption spectrum. I may illustrate its process in this way. Suppose you have the usual spectroscope arrangement, a beam of white light passing through a prism and projecting the familiar violet-to-red pattern on the screen. Now take a thin glass flask filled with a solution of blood and interpose it in the beam in such a way that the light must pass through the red fluid before it passes through the prism. Instantly, black lines appear in the spectrum where red had appeared before. The blood absorbs the red light, and leaves black shadows to mark the gaps in the spectrum. By this property of absorbing red light the hemoglobin of blood can be identified. Even minute traces of it can be detected. The black lines, or gaps in the spectrum, are in a detailed way characteristic of the absorbing substance. Thus these gaps in the spectrum—or as the physicist says—these absorption lines are to chemical substances what fingerprints are to human beings.

Medical science is very dependent on the spectroscope.

One of its most dramatic applications uses the instrument to detect the presence in body cells of certain chemical substances which absorb light of one color. A cell, of course, is too small to be seen, so a microscope is trained upon it to make the cell visible. Then the light from the cell is passed by the microscope through the spectroscope, and various parts of the cell are appraised, the light from each part being sorted into its component rays. In this way measurements are made of the light absorption in each area of the tiny structure, and by such means it has been shown that a certain unique chemical compound is present in excessive quantities in rapidly growing cells. The presence of this excess is particularly noticeable in the case of cancer cells.

Various combinations of microscope and spectroscope have been set up to detect, measure, and locate in cells infinitesimally small amounts of vitamins, minerals, and other substances. They have shown that the body is able by its natural processes to render harm-less certain poisonous compounds. This is true, for example, of specific substances which cause cancer. These cancer-producing compounds were originally detected by means of their characteristic absorption of light, and by the same means we now watch them change to new forms.

Recently the spectroscope was directed at another vital medical problem. It is being used to identify substances which are formed by certain glands of the body and released into the bloodstream. These glandular substances affect growth, sex characteristics, and muscular power. They control the essential chemical processes of the body, and without them life cannot go on. Yet, when they function abnormally, they interfere with life. They seem to be inti-mately bound up with serious disorders such as cancer, deformities of bones and joints, and the failure of heart and blood vessels. We have long realized the indispensable nature of these compounds, but lacked detailed knowledge of their actions and changes—knowledge which the spectroscope is now bringing to light.

Now that it is possible to separate important chemical substances one from the other and to measure and identify each one by the spectroscope, we know that a new absorption pattern means a new, hitherto undescribed compound. From the pattern we can even draw certain conclusions as to the arrangement of its constituent atoms. The spectroscope, for example, told us the composition of penicillin long before the chemist had final proof.

Thus the pioneering work of Newton, in sorting light into its colors, and the further studies of many other modern scientists in the same field have given us a powerful tool for medical as well as chemical and physical research. The fingerprint gallery of science, obtained by means of the spectroscope, has already solved major problems. It will surely bring additional facts to knowledge in the years just ahead. It will influence all our lives.

The Spectroscope: A Master Key to New Materials

By George R. Harrison

Dr. George R. Harrison is professor of physics, and dean of science
at the Massachusetts Institute of Technology.

In the past, mankind had of necessity to be content to use the
materials which nature provided. In Colonial days, for example,
men lubricated their machinery, oiled their boots and even filled
their lamps with oil taken from whales. For even so modern a
device as the automobile, the best tires have, until now, been made
of rubber prepared from latex drained from trees. Until fairly
recently women were pleased to wear stockings made of silk, a
moderately satisfactory plastic filament obtained from worms.

Every substance we use, whether oil, rubber, silk or one of the
thousand other materials which we consider essential to civilized
living, is composed of countless tiny molecules, and behaves as it
does because of the properties of these molecules. Oil molecules
when combined with oxygen release heat energy, so oil is good fuel.
The rubber molecule has a great deal of stretch, like a coiled spring,
and can be extended far beyond its normal length without breaking, so rubber tires are flexible and resilient, and will absorb bumps
and jolts. The molecules in silk combine some stretch with considerable strength and the ability to hold firmly to their neighbors,
so millions of these molecules can cling together to form a smooth,
tough fiber. Scientists have long known that the best way to understand a material is to understand the molecules of which it is composed.

We are now entering a new phase of scientific development
which might be called the production of custom-built molecules.
In earlier days chemists produced new substances by mixing chemicals together, letting them fizz more or less at random, and then
seeing whether the new substances obtained had properties which
would be useful. Today, however, they are learning to figure out
in advance how to build molecules which will have any desired
property.

Only a few tens of thousands of different kinds of molecules have been identified by chemists as occurring in nature, but they have been able to produce nearly a million new kinds of molecules—and thus new substances. This advance became possible when scientists learned now to take the molecules themselves apart. All molecules are made of atoms. There are less than a hundred varieties of atoms, and the main job of the chemist has been to learn how to rearrange these atoms in combinations to produce new and useful molecules and, hence, new and useful materials.

An outstanding example of a custom-built molecule is Freon. Ordinary home electric refrigerators used to be filled either with ammonia or sulphur dioxide, which had strong odors and could even poison the air if the refrigerator sprang a leak. All other available materials had been tried, but none was exactly suitable. Obviously a new and better molecule was needed. Like a tailor restyling an old coat, chemists took the carbon tetrachloride molecule, which came pretty close to being right, and replaced two of the chlorine atoms which it contained with atoms of fluorine. The result was a new substance, Freon, which proved ideal for refrigeration and, incidentally, for many other industrial purposes.

Another example of the custom-built molecule is nylon. Scientists worked for many years to find a means of producing a filament as fine, as strong, and as elastic as those of silk, and yet not so expensive. The first partially successful result was rayon. Rayon ultimately could be made much more cheaply than silk, but rayon stockings, as every woman knows, are inferior to silk stockings, because the molecules in rayon when stretched do not hold together as strongly as those in silk, so rayon stockings are more subject to snags and runs.

A short time before the recent war, chemists constructed a new molecule which holds to its companions even more strongly than do those in silk. The new molecules formed a material which we now call nylon. The molecules in nylon have some of the characteristics of the rubber molecule; and fibers of nylon show tensile strength and elasticity superior to silk, so nylon stockings came into great demand. Even so the chemist has not necessarily finished his custom-tailoring of the nylon molecule, for even nylons snag; however, there is no reason why he should not learn how to form new groupings of atoms into a super-nylon molecule. Eventually it will be as out-of-date to obtain textile fibers from worms as it already is to obtain fuel oil from whales.

The instrument which has enabled physicists to find out most about the structures of atoms, and chemists to find out how atoms fit together to make molecules, is the spectroscope. This device has unlocked even more secrets of nature than have its companions, the telescope and the microscope. The spectroscope is a very simple instrument, but it gives the answers to an incredible variety of scientific questions, from the size of an atom to the weight of a star, merely by dissecting a beam of light from the star or atom and measuring its component colors or wave lengths.

Any atom or molecule can be made to emit light by striking it a hard atomic blow and all the light which our eyes can see has originated in this way. Sunlight comes from atoms constantly stimulated by bumping into their neighbors at the terrific temperatures in the sun. An incandescent lamp emits light from atoms kept constantly agitated in its hot filament. Any substance, whether a drop of blood, a speck of putty, or an iron nail can be made to emit light by heating it until its atoms become stimulated. The light thus emitted, sent through a spectroscope, reveals many secrets regarding the atoms from which it originates.

Most of the ninety-odd kinds of atoms which form the chemical elements have been studied carefully by means of the spectroscope. Every student in a chemistry laboratory has dropped a pinch of salt into a flame and seen the bright yellow light which is characteristic of the sodium atom. Similarly copper atoms and iron atoms and the neon atoms of the electric signs all emit characteristic wave lengths of light, some invisible to the human eye, but all capable of being analyzed by the spectroscope. With this instrument the scientist measures the length of the light waves. They are only about 1/50,000th of an inch long, but the spectroscope will measure them to within a few trillionths of an inch, or a billionth of the thickness of a hair.

Once the scientist knows the lengths of the light waves, he can learn much about the atoms which emitted them. By solving a sort of crossword puzzle game for each atom, he has been able to determine the number of electrical particles in all of the kinds of atoms we know about, and to work out a picture of the electrical structure of each atom. Most important, he sees the disposition and strengths of the various electric and magnetic forces which make the atom able to hang onto other atoms to form molecules. To learn these tiny secrets of the atoms is a slow and difficult process; and even after fifty years at the job we have fairly complete pictures of only a few of the atoms. Enough information has been obtained, however, to assist the chemist greatly in designing new molecules and providing new materials.

I shall close with an example of molecular architecture of considerable recent importance. For years quinine, the specific for malaria, has been obtainable only from the bark of the cinchona tree. When the war came our supply of quinine was cut off, and our troops in the jungles of New Guinea needed a substitute. A chemically constructed molecule, atabrine, was found to serve, and has been most successful, though it does temporarily turn the skin of persons taking it a bright yellow. But very recently chemists have succeeded in building up from atoms the quinine molecule itself. New molecules useful against malaria have also been invented; and it seems probable that, so far as malaria is concerned, the dependence of the human race on natural material from a tree which grows in only one part of the world is gone forever.

Each year the gap grows smaller between the research scientist in his laboratory, dissecting the tiny atom with a beam of light in his spectroscope, and the industries which stand ready to provide a new material or device needed to improve the health, comfort and security of civilized living.

D D T

By Milton Charles Winternitz

Dr. Milton Charles Winternitz, a pathologist, holds the Anthony N. Brader professorship at the Yale University School of Medicine.

For twenty-three years after the first of the compounds now known as the sulfa drugs was made, its importance in the treatment of disease remained unknown.

Developed for the dye stuff industry, the sulfa compounds are an excellent illustration of the value of scientific research, undertaken with an entirely different and far less important application in mind. I am going to describe here a chemical compound that remained a useless curiosity for 70 years.

It is the insecticide, DDT.

DDT was discovered in the 1870's. The first application for it was found in 1939.

DDT is known by one of those descriptive names which the chemists find essential. They call it Di-chloro, di-phenyl, tri-chloro-ethane. It contains several closely related compounds. The story of all of these compounds is not yet known.

The scientific world had its first big news about the power of this chemical to kill insect pests when we learned in 1939 that as a one-per-cent dusting powder, it saved the Swiss potato crop from destruction by the Colorado beetle.

Its action soon was shown to be widespread and, as will be seen, this knowledge reached Great Britain and the United States at an opportune time.

The reports read like fairy tales. Relatively harmless for man and animals, it was said to kill many household pests, many of the almost innumerable varieties of insects that destroy crops, many of the blood-sucking varieties responsible for the spread of disease in animals and man. Its fatal action was said to be equally effective whether the insect ate the drug or merely touched it. As a film on surfaces it was reported to remain effective for several weeks after application. Only one flaw was detected. Although many insects are undesirable, there are many others which are useful to man, destroying plant pests and carrying out pollination. And DDT is not discriminating; along with the bad, it kills the good insects, including the lady beetles and honey bees.

Fortunately, when the story of DDT reached the United States, the men and facilities necessary for proof of its qualities were organized and busily engaged in the search for new insecticides. For war with Japan had cut off the supply of one chief insecticide, pyrethrum; and our main source of rotenone, a second of the few valuable insecticides, was lost with the conquest of Malaya.

So the Orlando, Florida, station of the Department of Agriculture was expanded. There, excellent co-operation was developed between the armed services, the civilian, industrial, and educational institutions, and the agencies of Government concerned with the problem. This pattern of co-operation which has emerged during the war, then wisely developed, broadens and enriches knowledge without interfering with the initiative of the individual in the execution of his own contribution.

And so when samples of DDT from Switzerland became available in October, 1942, the stage was set. Communication difficulties delayed transmittal of its chemical structure; but by the time this arrived, the active ingredient had not only been isolated and analyzed—it had actually been synthesized.

The many claims for DDT were sustained. Our need made production imperative.

One hundred and fifty tons had been used in Switzerland during 1942. Many times this amount is now produced in the United States each year.

As a ten per cent finely divided mixture in an inert base, DDT has been successfully used against an outbreak of typhus fever, a disease that flourishes in the cold months when war herds people together and prevents them from keeping clean.

Typhus reached Naples in March, 1943, and was spreading when Allied troops arrived. In four weeks the number of cases had risen from 36 to 311. Then the Director of the United States Typhus Commission took over. Each day twenty thousand, rich and poor alike, were dusted with DDT. In January 1,300,000 were dusted and nearly as many in February. The decline in the incidence of typhus was as abrupt as the rise had been steep. For the first time in history, a typhus plague had been arrested in midwinter. Dusting, DDT impregnated garments, and protective vaccination have removed the menace of the typhus-bearing louse and his flea relatives that transmit the plague.

The story of malaria and DDT is equally dramatic. The annual incidence of malaria is estimated as upwards of three hundred million. The severe types are encountered in tropical regions, but milder forms occur as far north as Sweden and as far south as Cape Horn. The yearly peacetime death toll of more than two million outnumbers that of any other infectious disease—a danger to our civil health and a threat to our military success. For centuries malaria has thrived in the chaos of war and the resulting sanitary breakdown. Millions of Allied troops had to be sent into tropical areas at a time when the usual quinine supply was unavailable and before the newer superior drugs were out of pilot-plant production. Malaria casualties in 1943, including only those sufficiently sick to require evacuation, were five times the total of all others, from bugs and bullets together. This grave danger is now past, thanks to prophylactic medication, personal hygiene, and regional sanitation.

DDT has a major role in both of the latter. It is fatal to all mosquito types that transmit malaria—to eggs and to larvae. Only the pupae are resistant. Because DDT is readily soluble in many oils, it is possible to disseminate clouds and sprays from the air as well as from the ground. The adult mosquito struck by a particle no larger than 1/5000 of an inch and containing an incredibly small content of DDT, develops tremors. It may die within 15 minutes and surely does within a day. The cloud, and especially the spray with larger particles, leaves a residuum effective for adult mosquitos and also for larvae. Its period of effectiveness varies with environmental conditions from days to weeks.

On interior walls and ceilings it has now been shown to retain its lethal effect for 300 days. This has been turned to marked advantage in control of fly-borne as well as mosquito-borne disease including dysentery, cholera, dengue.

The negligible danger of DDT as a dusting powder is increased in oil solution but so far no ill effects have been demonstrable in men even after unusual and protracted exposure.

DDT is now available for other than military needs, and it has demonstrated its supremacy in the control, not only of the great majority of insects which transmit diseases to men and animals, but also of many insects responsible for untold damage to crops and forests. Indeed only a few forms escape, like the mosquito pupae and other varieties whose outer casings are rich in a compound in which DDT becomes concentrated.

We are aware of possible undesirable results from its wholesale use on insects essential for pollination, on the distribution of birds and on the balance between many forms of life in the environment.

These questions are unanswered; and until they are, it is fundamental that the use of DDT be safeguarded.

The unchallenged position DDT now enjoys will be contested.
Many thousands of compounds are now being studied and, rumor
has it, rivals of DDT are already here. These thousands are only
a small fraction of those on the chemists' shelves.

Few have been investigated thoroughly. Let us hold fast to the
pattern of co-operation in scientific research to profitably developed
during those years of war. Perhaps among the chemists' forgotten
curiosities may be found the solution of some of our other pressing
problems.

The Story of Streptomycin

By Selman A. Waksman

Dr. Selman A. Waksman is professor of microbiology at Rutgers
University, and microbiologist in the Agricultural Experiment Station
of the State of New Jersey.

CHEMOTHERAPY, by which we mean the use of chemical substances
introduced into the human body to combat infectious disease, is
the development of barely fifty years of chemical and medical research. The first landmark in its history was the discovery of the
value of arsenic compounds in the treatment of syphilis and other
protozoan infections—an advance made by Paul Ehrlich in the first
decade of the present century. A second landmark was the introduction, a mere dozen years ago, of the sulfa drugs. These sulfonamides were found to be highly effective against a number of bacterial diseases, and they quickly opened up a new era in chemotherapy. The third landmark of our new science was the discovery
of the antibiotic drugs—and it is one of these, the antibiotic known
as streptomycin, that I shall discuss here.

First let us understand what an antibiotic is. In its simplest definition, an antibiotic is a drug that is not manufactured by man, as
sulfonilamide is, but rather derived from nature as a by-product of
some living process. Penicillin, for example, is a substance produced
by certain species of green molds. Similarly, streptomycin is a sub-

stance produced by another microbe. Somehow these microbes have developed the faculty of producing and exuding substances, namely the antibiotics, which are capable of inhibiting the growth and even destroying disease-producing bacteria and other microbes.

The name of these substances is derived from anti or against and biotic or living; in other words they interfere with the living processes, in this case the disease-producing germs.

Antibiotic drugs differ greatly from ordinary disinfectants and antiseptics, not only in their origin, but also in their chemical composition, in their antibacterial properties, in their mode of action upon bacteria, and in their effect on the body's tissues. They are able to destroy the pathogenic bacteria in the blood or in other body fluids and tissues without causing injury to the human body; in other words, they are nontoxic.

Streptomycin is produced by a living organism known as *streptomyces griseus,* a microbe which occurs naturally in garden soils, river muds, peats and compost heaps. Not all strains of this microbe are able to produce streptomycin, however. Only very few strains or cultures have this faculty. These cultures were first isolated in the laboratories of the Department of Microbiology of the New Jersey Agricultural Experiment Station of Rutgers University. This discovery came after many years of minute and exhaustive research. We were interested, for many years, in the microbes of the soil, in their mode of living, and in their effects upon one another as well as upon the fertility of the soil.

We had learned that some of these microbes have the capacity of producing substances which help others or which destroy others. It is the latter that received special consideration when we started, in 1939, a comprehensive study of the utilization of soil microbes for combating disease-producing germs. We succeeded in isolating a series of substances, which we designated after the microbes that produce them. But none of these proved to be, for various reasons, a drug that could be used for chemotherapeutic purposes, until finally, in 1942, we isolated a substance that we designated as streptothricin. This drug proved to have highly desirable properties for combating a variety of infections resistant to penicillin or to the sulfonamides. However, on further study it proved to leave in the animal body a certain residual toxicity, which could produce

highly undesirable effects. We continued our search for new antibiotics, until, late in 1943, we isolated streptomycin which was
similar in many respects to streptothricin, but which did not have
the undesirable property of the latter, since it was considerably
less toxic to experimental animals. This suggested that it would
be a safer drug for the treatment of diseases in the human body.

Experiments were immediately instituted in animals to determine what microbes were affected by streptomycin. It was
found that the new antibiotic was especially successful in the treatment of infections caused by those bacteria known to scientists as
the gram-negative, whereas the bacteria against which penicillin
was most effective are mostly of the gram-positive type. The gram-
negative bacteria, on which our new antibiotic is effective, include
forms which cause the diseases of plague, cholera, whooping cough,
tularemia, typhoid, dysentery, certain forms of influenza, various
infections of the bladder and kidney, undulant fever, and a number
of others. It is an interesting fact, and a highly fortunate and important one too, that most of the disease germs which streptomycin
can conquer are very little affected, if at all, by penicillin and the
sulfa drugs. Thus, streptomycin gives us mastery over diseases
which penicillin and the sulfa drugs cannot cure. Streptomycin is
also effective against certain bacteria which after prolonged treatment with penicillin have become resistant to that drug. Thus, it
supplements and to a certain degree reinforces the older drugs, and
thus fills in gaps in our battle front against infectious disease.

On the basis of the chemical and biological properties of streptomycin, the body's tolerance of its presence, and its extraordinary
activity against various bacteria, the conclusion seems justified that
this new drug is one of the safest chemotherapeutic substances yet
known. It has now been used successfully in the treatment of a
variety of infections caused by the bacteria listed previously. Some
highly encouraging results have also been reported in the treatment
of certain forms of tuberculosis. However, great caution must be
exercised in extending hope that a cure for tuberculosis has finally
been found. The results are highly suggestive and serve as a
stimulus for further search of means for combating this dreadful
disease which has afflicted mankind since time immemorial.

Streptomycin has been available to the medical profession for nearly three years. It has found extensive application in the treatment of a number of diseases. Of particular importance is its utilization in the treatment of certain forms of tuberculosis. The numerous dramatic recoveries that have been reported by many investigators indicate that this chemical compound, the product of a lowly organism, is a powerful weapon against many baleful and destructive infections.

At present some ten companies in the United States are engaged in the manufacture of streptomycin. The microbe is grown in large tanks which hold from 5,000 to 15,000 gallons of culture fluid.

The streptomycin is then extracted from the culture and purified by suitable chemical procedures. The amounts available for civilian use have been until very recently still insufficient to satisfy more than a fraction of the needs. Lately, however, some of the large plants have been completed and production is increasing rapidly. For example, in the case of tuberculosis about 100-150 grams of pure streptomycin are required for the treatment of each patient. Since a gallon of culture fluid yields only 0.1 gm of pure streptomycin, about 1,000 to 1,500 gallons are required to produce the amount needed for one patient. It is expected that by January, 1948, about one million grams of streptomycin will be produced monthly in this country.

The discovery of streptomycin, following that of penicillin, points to the possibility of isolating other antibiotic drugs from microorganisms. These new agents open broad horizons both for the chemist and for the medical man. Perhaps from the microbe the chemist will get pointers, derive new knowledge, that will assist him in synthesizing new drugs. For the doctor, recent developments open a new epoch in clinical medicine. Back in the 1920's doubt was often expressed whether a drug would ever be found for the treatment of generalized infections caused by bacteria. Today we have the sulfa drugs, which are products of the laboratory, and the antibiotics, which are produced by microbes, and between them this great need is being served.

One may look forward to the time when the physician will have at his disposal a large number of drugs, each a specialized tool of chemotherapy, each especially adapted to the treatment of a particular disease.

CHAPTER 6

ATOMS AND MOLECULES

It is a real feeling for science that leads a small boy to take an alarm clock to pieces. He wants to see what it is made of and how it works.

The same sort of motives have led scientists to take apart matter to see that it is made of atoms and molecules, and to take these, in turn, apart to see that they are made of still more basic particles: electrons, protons, and neutrons. In the present chapter we will get a glimpse—at times a frightening one—of how successful these curious scientists have been.

We refer to particles such as electrons, protons, or neutrons as "ultimate" particles. This simply means that at the present stage of scientific progress we know these particles only as structureless, indivisible objects which have certain properties. The scientist does not know why they have these properties, nor does he ask.

When the scientist takes matter apart, it is his chief concern, like that of the small boy, to explain the properties of the whole in terms of the properties of the parts. This explanation is not, of course, an ultimate one. Indeed it is impossible to think of explaining any one idea except in terms of other ideas, ones which are usually considered more basic or more familiar.

However the scientist, in his explanations, does not necessarily ask that the central ideas he uses for explaining be either easy or familiar. He knows that central ideas which explain successfully for a long time become familiar and hence are eventually thought of as easy.

The scientist is happy about his explanations when a wide range of complicated and diverse phenomena are explained in terms of just a few central ideas. He is pleased if his explanation unexpectedly also covers phenomena which were not part of his original problem, just as the small boy would be pleased to recognize that the spring in the alarm clock works the same way as the spring which drives one of his toys.

The scientist finds satisfaction if his explanation suggests, and

96

in turn explains, some new experiments which no one would otherwise have thought of doing. He is particularly happy if his explanation gives him new ability to predict phenomena or new power to control nature or modify it to better use.

But the scientist does not worry if his explanation, like that of the poet or the theologian, has at its core an unexplained mystery. He only demands that this basic mystery be recognized and clearly stated, and he always strives to push this mystery one step further back. His most recent advances have taken the atom and the molecule, discussed in this chapter, out of the realm of ultimate mystery. Perhaps tomorrow he will have advanced beyond the electron.

W. W.

Within the Atom

By Hans Albrecht Bethe

Dr. Hans Albrecht Bethe, a professor of physics at Cornell University, was, during the war, in charge of the Theoretical Physics Section at Los Alamos, New Mexico, where the atomic bomb was developed, constructed, and tested.

THE atom is the hero of the day. It is the most democratic hero you can choose, because it is everywhere and in everything. All matter is composed of atoms. Indeed, matter consists of nothing but atoms, and there are incredible numbers of them. A spoonful of water contains a million billion billion atoms.

The classical idea of the atom pictured it as solid and indivisible. In fact, the word atom means that which cannot be divided. About the beginning of this century science discovered that the atom itself is made up of smaller parts; in other words, it has a structure. In 1910 the great British physicist Lord Rutherford stated on good evidence that every atom consists of a positively charged nucleus surrounded, like a central sun, by a negatively charged planetary system. The planets of this atomic world were named electrons, and each electron is a particle of negative electricity.

It was found that the number of electrons revolving around the nucleus depended on the number of charges of positive electricity that were carried by the nucleus. Thus, the hydrogen atom has one unit of positive charge—and it has one revolving electron. Uranium, the heaviest natural element, has 92 units of positive charge, and we find that its nucleus is surrounded by 92 revolving electrons. Between these two extremes—hydrogen the lightweight and uranium the heavyweight—are all the various combinations of positive and negative charges which exist in nature and which constitute the varieties of atoms.

Thus, to sum up our picture, we have found that atoms consist of nuclei and electrons. The nucleus is the massive center, which contains almost all the atom's mass. The electrons are the electrically negative particles which revolve around the nucleus. It is the number of electrons in an atom that governs the chemical properties of the atom. The electrons, for example, determine that one atom of oxygen will unite with two atoms of hydrogen to form the familiar molecular pattern, H_2O, of water.

While the modern theory of atomic chemistry was being developed, physicists went on to explore the atomic nucleus and found that it, too, had a structure. To be sure, in the one case of hydrogen, that lightest of the atoms, the nucleus was found to consist of a single particle—but in all the other ninety-one elements the nucleus was itself a combination of yet smaller particles. Experiments revealed that these particles of which the nucleus is built were of two kinds—protons and neutrons. Lord Rutherford discovered and named the proton, and some years later one of his students, Sir James Chadwick, discovered and named the neutron.

In mass or weight protons and neutrons are about equal, but in electrical properties they are quite different. The proton is positively charged, and the number of positive charges in the nucleus is equal to the number of protons contained. Thus hydrogen, with its one positive charge, has one proton. Uranium, with 92 positive charges, has 92 protons.

The neutron, on the other hand, carries no charge at all—is electrically neutral, hence its name. But it weighs approximately the same as the proton. The oxygen we breathe has a nuclear structure made up of 8 protons and usually 8 neutrons—and its weight therefore is 16. Uranium—the kind used in making the bomb—has 92 protons and 143 neutrons, giving it an atomic weight of 235. Atomic weight is the sum of the number of protons and neutrons carried in the nucleus.

The neutrons and protons within an atomic nucleus are held together by the most powerful forces known. Remarkably little is understood of these nuclear forces, even after many years of research. We do know that they are enormously strong—more than a million times stronger than the chemical forces which hold oxygen and hydrogen together in the water molecule, while these chemical forces in turn are many times stronger than the elastic forces which hold together a lump of steel.

There is a direct way of measuring the strength of nuclear forces. It depends upon the fact that the combined mass of all the neutrons and protons inside any given nucleus is about 1 per cent less than the sum of the masses of the individual neutrons and protons. This fact tells us that when the neutrons and protons are put together to form the nucleus, some of the mass of the individual particles is converted into energy in accordance with Professor Einstein's law of the equivalence of mass and energy. And by measuring the loss in mass we are able to compute from Einstein's equation the strength of the nuclear forces. I can assure you it is enormous. For instance, one ounce of mass is equivalent to the energy output of the great power plant at Boulder Dam for a whole month. Therefore, the observed small difference in mass in the atomic nucleus indicates that the nucleus contains considerably less energy than the separate protons and neutrons of which it is composed, and this large energy difference measures the strength of the nuclear forces. It is worth noting that energy would have to be supplied in order to tear the nucleus apart into its protons and neutrons—therefore such atom splitting would not be a source of atomic energy.

With one exception, no nucleus has been completely split into protons and neutrons. The more usual experiments consist of the transformation of one kind of nucleus into another, and this is what is popularly called "splitting the atom." These transformations can be initiated by bombarding a nucleus with some form of minute projectile. Protons have been used, but since the proton carries a positive charge, and since the nucleus of every atom is also positively charged, the nucleus tends to repel any proton moving toward it. Thus only by accelerating the protons to very high velocities can physicists score an occasional hit.

The neutron was discovered in 1932, and as soon as it was tried it proved to be an ideal projectile for this purpose. For since it carries no electrical charge, it is not subject to forces of repulsion.

Several hundred nuclear transformations were investigated in the 1930's and they had one result in common: when the bombarded nucleus broke into two fragments, one of them was always very small, while the other contained all the rest of the nucleus. This could hardly be called atom splitting.

But in 1936, for the first time, a heavy nucleus was split into almost equal parts. It was found that when a neutron hit the nucleus of Uranium-235, the nucleus separated into two fragments, one weighing about 100, the other about 135. This is nuclear fission and is the basic principle of the atomic bomb.

Immediately after the discovery of this process, physicists were able to calculate the amount of energy set free by fission, following Einstein's principle. True, the difference in mass between the uranium atom and its fragments was only one-tenth of 1 per cent. But, as we have seen, this still corresponds to enormous energy.

The most important fact about fission is that neutrons are emitted in the process. Let us suppose that in a fission two neutrons are emitted. Then, if we supply just one neutron to a large block of Uranium-235, it will cause the fission of one atom, that will lead to the emission of two neutrons, each of these will produce fission, resulting in the emission of four neutrons, and this multiplication will continue indefinitely. As the freed neutrons multiply, the energy stored in the uranium nucleus is liberated. If it is not stopped, the process will go on until all the uranium in the block is split.

If unchecked, such a nuclear chain reaction leads to the violent explosion of the atomic bomb. But the chain reaction can also be perfectly controlled and may some day be used for the production of atomic power. We see, therefore, that the release and control of atomic energy is now a reality. But the physicists have not reached their goal. They are still seeking to understand the nature of the gigantic nuclear forces.

The Atomic Nucleus

By Isidor I. Rabi

Dr. Isidor I. Rabi, recent Nobel Prize winner, is professor of physics and executive officer of the Physics Department at Columbia University.

If the uranium atom were enlarged a thousand million times, it would be about a foot in diameter. If its weight were increased proportionately to the increase in volume the atom would weigh about a thousand pounds. In the center of this magnified atom we would find a kernel about the size of a minute grain of sand. This is the nucleus. The part of the atom outside the nucleus consists only of electrons—and in the case of uranium there are 92 of them. These electrons are very light particles, and they move around the nucleus in orbits determined by the electrical forces which control them. On our scale of magnification, the total weight of the 92 electrons would be a quarter of a pound, and all the rest of the thousand-pound mass would be in the tiny nucleus. In other words, that magnified kernel, about the size of a small grain of sand, would weigh nine hundred and ninety-nine pounds and twelve ounces. A thimbleful of uranium nuclei would weight thousands of tons.

The nucleus is strikingly different from the electrons not only in mass but also in electrical properties. For, whereas the electrons are negatively charged, the nucleus is positively charged. This is true, not only of uranium, but of all the elements.

For every atom, then, this is the pattern of structure: a central positively-charged nucleus around which a lightweight negatively-charged electron or group of electrons moves at high speeds. In the case of the simplest hydrogen atom there is one revolving electron, and the nucleus carries a single positive charge. As you pass up the scale of atomic complexity, the number of electrical charges increases. Indeed, it is the change in electrical charge that marks the change to a new element. Thus the light-weight gas, helium, which is next to hydrogen in atomic simplicity, has two positive charges on its nucleus, and two negatively-charged electrons in motion around this nucleus. Oxygen, to take a common element of the air which is known to all of us, has eight positive charges on its nucleus and, correspondingly, eight electrons whirling about this nucleus—whereas the inert gas nitrogen has only seven nuclear charges and seven encircling electrons.

We know far more about the electrons than we do about the nucleus, but our assignment here is to examine the nucleus. We shall have to use powerful research tools, for this dense kernel is so very small, and is so masked by the surrounding electrons and by its own strong positive electrical charge, that its secrets are indeed well guarded. Vast energy is locked within the nucleus. The atomic bomb gave evidence of that. In order to penetrate to the nucleus we must apply energies comparable to those already within the nucleus, and this involves instruments of high power. The cyclotron is one such instrument; the uranium pile, another. A very potent device is the recent invention known as a betatron, an apparatus for accelerating electrons to velocities approaching the speed of light. Nature itself has given us one of the most powerful agencies for nuclear studies. I refer to the cosmic rays. These mysterious radiations, which come in from outer space, make available to us energies far beyond those which any man-made device is likely to achieve in the near future.

By the use of research tools such as those just mentioned, physicists have penetrated to the nucleus and have found it an exceedingly complicated structure. This structure is still far from being completely understood, but except for the one case of light-weight hydrogen we know that nuclei are not single indivisible particles but are composite structures. To the best of our knowledge atomic nuclei are made up of two kinds of particles: protons and neutrons. The protons each carry a positive electrical charge, and it is they that are responsible for the charge on the nucleus. Thus, in the nucleus of the oxygen atom which, as I said above, carries eight positive charges, there are eight protons; in nitrogen there are seven protons and seven positive charges; and so with each chemical element. The number of nuclear charges is always equal to the number of protons.

The other building block of the nucleus, the neutron, is slightly more massive than the proton and about the same size, but it has no electrical charge whatever and therefore is electrically neutral. Many atoms have in their nuclei equal numbers of neutrons and protons; others have more neutrons than protons. The proportions vary.

We picture the nucleus, therefore, as a very tiny kernel made up of protons and neutrons. Since all protons are charged with positive electricity, they repel one another. Inside the nucleus this mutual repulsion is extremely intense because the protons are so close together. If there were not other forces within the nucleus to counteract this electrical repulsion, the nucleus would instantly explode. But there are present mysterious forces of attraction between proton and neutron, between proton and proton, and between neutron and neutron. These forces of attraction are different from any other kind found in nature. They are not like gravitational or the usual electrical forces. The nuclear forces are not only more power-ful, but also they do not seem to take hold until the nuclear par-ticles are practically in contact. Although physicists have worked for years on the problem of the nature and origin of these adhesive forces, little progress has been made. It was possible to deal with the problem of the atomic bomb, for it involved a few specific nu-clear properties which were understood. But to understand the gen-eral nuclear forces, we shall need new ideas and principles of which at present we have no hint.

The mass of the proton is 1840 times that of the electron, but its electrical charge is of equal magnitude, though opposite in sign, being positive whereas the electron's charge is negative.

Protons have another and somewhat mysterious property known as spin. That is to say, they rotate. Just as all protons are identical in mass and in positive electrical charge, they all have exactly the same amount of spin. Because of this spin, the motion of a proton within the nucleus has many of the properties of a spinning top, or gyroscope.

The rotation of electricity is always associated with magnetism. So it is with the spinning proton. It is a little magnet with a north and south pole oriented in the direction of the spin. From the gen-eral relations which are expected to hold true between mass, spin, and electrical charge, it should be possible to predict the strength of the proton magnet. However, such predictions have failed com-pletely. The measured strength turns out to be almost three times the predicted value. This discrepancy is not understood. It may turn out to be a clue to the nature of the proton and its nuclear forces.

The neutron also rotates, with a spin equal to that of the proton, and the neutron too, is a small magnet. Its north and south poles are arranged in the direction which corresponds to the rotation of negative electricity, even though the neutron is known to be electrically neutral. Any detailed explanation of the magnetism of the neutron is completely lacking.

There is another remarkable behavior of at least some nuclei. It is the property of emitting electrons. One of these nuclei, with-out any external influence at all, will suddenly shoot out an elec-tron. There is not enough room within the nucleus for an electron to exist there, and its emission seems to be the result of spontaneous generation of the particle within the nucleus. The idea has been suggested that the ejected electron is a by-product of the transformation of one of the nuclear neutrons into a proton. It is indeed true that after emission of the electron, the nucleus has one proton more than it had before, and one neutron less. Here again an adequate explanation is lacking. This mysterious transformation of a neutron into a proton with the simultaneous emission of an electron is probably another facet of the many-sided problem of the nature of the nuclear forces and of the structure of proton and neutron.

I have tried to stress here not so much things that are known, but some of the limitless unknown. Now, as almost never before, there is unbounded opportunity for young men and women to make great discoveries. Newer and more ingenious experiments have to be designed. Newer and more profound ideas and guiding principles will have to be discovered before the nature of the nucleus is fully comprehended. The great accomplishments of the past have opened still broader and more fundamental fields of investigation, things undreamed of a generation ago. The more we learn of nature, the more subtle and beautifful her laws become. We can be sure that the next generation of scientists will not fail to take up this challenge and make new discoveries and raise new problems for future generations to solve.

A View of the Molecular World

By John G. Kirkwood

Dr. John G. Kirkwood, a physical chemist, holds the Todd professorship in chemistry at Cornell University.

Every material object in the world is composed of almost unbelievably tiny units called molecules; and each of these molecules is, in turn, composed of still smaller and simpler units called atoms. The everyday behavior of all of the substances making up the world in which we live—substances such as the leather in your shoes, the glass in your windows, the iron or steel in your stove, and the sugar on your table—the everyday behavior of all of these is determined by the detailed architecture of the molecules of which the substances are composed. Thus the scientist wishes to know how the molecules in question are built up out of the still smaller units, the atoms; and how the atoms are held together, by chemical bonds, in definite structural patterns. Finally, how are the proper- ties of the resulting substances related to the architecture of their molecules? Only when these fundamental questions have been an- swered, can satisfactory replies be found to such everyday ques- tions as: Why is an alloy steel strong? Why is glass brittle? Why can rubber be bent and stretched?

These molecules and atoms are almost unimaginably small. An ordinary sized atom would have to be magnified something like a million times before it would be visible to the eye as a tiny speck. But although molecules are much too small to be seen with our eyes, we can build instruments to see them for us and to record their behavior for our study. One such instrument is the spectro- graph, which measures the wave length,—that is to say, the color, —of the light emitted and absorbed by molecules and atoms. Such observations, when properly interpreted, provide us with rich infor- mation concerning molecules as engineering structures, telling us how strong are the chemical joints between the atoms of which the molecules are composed; and telling us of what kinds of internal motions and vibrations they are capable. Other instruments record on photographic plates the telltale patterns produced when the molecules of a substance deflect beams of X rays or electrons. These patterns are as characteristic as fingerprints; and from them we learn the size of molecules, the distances between their com- ponent atoms, and how they are packed together to make up the materials of our everyday life.

Some molecules contain but few atoms and possess relatively simple structures. Other giant molecules contain many atoms and are architecturally very complicated. The convenient scale of length in the molecular world is the Angstrom unit, equal to four-billionths of an inch. Some molecules are only a few Angstrom units in length, while others are much larger. Thus simple molecules like water, composed of one oxygen atom and two hydrogen atoms, are but a few Angstroms in length. But giant molecules like those of the proteins, cellulose, and rubber range in length from hundreds to many thousands of Angstroms. Some giant molecules, for example, those of the protein of egg white, are shaped somewhat like a football. Others, for example those of the muscle protein, myosin, and the molecules of natural and synthetic rubbers, are long, flexible, and threadlike. Both natural and synthetic rubber owe their characteristic elastic properties to the threadlike structure of their molecules, which have a tendency to get tangled up. But if we apply a pull to a piece of matter composed of the long tangled-up rubber molecules, then the specimen stretches considerably, because the mixed-up network of molecules untangles a bit, even though reluctantly. On the other hand, in crystalline substances, for example common table salt and the metals, the molecules and atoms are arranged in a most orderly manner, in regular three-dimensional patterns which extend throughout the entire crystal. It is a little hard to visualize those regular solid patterns of atoms in a crystal. It is a little like the repeated pattern on wallpaper, except that the wallpaper pattern is only two-dimensional or flat, whereas the crystal pattern is three-dimensional or solid.

After our brief glimpse at the structure of molecules, it is natural for us to ask how they are put together to form the materials of the everyday world, and to attempt to discover how it happens that under the same conditions, some materials like air are gases, others like water are liquids, while still others like salt and steel are solids.

Two facts furnish the key to the answers to these questions. The first is that molecules, like the sun and the planets, attract each other. The inter-molecular attractive force is, however, primarily electrical rather than gravitational in nature. The second important fact is that molecules are in a constant state of motion. Unlike the ordered motions of the planets, the customary motion of molecules is more a chaotic and random dance recalling jive and jitterbug. Of course the motion is on far too small a scale for us to see. But we can feel it. What we feel is heat. When a substance is cold its molecules are dancing sluggishly; when hot, its molecules are dancing briskly.

The outward appearance of a substance which we recognize as a crystal, liquid, or gas, depends upon a compromise between two sets of influences. On the one hand, the attractive forces between the molecules tend to keep the molecules in well-ordered arrays like accurately marching soldiers. On the other hand, the disordering influence of molecular motion, tends to mix the molecules up like a rioting crowd. At sufficiently low temperatures, the disordering heat motions are weak; the discipline of the forces between the molecules predominates. Therefore at low temperatures we find many substances in the crystalline state, with the molecules arranging themselves in the ordered pattern of a crystal lattice. The structural details of this crystal pattern are at far too fine a scale for observation with the eye. But they can be seen with X rays. Reflected from a crystal, the X rays record themselves on a photographic plate in a characteristic pattern from which, with some ingenuity, the structure may be deduced. The beauty and symmetry we admire in the facets of gems and in certain minerals reflect the symmetry and order of the crystal lattice.

As the temperature of a crystal is raised, the pattern of its atoms is disordered more and more by heat motion in the form of sound waves traveling back and forth in the interior of the crystal. These waves can be likened to those which are produced in a violin string by the action of the bow. Fortunately for our comfort, the pitch of these sound waves is so shrill that our ears are not affected. When one continues to heat the substance, the thermal disorder eventually becomes so serious as to throw the regular ranks of the crystal lattice into complete disorder. Then the melting temperature has been reached, and the substance is transformed into a liquid. This transformation is a common place phenomenon of our daily life, observed in the melting of snow and ice.

Because of the fluidity of liquids, which allows them to be poured into vessels of any shape, we are accustomed to regard liquids as having no structure. This is not quite true. On the molecular scale, liquids possess a residual trace of regular structure, which, as in the case of crystals, can be observed with the aid of X rays. X-ray photographs of liquids lack much of the detail of those of crystals and what detail they possess is blurred and indistinct. We are forced to conclude that, although crowded conditions prevail, military order no longer controls the arrangement of the atoms and molecules in a liquid, as it does in a crystal. Nevertheless, each molecule maintains a trace of order with respect to its near neighbors, which locally resembles the more extensive order existing in the crystal lattice. Its efforts to control the pattern of its neighbors are opposed by heat motions, and these efforts only affect a few of its nearest neighbors.

To illustrate some of the foregoing statements, let us consider the case of water. In an ice crystal, the lattice pattern is an open structure in which each water molecule has four neighbors. When ice melts, the lattice as a whole is destroyed, but each molecule nevertheless keeps four neighbors arranged in a partially collapsed form of the local ice structure in which each water molecule has the open ice structure; liquid water is denser than ice at the melting point. Hence ice floats on liquid water.

In fact, this local liquid structure continues to collapse between the melting point and a temperature of four degrees Centigrade. In this temperature interval, therefore, liquid water increases in density. Above four degrees, increasing thermal disorder expands the neighbor structure and the density diminishes with increasing temperatures. Were it not for the fact that the open ice structure collapses on melting, ice would sink in liquid water, as do most crystals in their melts. It would take us too long to explore the consequences of such a state of affairs on geological events, on the weather, and ultimately on our daily lives; but these consequences would be serious and far-reaching, so that the arrangement and behavior of these water molecules, in liquid water and in ice, is actually a matter of direct and practical concern to each one of us.

As the temperature of a liquid is raised, thermal disorder finally completely overpowers molecular attractive forces. The molecules are then torn asunder, and the liquid is transformed into a gas. This we observe when the kettle boils. Of the structure of a gas, little need be said. Each molecule leads a solitary but active existence, traveling alone over long stretches of distance and rudely jostling any neighbor which chances in its path.

In addition to satisfying their scientific curiosity, chemists and physicists have been able to put their investigations of molecular structure to good use in ways which could not at first have been anticipated. Apart from their intrinsic scientific interest, studies of molecular structure and of the structure of materials on the molecular scale have contributed directly to the solution of many technical

problems. I shall mention only one example. Spectroscopic studies
of the modes of vibration of the water molecule and of hydrocarbon
molecules have provided basic information needed for the operation of high pressure steam power units, and for the control of
the cracking process used in the manufacture of the high octane
gasoline which will power your automobile or airplane in the post-
war world.

Molecular Architecture and Medical Progress

By Linus Pauling

Dr. Linus Pauling, a physical chemist who has been concerned with
the applications of chemistry to biological problems, is chairman of
the Division of Chemistry and Chemical Engineering at the California
Institute of Technology.

THE molecule of Penicillin G contains forty-one atoms. This wonderful substance, penicillin, opposes certain deadly bacteria, and in
a few years it has saved the lives of tens of thousands of people.
DDT kills insects; and it has been the means of stopping epidemics
by destroying mosquitos, lice, and other agents which transmit
infectious disease. Morphine, ether, and other anesthetics allay pain
and put us to sleep. Still other substances, such as adrenaline, stimulate the heart and wake us up.

Why? Why do these various drugs have these different effects
on our bodies? What is the secret of the specific response which
each invokes?

We do not know the full answer to this question, but we are
sure that, for each substance, part of the answer lies in the details
of the structure of the molecules of the substance. To find the full
answer we must first of all determine the precise arrangement of
the forty-one atoms in the molecule of penicillin, and of the twenty-
eight atoms in the molecule of DDT. This knowledge is needed as
the first step toward understanding the power of penicillin to kill
bacteria, and the power of DDT to destroy insects. And so for
morphine, adrenaline, and all the rest—the secret of their physiological action lies in their molecular architecture.

Our task, however, is really two-fold. First, we must determine the structure of the drugs which produce these physiological effects. And second, we must determine the structure of the enzymes, nerve fibers, and tissues of the living organism which react to these drugs in their characteristic ways.

Much progress has already been made on the first of these problems. Chemists have worked out the architecture of many substances which have medicinal effects. In the case of chloroform, for example, it has long been known that its molecule consists of five atoms—one atom of carbon, one of hydrogen, and three of chlorine. Back in the 1880's, chemists found that the three chlorine atoms and the one hydrogen atom are compactly arranged in space around the carbon atom. The three chlorine atoms may be considered as lying at the three corners of the base of a three-sided pyramid, with the hydrogen atom at the apex, the carbon atom being inside the pyramid at its center. The chemists also discovered that each of the four outer atoms is held by a very powerful chemical affinity to the single carbon atom within. This general picture was obtained by chemical methods developed long ago. But within our time, beginning in the 1930's, scientists have obtained a far more precise knowledge of the structure of the chloroform molecule. They have even determined the submicroscopic distances which separate the carbon atom, within the molecule, from the four atoms which are grouped around it.

In order to measure such distances we have to give up our familiar units of measurement—they are too coarse for this molecular world. We make use of a special yardstick known as the Angstrom unit. In the span of the familiar household inch there are two hundred and fifty-four million of these tiny units. This, then, is our molecular yardstick, the Angstrom—a unit which measures one two-hundred-fifty-four-millionth part of an inch.

It is difficult to visualize this dimension. To get some picture of what it means, let us examine a wineglass full of liquid chloroform, and let us assume that everything is magnified by this linear factor 254 million, which converts one Angstrom unit into an inch and which correspondingly magnifies one inch into four thousand miles. On this scale, a man would be about two hundred and fifty thousand miles tall—which is the distance from the earth to the moon.

On the same scale, the wineglass would be as big as the earth, and the chloroform molecules filling the glass would each measure about seven inches across.

The shape of the chloroform molecule, you remember, is that of a triangular pyramid, with the carbon atom inside and the four-corner points of the pyramid occupied by the three atoms of chlorine and the one atom of hydrogen. On our magnified scale, we can picture the inside carbon atom as about the size of a walnut, the three chlorine atoms as small oranges, and the hydrogen as a tangerine. On this same scale, the distance from the walnut, representing the carbon atom, to each of the oranges, representing the chlorine atoms, is 1.76 inches—a distance corresponding in molecular dimensions to 1.76 Angstrom units. Similarly, the distance from the walnut—the carbon atom—to the tangerine—the hydrogen atom—is 1.09 inches—corresponding, on the molecular scale, to 1.09 Angstrom units.

Our giant wineglass, as big as the earth, would be filled to the brim with billions of billions of these seven-inch molecules. And these molecules would not be resting quietly on each other in the wine glass, but would be jostling one another and rolling over one another in vigorous motion. Very often one of the molecules, at the surface of the liquid, would break away from its neighbors and would escape into the air, where it might impinge on a nerve ending within our nose, and cause us to become aware of the characteristic odor of chloroform; or it might, with many others, be inhaled, and cause us to lapse into unconsciousness.

Chloroform is not the only molecule whose dimensions are known. In recent years scientists have determined with similar accuracy the structures of several hundred substances.

These substances represent a variety of architectural complexities—ranging from small molecules of only two or three atoms to much more complex molecules built of fifty or sixty atoms. Most of our knowledge of the structure of these substances has necessarily been obtained by indirect means.

I remember, as a boy in Oregon, looking at a distant arc light through the fabric of an open umbrella. I could see the light, itself, and above it and below it, and to the right and left, there appeared something more—a pattern of spectra, the familiar colors of the rainbow. This pattern of colors was caused by the interference and reinforcement of the light waves which passed through the meshes of the fabric, and the angular spread of the pattern was determined by the ratio of the wave length of the light to the distance between the meshes of the cloth. Knowing the wave length of the light, one could use the observed pattern to calculate the distance from one thread to the next. One could also infer from the nature of the diffraction pattern the type of weave, and thus determine the structure of the cloth.

The investigator of molecular structure follows a similar procedure. He may, for example, use a beam of electrons—instead of the rays from the distant arc light.

The molecules of the chemical compound which he seeks to measure are analogous to the fabric of the umbrella. When the beam of electrons passes through the molecules, the electron waves are scattered into a diffraction pattern which is photographed—and by analyzing this photographed pattern the scientist learns how the atoms are arranged in the molecule and how they are spaced with reference to one another. The structure of a number of drugs has been analyzed in just this way.

But working out the architecture of drugs and other chemical compounds is only half the job. There remains the task of determining the structure of that part of the living creature on which the drug or other chemical acts. And this task is extremely difficult, because of the extreme complexity of many constituents of living matter. For example, the molecule of penicillin consists of forty-one atoms—but the molecule of hemoglobin, one of the important constituents of the red blood cell, consists of ten thousand atoms. Other protein molecules are larger still. Some containing twenty thousand, one hundred thousand, even one million atoms to a single molecule have been weighed. But although we can weigh them, we do not yet know the exact architecture of a single one of these protein molecules.

This then is the great problem of modern chemistry—the determination of the molecular architecture of the proteins and other complex constituents of the living organism. *This problem must be solved*. The progress of medicine depends on its solution.

When once a real understanding of the physiological activity of chemical substances is obtained—when we know what are the structural features of the penicillin molecule which give it its power, what is the method of attack of the poliomyelitis virus on the molecules of the nerves of the victim of infantile paralysis, what relation the cancer-producing molecules of polynuclear aromatic hydrocarbons bear to the molecules determining cell division—when we know these things, then medical progress will be swift. The medical research man then will be a molecular architect. He will be able to draw the atomic blueprints for promising pharmacological compounds in order that chemists may synthesize them and biologists may test them. He will be able to analyze and to interpret the structures of enzymes, tissues, and viruses to learn the mechanism of disease and hence the way of combatting diseases.

When this time comes—and it is coming—medicine will indeed have become an exact science.

Isotopes in Atomic Research

By Harold Clayton Urey

Dr. Harold Clayton Urey, winner of the Nobel Prize in chemistry for his discovery of the heavy isotope of hydrogen, is now distinguished service professor of chemistry in the Institute of Nuclear Studies, University of Chicago.

Since the atomic bomb exploded over Hiroshima and Nagisaki, it seems much easier to talk about isotopes. Everyone who reads the newspapers now knows that isotopes exist, that uranium-235 is the explosive kind and that the uranium-238 is not explosive. We also know that the separation of these two isotopes was necessary before the uranium-235 bomb could be made, and that it was a difficult industrial problem to separate even small amounts.

While frequent references to these subjects in the newspapers have made us familiar with the terms, I think you may be interested in a more precise discussion of isotopes—what they are, why we wish to separate them, and the methods by which this is accomplished.

In the first place, let us understand that isotopes are simply atoms of the same element but of different weight.

Professor Bethe, in his paper which opens this chapter, discussed the three primary particles—protons, neutrons, and electrons. The protons are positively charged massive particles which reside inside the atomic nucleus. The electrons are the negatively charged particles which revolve around the nucleus. The third kind, the neutrons, are electrically neutral, and like the protons are found only within nuclei. Neutrons have about the same mass as protons, and the weight of an atom is the sum of the weights of its protons and neutrons. (Electrons, I may say parenthetically, are so extremely light that their masses can be ignored in discussing the weight of the atom.) The weight of an atom, therefore, is the sum of the weight of its protons plus the weight of its neutrons.

Now, the number of protons in the atoms of any one element is always the same. In the case of uranium, for example, and no matter which isotope of uranium we are talking about, each atom has exactly the same number of protons—92. There is one kind of uranium which weighs 234, another kind which weighs 235, another 238, still another weighing 239. Since each has exactly 92 protons, the weight differences can be accounted for only by differences in the number of neutrons. Therein is the explanation of isotopes. The uranium-238 has 146 neutrons in its nucleus, whereas the explosive isotope, the uranium-235, has three fewer neutrons.

As you go through the list you find that almost every chemical element has atoms of different weight—that is, has different isotopes. Most of the hydrogen in the world weighs around 1 unit, because its nucleus consists of a single particle, a proton.

But there is a small proportion of hydrogen atoms which have a double-weight nucleus, consisting of a proton and a neutron. Other elements also consist of mixtures of isotopes. Carbon, for example, has two isotopes, nitrogen two, oxygen three, and so on.

I hope it is clear, from this rather abbreviated explanation, what isotopes are. They are atoms of the same elemental substance, which differ from one another in weight, and these differences are accounted for by the varying numbers of neutrons in their nuclei. The atoms which have few neutrons in their nuclei are called the light isotopes, and those with the most neutrons, the heavy isotopes.

But why should we want to separate isotopes? The answer is easy. It is only by separating, by isolating the material he is interested in, that the research man can investigate its properties. In the case of uranium, as soon as it was found that the rare uranium-235 was the isotope subject to fission or splitting, it became a major task to separate it from the more plentiful uranium-238.

The separation problem is difficult because we are dealing with a mixture of atoms of the same chemical element, whose differences in physical properties are usually very slight.

Simple distillation of water is sufficient to separate the light isotopes of hydrogen and oxygen from the heavier ones—the light atoms are more readily carried over in the vapor. Similarly, the relative number of isotopes of carbon and oxygen in the carbon dioxide escaping from your glass of soda water differ from the relative numbers of these isotopes that remain in solution. This distillation or chemical method has been used to separate isotopes of hydrogen, carbon, nitrogen, and sulphur; and its feasibility for the separation of lithium, oxygen, and perhaps potassium, has been indicated. But unfortunately the differences in mass become relatively smaller as we take up elements of higher mass, and the method does not look promising for elements above atomic weight 40. So we try other methods.

If you have a gas or liquid between two plates, keep one plate hot and the other cold, the lightweight isotopes will tend to move toward the hot surfaces and the heavy ones toward the cold surfaces. Considerable separation can be attained by this so-called thermal diffusion method.

Another method uses centrifugal force. In rapidly rotating centrifuges the heavy isotopes move outward to a greater extent than the light ones. This method seems feasible for quite a number of elements, though difficult.

Not one of these three methods—distillation, thermal diffusion, or centrifugation—proved practicable in the case of uranium. In some ways I was sorry about this, but in some ways quite glad.

In a war problem, one wishes to get the work done as rapidly as possible and thus shorten the war. On the other hand, if the uranium isotopes could be separated by an easy method, they could be separated in almost any garret or basement laboratory. Hence atomic bombs could be made without the necessity of large industrial plants. And, of course, if they could be made in that way, it would be difficult to know whether people were making them, and the whole problem of control of the atomic bomb would be much more difficult than it is.

Since the easy methods would not work, we had to turn to more difficult ones—and first of all to separation in electromagnet fields. In this method the uranium atoms are given an electrical charge, and the stream of these electrified atoms is shot between the poles of a powerful magnet whose effect is to cause them to pursue a circular path. But the greater inertia of the uranium-238 causes it to resist the pull of magnetism more than the lighter uranium-235; hence the two isotopes become separated.

The other method used was the diffusion method. This depends on the rate at which gaseous molecules flow through porous material. You can set up a system, for example, in which air flows through blotting paper, and because the atmospheric nitrogen is lighter than the oxygen, the nitrogen will flow through more rapidly. In the same way the lighter uranium-235 atom diffuses more rapidly than the heavier 238. The separation is very small. To change the relative abundance of the isotopes by large amounts requires that the process be done over and over again thousands of times—and this is one reason for the mammoth size of the separation plants pictured in the newspapers.

What of the future? Since uranium isotopes are the most difficult ones to separate, and since we have succeeded with them, we are confident of our ability to separate the isotopes of any element. However, it takes a very valuable isotope to justify the immense amount of work done on the atomic bomb project. Mostly we do not wish isotopes that badly. We should note, however, that a few years ago we did not want uranium isotopes. Nitrogen isotopes are now articles of commerce. Hydrogen isotopes have been separated in large quantities. It may be that some day we shall want isotopes of lithium, boron, carbon, or sulphur—so it is well to have methods in advance.

We are at the beginning of a vast new chemistry—one concerned with changes taking place within the nuclei of atoms. Part of this work involves securing separated isotopes for these studies. To the layman, what has already been done may be the most interesting, but to those of us who work in this field, it is the unknown thing ahead that has maximum interest. Particularly, young men and women should realize that science is an ever-expanding universe with always the most interesting discoveries still to be found.

The radioactive isotopes produced by methods used in making the atomic bomb will have many uses in studying chemical and physical processes both for purely scientific and industrial work. They should have many uses in medicine. They can be made by methods which for the most part do not require the separation of isotopes by the methods that I have indicated. At the same time the separated isotopes particularly of hydrogen, carbon, nitrogen, oxygen and sulphur should also be useful for similar studies. For example, we can use both stable and radioactive isotopes to follow elements through complicated systems such as living animals. Thus nitrogen in food, if it is heavy nitrogen, can be followed through the complicated chemical processes that occur in an animal body. Or radioactive carbon or heavy carbon may be followed in the same way. During the next 25 years we should learn a great deal about such processes.

During recent years we have heard much about the usefulness of science, that is, the justification of science on the basis of its usefulness for peaceful or military things. I believe this point of view is not as broad as it should be. Science is an end in itself, just as literature and art are. Our primary objective should be to learn fundamental things about the behavior of natural phenomena. We wish to know all about the structure and behavior of the heavy nuclei of atoms, what holds the proton and neutrons together, the details of the splitting of atoms, why they are stable or radioactive, what new fundamental particles there may be in nature beyond protons, neutrons and electrons, and many things of this sort.

The separation of isotopes is only one of very many modes of attack on these fascinating problems in our study of these very small and energetic nuclei of atoms.

The Atomic Age

By J. Robert Oppenheimer

Dr. J. Robert Oppenheimer, previously professor of physics at the University of California, and during the war the head of the atomic bomb laboratory at Los Alamos, New Mexico, has been elected director of the Institute for Advanced Study, Princeton, New Jersey.

In the hour before dawn one day in the summer of 1945, the hills of the Jornado del Muerto, a desert stretch in New Mexico, were briefly lighted with a light no man had ever seen before. We who were there knew that a new world lay before us. It is my privilege briefly to tell here what is discernible to us in the outlines of this new world.

Let me be clear on one point: no great new principle of nature was discovered or revealed in that first atomic explosion. The bomb which we there tested was based on the broad foundation of a century of physical science. In its design were embodied the great principles of the behavior of radiation and matter, as they were worked out in the closing years of the last century and in the first three decades of this. Into this bomb was built the experience of the world's laboratories on atomic nuclei and their reactions. In this bomb was built the discovery, made only a few months before the outbreak of the war, that a neutron could induce the fission or splitting of the heaviest nucleus into two almost equal components. This break-up of the nucleus is accompanied by the liberation of a large amount of energy, and of enough neutrons to cause this fission to spread to more and more nuclei if the material and circumstances are right. Our job in the war projects was to make the circumstances right.

If there was any surprise in this first explosion, it lay not in any great new discovery. It lay rather in the fact that what happened was so like what we thought would happen—that the physical science which had been built into this new weapon was such a sure and reliable guide.

With trivial exceptions, all the power that is used on earth derives from nuclear reactions which take place in the sun. The nuclear reactions which took place in the New Mexican desert were of a different kind, and are subject in quite a different way to man's control.

It seems to be a general impression that there are serious and fundamental problems in controlling the release of this energy and in making it useful for the purposes of society. This view is based on misconception. More than two years before the test in New Mexico, another great experiment was carried out at the Metallurgical Laboratory in Chicago. In this experiment, conditions were so arranged that the fission of one uranium atom in a great mass of uranium and graphite produced, through the neutrons it generated, the fission of a second atom, and so on indefinitely. The experiment could be run with the rate of fission and the rate of energy release adjusted within wide limits by a simple control. This was the first self-sustaining fission chain reaction.

Since then many varied devices have been designed and built, each of them generating appreciable quantities of energy, all of them based on maintaining a controlled nuclear chain reaction. Some are small, some enormous; and the power which they generate also varies by large factors: but all were made as a part of the program of developing atomic bombs and all have one feature in common: they do not develop energy at a high temperature.

The technological problem of operating such units to produce energy at a temperature high enough to make it profitable to generate electrical power, or to provide steam for heat or for industrial uses, appears to be capable of solution in many ways in the very near future. We see no real limitation on the availability of nuclear fuel. Therefore we may look forward to the widespread application of such sources of power to the future economy and technology of the world.

One word of warning may be appropriate: a unit of this kind, operating, let us say, at a thousand kilowatts, produces radiations equivalent to those from ten tons of radium. If men are to be anywhere around such units, this radiation must be absorbed by shields of very appreciable bulk. For this reason alone, we do not think automobiles and airplanes will be run by nuclear power units—not, at least, until a new idea supplements our present knowledge.

But the fact that nuclear-energy units require an insignificant amount of fuel makes us think that they will be applied to extend the present uses of power in our economy. We do not expect petroleum or coal to become outmoded as fuels. It is clear that although useful power plants may be only a few years away, the full adaptation of the new possibilities to a living economy will be a matter of many more years than that.

It is in just those radiations and radioactivities which made the power plants so intractable that most scientists see one of the greatest benefits of the atomic age. These radiations hold particular promise in the fields of biological, biochemical, and medical studies, where they should provide tools of immense power, both for the treatment of disease and for the attack on fundamental problems.

Of course time and work can show what the content of these developments will be. Even for the field of physics there will be new possibilities. I may give one example: the neutron is a constituent of atomic nuclei, but it does not occur free in nature, where its properties can be studied. Neutrons do occur in great numbers among the fragments of the chain reacting systems, and it is there that their somewhat unfamiliar behavior will best be explored. Of this whole field of research we see very much less than the mariner sees of the iceberg. That is what is meant by research.

The explosion in New Mexico was neither a controlled source of power nor a research tool—it was a weapon. Within a few weeks it was to be a weapon used against human targets in the strikes of August 6th and 9th, 1945. Today this is the aspect of the atomic age which is most prominent—and most rightly prominent—in all our thoughts. There does not seem to be any valid doubt that atomic weapons can be made, made plentifully, made cheaply, and indeed be made very much more destructive than the one we tested in New Mexico. There does not seem to be any valid hope that defenses against such weapons can be made effective against attack based on surprise, or that specific defenses against such weapons, other than the destruction of enemy bases and enemy carriers, will be developed in the future. There is, to my mind, little valid foundation for the belief that in a world torn by major wars these weapons, for tactical or humane reasons, will be left unexploited.

Often before, men have claimed that a weapon had been found so terrible that wars would cease; often before, men have pointed to the increasing technical and social interdependence of the peoples of the world and argued that wars should cease. The fact that these arguments have not prevailed does not mean that they will not prevail today. The fact that increasingly terrible wars have been waged does not mean that we should prepare to wage still more terrible ones in the future. It is not in this sense that history is to be ready. For this is what is new in the atomic age: a world to be united, in law, in common understanding, in common humanity, before a common peril.

CHAPTER 7

PHYSICS AND MATHEMATICS

PHYSICS IS among the most broad and inclusive of all the branches of science. The fact that we call practically all of the events taking place about us "physical phenomena" illustrates how extensive and how close is the contact which physics has with all aspects of nature.

At one extreme physics may sound abstract and even mysterious, when it deals with problems of the ultimate constitution and behavior of matter. At the other extreme physics can seem utilitarian and down-to-earth when it teams up with engineering to solve practical problems. Both of these impressions as to the role of physics, however, are likely to be illusions. The so-called practical problems often require deep theoretical knowledge, and the abstract equations of today are the atom bombs of tomorrow.

The preceding chapter described modern science at the level of atoms and molecules where physics and chemistry merge into one field. The present chapter is concerned with the broader aspects of physics alone.

Here for example we find a story of classic experimental physics —the study of high pressure phenomena—and an illustration of basic physics leading to a whole new field of practical applications —the field of polarized light phenomena. Here we learn that measurement is an essential characteristic of science and that precise standards of measurement are needed by both science and industry.

It has long been popular to speak of the kinship of mathematics to music, but one contributor to this section, out of his experience both as a physicist and an amateur painter, gives an account of the less familiar but equally interesting relationship between physics and the pictorial arts.

In the final section, returning to the more fundamental aspects of all quantitative science, we are shown the central role which mathematics plays whenever science tries to describe the laws of nature.

W. W.

Effects of High Pressure

By Percy W. Bridgman

Dr. Percy W. Bridgman, who received the Nobel Prize for his research in high pressure, is professor of physics at Harvard University.

LIFE is pretty much a surface affair so far as our world is concerned. Even when we make our loftiest airplane flights or descend into the deepest mines, we never get very far from the surface of the earth. The substances which we encounter in our daily life are similarly conditioned by the pressures, temperatures, and other circumstances which prevail at their outer surfaces.

And yet, only an infinitesimal fraction of the matter in the universe is found at the surface of planets and stars. All except this very minute fraction is buried beneath the surface where conditions are very different. If we want to understand how the world is constructed, and how it works, we must know the properties of matter under the conditions that prevail in the interiors of planets and stars. This problem of the interior has two main aspects: to find the effect of high temperatures and to find the effect of high pressures.

During the last forty years and more I have given a great deal of thought and experimenting to the second part of the problem, namely to find the effects of high pressures on the properties of matter, and I should like to describe for you some of the results.

Perhaps the best way to begin is to set the scale. The engineer has long used as a convenient unit the pressure of the atmosphere at sea level, which is approximately 15 pounds to the square inch. The pressure at the deepest bottom of the ocean, about six miles down, is one thousand times as great as atmospheric pressure. The pressure in a large cannon is, in turn, two or three times greater than deep sea pressures. But the pressure at the center of the earth is more than a thousand times the pressure in a large cannon, or about three and a half million atmospheres.

Pressures as high as those of the earth's interior are beyond anything that can be controlled in our experimental laboratories at the present time. We can, however, control and study pressures which are an appreciable fraction of this. The highest pressure which I have produced and measured is a little over four hundred thousand atmospheres, or something more than one-tenth the pressure at the center of the earth. Nearly a third of all the material composing our planet earth exists at this or a lower pressure, so, in experimenting with this pressure, we are exploring a condition which affects a very appreciable fraction of all the material in the earth.

Actually, there is very little that can be done in the laboratory at four hundred thousand atmospheres. We can attain it, record it, and that's about all. But at pressures of one hundred thousand atmospheres—corresponding to about seven hundred and fifty tons per square inch—it has been found possible to make measures extensive enough to be significant, and there is a wealth of new and interesting effects found at still lower pressures.

You may wonder how we produce these great pressures of many tons to the square inch. We use a fluid medium to transmit pressure, following in general the principle of the hydraulic ram. One of the first problems was to prevent leak of the fluid. After some study the answer was found. By a special design in the shape and arrangement of the packing we found it possible to make the pressure itself automatically tighten the packing. As a result, the higher the pressure, the less the fluid can leak. With a packing of this sort the ultimate limit is set not by leak, but by the strength of the vessels within which the tremendous pressures are produced.

Several materials have been developed in recent years which have proved useful to provide vessels of high strength. One of these is carboloy, an alloy of tungsten carbide.

Under compressive stress carboloy is more than twice as strong as steel. The strength of the vessel can also be raised by improving the structural shape. It is possible, by suitable design, to make the pressure itself automatically support the vessel. This may be done by completely enclosing the high pressure vessel within another vessel in which the pressure is lower, thus employing a sort of cascade effect.

Water, metals, and many other ordinary substances are usually described as incompressible, but pressures have beeen reached in the laboratory which actually reduce water to one half its original volume. The same pressures applied to iron have reduced its volume by only 5 per cent. On a cosmic scale the effects of pressure on the volumes of ordinary substances are highly important. Thus, the center of the earth is thought to be composed of iron squeezed to one half its normal volume by the enormous pressure.

Pressure not only changes the volume of a substance, it also changes the temperature at which the substance melts. If the substance is one that expands when it melts, and nearly all substances do expand, then its melting temperature is raised by an increase of pressure.

The rise in melting temperature may be very considerable. Take the case of mercury, for example. Under ordinary conditions mercury is liquid and freezes only when the temperature is reduced to 40 degrees below zero. But when it is squeezed with a pressure of twelve thousand atmospheres, mercury freezes solid at room temperature. The experiments indicate that the freezing temperature increases progressively with increase of pressure. That is to say, the higher the pressure, the higher is the temperature at which the substance will freeze. This evidently has important geological implications. It means, for example, that the interior of the earth is maintained solid by the pressure, although the interior temperature is much higher than the normal melting temperature.

Water is an exception to the rule just stated, for water is an abnormal substance that expands when it freezes, as many of you know if the milkman leaves his bottles outside on a cold morning. Because of this peculiar property of water, it results that when the pressure is raised, the freezing temperature of water goes down instead of up. In this way, by increasing the pressure, the freezing temperature of water can be progressively lowered from the familiar 32 degrees Fahrenheit until it reaches eight degrees below zero.

This occurs at two thousand atmospheres, and at that pressure an extraordinary thing happens; the ice gives up its struggle against overwhelming force and collapses into a new kind of ice, which is denser than water instead of lighter. Because it is denser, the melting point of the new ice therefore rises when increased pressure is imposed. But this new kind of ice also presently gives up the struggle, and is replaced by another. In all, six new kinds of ice are known, produced by high pressure, and one of them—when at a pressure of forty thousand atmospheres—melts at the temperature of melting solder. This is hot ice in very truth. Not only water, but many other substances can be forced by pressure to take new solid forms. Some hundreds of these have been studied. The record is at present held by the ordinary camphor used by our mothers to keep moths out of woolens. Under pressure, camphor can occur in 11 different forms.

Every property of a solid or a liquid is altered by pressure, and often by very large amounts. I shall mention only one more of these, namely the property that determines how the substance shall flow when sufficient force is applied to it. If the substance is a liquid, this property which resists flow is called viscosity.

Molasses, for example, has a much higher viscosity than a thin sugar syrup. The viscosity of a liquid may be enormously increased by pressure. Increases of as much as ten million fold have been attained at twelve thousand atmospheres. This means that a liquid may become as stiff as glass under the action of pressure, and without undergoing any sharp freezing. If the substance is a solid, the corresponding property is called plasticity. The plasticity of some metals is greatly increased by pressure, and as a result they will support great deformations without breaking. Ordinary steel, for example, becomes highly ductile. I have observed a piece of steel stretched out locally to three hundred times its initial length without breaking. This happened when the steel was under a pressure of twenty thousand atmospheres. At the same time the strength was notably increased. It is certain that such effects of pressure on the flow properties of solids have played a dominating role in the architecture of the earth, as anyone may see who visits a geological museum or inspects the twisted rock strata on any cliff in the mountains. Thus, even at the surface of our globe we may observe the continuing effects of pressures imposed in the remote geological past.

Polarized Light

By Edwin H. Land

Mr. Edwin H. Land, the inventor of Polaroid light polarizing film, is the president and director of research of the Polaroid Corporation.

For centuries, light has been a puzzle and a challenge to the scientists. The physicists have had controversies about the nature of light—particularly as to whether it is formed of particles of some sort, or whether it is formed of waves in some strange and all pervasive medium.

But whatever the basic nature of light, it is always agreed that there is associated with light a vibration. If this vibration takes the form of an orderly flat ribbon, then one says that the light is polarized: if the vibration is helter-skelter in all directions, then the light is not polarized. In the present paper we will be considering light that is polarized.

Just as everything in the world is more or less colored, so also everything in the world sends forth or reflects light that is more or less polarized. But while our eyes can see the colors, they cannot see the polarization. In order to see the polarization, we must make special glasses for our eyes to look through. This special glass which polarizes looks like ordinary window glass. But it knows polarized light from ordinary light. It will let ordinary light go through it, and convert it into polarized light. But as for polarized light, it will sometimes let it through and sometimes stop it.

If you keep in mind that polarized light corresponds to a flat ribbon vibration in a straight line, while unpolarized light corresponds to a helter-skelter vibration, then I think you can see why it is possible to have a special glass that sometimes lets polarized light pass through, and sometimes does not. It is somewhat analogous to what happens if you try to throw a stick through a picket fence. The stick will have no chance to go through unless it is parallel to the open slits in the fence.

Consider what happens, then, if you go outside and look at the world through a piece of polarizing glass. When you look at the shiny asphalt of the street, all the shine disappears. When you look out across the ocean, the water-glare is gone. Our Army and Navy put this effect to good use in goggles and in Naval range finders. The glare, because it is polarized, is stopped by the polarizing glass. It is stopped unless you happen to have turned your glass the wrong way.

Polarizing glass has a kind of optical grain, an asymmetrical optical texture, corresponding to the open slits in the fence we spoke of. Cut a piece in half, put the two pieces on top of each other with their cut edges parallel, and you can see right through them. But if you turn one over the other, they begin to darken.

When their cut edges are at right angles, they are black. You can't see through them at all, just as you couldn't throw any stick through two picket fences whose slits were at right angles to one another. If you wish to look at something which is too bright to look at—for example, a plane as it flies into the sun—you can do it comfortably and effectively by arranging a pair of polarizers so that one can be turned over the other in your goggle or in your machine-gun sight.

You can get this same control no matter how far away you place one of the polarizers. Covered with polarizing glass, a light a mile away, or 100 miles away, will blink on and off if you will turn your polarizer like a wheel as you look through it.

If we look at the sun in an eclipse, we will see its corona go light and dark as we turn our polarizer. Thus its light is polarized. So is the light from the spiral nebulae. Even the light of the sky is polarized by the lopsided scattering of the sunlight by the particles in the atmosphere, so that we can darken it without changing its color or darkening the rest of the scene. All crystals have their individual effects on polarized light so that we can tell one from another by examining them between polarizers.

Perhaps the best way of getting the feeling of how light gets polarized is to know how polarizing glass is made; and we will now abandon our previous picket-fence analogue and use another which is more accurate. First, imagine a good-sized paint brush with bristles of a special kind. Imagine that the bristles become finer and finer, so fine that you need a microscope to see each individual bristle, and at last too fine to be seen even in a microscope. If you had such a paint brush with such fine, special bristles, and if you looked through the brush, you would first of all find that it would appear an even dark gray like a dark piece of glass; and you would also find that you had a polarizer. When light came through the bristles of such an imaginary paint brush, those vibrations in the light that were in the long direction of the bristles would be removed, and those vibrations in the light across the direction of the bristles would come through. If you held two such paint brushes on top of each other with the bristles parallel, you could see through them both; but when you rotated them so that the bristles in one brush crossed the bristles in the other, you would not be able to see through them.

You can now see why we abandoned the picket fence idea, for it is too crude to serve as more than a first introduction. As our more correct paint-brush picture has indicated, the stick that goes through the picket fence is, paradoxically enough, the one which is crosswise to the open slits! And neither in the fence nor, for that matter, in the paint brush ought one to think of ordinary open slits. Actually, in the case of the paint-brush analogue, the bristles represent directions of an electronic field with which the light interacts.

In making actual polarizing sheets, we create a brushlike structure inside of a plastic sheet—a clear, tough plastic called polyvinylalcohol. First, we stretch it in one direction so that the long, tangled molecules straighten out, all parallel to the direction of stretch. Then we dip the sheet into a solution like the ordinary tincture of iodine in your medicine chest. The rusty brown iodine is instantly and rather miraculously transformed. It now has two different colors. To polarized light vibrating in one direction, it is perfectly white and clear; to polarized light vibrating in the other direction, it is black. The sheet has become a light polarizer, ready to be sandwiched between plates of glass or waterproof sheets of clear plastic, to be used in goggles and range finders.

The stretched-out plastic provides the molecular grain or structure. The iodine contributes the light-absorbing asymmetry. We have produced a practical analogue of the imaginary bristle brush.

One of the great technical advantages of the polarizer is that it enables one to control the brightness of light without altering its color. It enables us to label light, to put a tag on it, to say that this particular light is to go here but not there; whereas this other light, polarized in a different direction, is to go there but not here. Thus, in automobile headlights, one can light up the road brilliantly with a headlight that is itself nearly invisible to the driver facing into it. In submarine periscopes, we can sort out the glare from the water while we let through the useful image of our target. In the future, perhaps, we shall have three-dimensional motion pictures— even three-dimensional television—in which, with polarizers, we can sort out for each individual eye in the audience the proper picture from the two which are always on the screen and so create the three-dimensional impression.

The history of polarization is an excellent example of the continuous interplay between pure and applied science. From 1669, when an effect due to polarized light was first observed, until about 1935, polarized light was used only in the laboratory. Scientists used it to develop theories about the essential nature of light and to help in their study of crystals.

Not until after 1935 did any large scale, practical application of polarized light take place. Without the centuries of interest in polarization by scientists who loved science the way musicians love music, and who had no practical purpose in mind, the modern synthetic polarizers that open up whole industries for us would have been impossible.

But these new modern polarizers, and the techniques of the industries they create, will help us come to an understanding of what happens when a molecule polarizes light, and will contribute also toward answering one of the most fascinating of all questions in pure science: What is light?

Thus, applied science, purposeful and determined, and pure science, playful and freely curious, continuously support and stimulate each other. The great nation of the future will be the one which protects the freedom of pure science as much as it encourages applied science.

Science and Standards

By Edward U. Condon

Dr. Edward U. Condon, previously at Princeton University and the associate director of the Westinghouse Research Laboratories, is now director of the National Bureau of Standards, Washington, D. C.

ONE of the foundation stones of science is man's faculty for measurement. This is conspicuously true of physics, chemistry, and engineering. And measurement is also playing an increasingly important part in the biological sciences and in their applications to agriculture, medicine, and psychology. Some have even said that "Science *is* measurement," and we recall the oft-quoted remark of Lord Kelvin to the effect that a thing is very poorly understood until it has been measured.

In order to make a measurement we must have a yardstick, a pound weight, or some other standard which is accepted by all as the unit. The determination of suitable standard units is very delicate business, however. Measurements in atomic physics, for example, are extremely complicated. Since an atom is only about one one-hundred-millionth of an inch in diameter, the problem of weighing it, clocking its speed, and determining its energy calls for subtle techniques and fine standards. Not only atoms and molecules, but large bodies, even such immense things as stars and planets, depend for their measurement on highly refined instruments and methods.

Several years ago the newspapers carried headlines stating that a Government physicist was weighing the earth in a little underground laboratory in Washington.

Actually, the object of Dr. Heyl's experiment was to determine the constant of gravitation. There was already in existence a value for this basic constant which had been determined thirty years before, but Dr. Heyl had devised a more delicate machine, and by this means he was able to measure the constant of gravitation with increased accuracy. With the closer determination of this important constant of nature, it was possible to calculate the mass of the earth more accurately than had ever been done before, and thus, in that sense, the scientist did weigh the earth. Incidentally, the mass of the earth turns out to be some 6,570 million million million tons This measurement of the constant of gravity was carried out in one of the Government laboratories, known as the National Bureau of Standards. This Bureau was established in 1901 as part of the Department of Commerce. The primary job of the Bureau of Standards is to provide the basic standards of measurement in physics, chemistry, and engineering. These standards range from such minute things as the wave lengths of light and the momentum of electrons up to such gross things as the standard yard and the standard pound.

As science expands and technology becomes more complex, better methods of measuring must be devised. Also new sorts of things must be reduced to measurement.

For example, great improvements have recently been made in the methods of measuring and specifying colors. This makes possible improved color matching of such different and yet common things as the tiled walls of a kitchen and the dyed textiles of the curtains in that kitchen. In similar fashion, but in a field far removed from the kitchen, we are now witnessing the rapid development of a whole host of new ways of measuring the strength of artificial radioactivity. The radioactive isotopes produced by the uranium piles are important to medical research, but they can be safely used only if the correct dosages of the radiation are known. Similarly, these measurements of radioactivity are highly important to insure the safety of workers in the atomic energy projects.

Each new kind of quantity which presents itself for measurement brings new scientific problems. The attempt to develop a method of measuring often reveals serious gaps in our knowledge of a subject. As a result, in order to measure the thing or its properties, we may have to study it in a very fundamental way through a far-reaching program of research. Thus, measurement leads to fundamental knowledge—and the National Bureau of Standards is, in fact, the Federal Government's central agency for basic research in physics, chemistry, and engineering. Because it was central in research in the physical sciences, the Bureau of Standards was naturally chosen to do the pioneer work in the development of atomic energy. Only after the scientific foundations of the study of uranium were far advanced and its application brought to the status of an engineering and construction job, was the project turned over to the Army for industrial development. Even after this was done, chemists of the Bureau of Standards continued to exercise watchful control over the purity of the uranium used. Purity is highly important, for if the metal were contaminated, even to the slight extent of a few parts per million, the whole project would be rendered inoperative. The purity of all the uranium being used for atomic energy is still controlled at the Bureau of Standards by methods originated by the Bureau's chemists.

The Bureau's contributions to the winning of the war covered a wide field. They ranged all the way from special studies of the corrosion of metals to the development of aeronautical instruments. In the latter field, a group at the Bureau of Standards developed the proximity fuse for mortars and bombs dropped from airplanes. Another instrument improvement led to the development of the Bat, one of the Navy's flying bombs. It was the only radar-guided missile to see service in the war.

Because of its responsibility for measuring the fixing standards for radio waves, the Bureau has become a center of research in practically all factors affecting radio communication. During the war, this work was considerably expanded, because of the vital importance of radio to all branches of the service, on the land, at sea, and in the air. The electrical properties of the upper atmosphere directly affect the transmission of short-wave radio, and these electrical properties in turn depend on activities of the sun, particularly those related to sunspots. All these problems have been subjects of intensive study by the Bureau of Standards, and with the termination of war, Congress has continued the work as a new unit of the Bureau known as the Central Radio Propagation Laboratory. This laboratory maintains observing stations at various points in the United States, in the Pacific and in the West Indies. It also co-operates with similar services of other nations.

With the passing of the great load of war work, the Bureau of Standards is now able to re-establish and extend many services to the American people which were necessarily curtailed during the emergency.

One of the most important is research on building materials and structures. Many of these studies are made co-operatively for the National Housing Agency. In view of the urgency of the housing situation, we are enlarging this program very extensively in the near future.

There is one phase of housing research which tests various kinds of house constructions for fire resistance. Over the years, a small but persistent program of study has explored this field. This study has led to a better understanding of what factors make a building more fire resistant. It has paid vast dividends in reducing loss of life and property by fire.

Another activity that can now be stepped up is that of helping business develop standards for consumer goods. Before the war there were several important projects in this field. One was directed at the development of machines for testing the quality of silk stockings and the wearing characteristics of shoes and of carpets. Already under way are projects to provide improved standard dimensions for various garments, based on a wide and representative sampling of body measurements. These projects are expected to result in savings to those who make, those who retail, and those who wear clothes.

It is clear, I hope, from this brief review, that the National Bureau of Standards serves in a dual capacity. First of all, the Bureau is a center of fundamental research—an agency for the exploration of nature and the discovery of new knowledge. The second function of the Bureau is to apply its knowledge to purposes of measurement. This second function involves co-operation with business and industry in arriving at standards of quality for a great variety of commodities. Its measurements provide the specifications for Government purchases, and they also guide industry, business, and the consumer to standards of quality based on scientific knowledge. The Bureau of Standards is therefore a national laboratory both of pure science and of applied science. It is dedicated both to the search for knowledge and to its useful application.

Physics and Art

By Herbert E. Ives

Dr. Herbert E. Ives, a research physicist of the Bell Telephone Laboratories known for his work in optics, color photography, and color measurement, is also an amateur painter.

It may seem to some of you that physics and art represent two extremes of human interest. Art deals with the intangibles of beauty; physics with the practical, the measurable, the exact. Yet historically the two have marched hand in hand. Four hundred years ago Leonardo da Vinci recognized the relationship: for, when Leonardo wrote his celebrated "Treatise on Painting," he harped throughout on mechanics and optics. Some three hundred years later, when Helmholtz studied the eye as an optical instrument, it inspired him to write his series of lectures "On the Relation of Optics to Painting."

Throughout the ages, the task of the artist has been to reproduce aspects of the world about him, as appraised by his senses. Many mediums have been tried—painting, sculpture, music, and the rest —but whatever the medium, the problem is not simple.

The painter, for example, depicts upon a flat surface that which in nature extends as far as the eye can reach. He must compress between the white of his canvas and the mere murkiness of his blackest pigment the glare of sunlight, the gloom of night, and all the shadings between these extremes. He must suggest motion and portray life with means that essentially are static and inanimate. In this quest the painter has at all times been guided, as was Leonardo, by the principles of natural philosophy, or as we now call it, the science of physics.

The nature of space has long been studied by the physicist; at the same time, the depiction of space has been the problem of the artist. In the ivory carvings of prehistoric man, the deer and the mammoth were separated from the rest of space by scratched outlines. Eventually, shadings were added to indicate shadows. As these shadings appear we have the beginnings of physics applied to art, for the shape of the shadow is determined by the straight

136

line along which light travels from the sun to the earth—the rectilinear propagation of light, as the physicist would say. With shading, paintings began to show relations in space—began to have extension or depth.

The greatest advance from the fixed plane of the canvas came with the Renaissance, when the principles of geometrical perspective were grasped. Before that there was little distinction in size between the near and the far. In primitive art, the distant horse might dwarf the near-by castle. Another convention of primitive art was to place distant objects above near ones, as though ascending a spiral staircase. It was in fifteenth-century Padua, where schools of "artists and geometricians" flourished, that science and art learned about the law of inverse squares. According to this law, an object when removed to twice the distance, occupies one quarter of the original angular field. Because of this law, which is well-nigh universal in physics, from gravitation to illumination, objects in a painting grow smaller toward the horizon and parallel lines converge to a vanishing point.

Artists henceforth were to lay out their pictures on the flat canvas just as the lens of the eye spreads a picture on the retina, according to the laws of geometrical optics.

The eye is a physical instrument—a camera obscura in the old langage of natural philosophy. The artist needs to know its properties, not excluding its defects. Like any other camera it does not define all objects sharply at once. If a near object is crisp, a remote object is fuzzy. So, when the artist added to his geometrical perspective a blurring of outline in distant objects, he further simulated the effect of space—as perceived by a creature with one eye.

But we have two eyes. Each of our eyes sees a different view, one a little around this side of the object, the other a little around the other. This gives us the most vivid of our sensations of depth. We call it stereoscopic vision. The English physicist Wheatstone invented a marvelous instrument called the stereoscope, which uses two slightly different views, one for each eye, to make a truly three-dimensional picture. The painter cannot do this with a single painting, but by a proper lateral blurring or even doubling of distant objects in a picture he manages to create the impression of reaching a little farther into space.

There is one more device which the artist can use—aerial perspective, which is closely related to physics. John Tyndall, famous experimenter of the Royal Institution in London, made many tests of light scattered by a milky liquid. He found that the scattered light was bluish—while the direct light was yellowish. Artists today use this effect to differentiate near objects from far, by veiling the distant objects with bluish haze, or by reddening objects illuminated through the haze.

We thus come to color. The primitive artist sought a pigment for every color, tint, and shade. His palette tended to resemble the Chinese type-setter's case, with a symbol for every word. It was early found that by mixing a few pigments, others of different colors resulted. Da Vinci in his treatise approached this problem, described a few simple mixtures, and then postponed the study to a future book. He never wrote that book, and the principles of light composition and color mixture had to wait until physicists like Newton, Young, Maxwell, and Helmholtz experimented and discovered them. Newton showed that all colors are present in white light. He demonstrated that the colors of objects are caused by the portions of white light which they absorb or reflect. Young showed that mixtures of red, green, and blue light will produce all the others. As a consequence it was recognized that three pigments which absorb these primary colors would suffice for the artist's palette.

These pigment colors—the simplest alphabet of color—are a bluish green, a magenta, and a yellow—not the red, yellow, and blue often cited. The results of these findings have been widely used in color photography and in color printing, but not so generally by painters as yet. When understood by the painter, the principles of color mixture enable him to think in terms of color itself rather than in terms of cadmium sulphide or chromium oxide.

The study of photometry and illumination has clarified the age-old problem of putting all the gamut of light values on a canvas. Between the whitest white pigment and the blackest black is a range of about twenty to one; between sunlight and moonlight, the range is a million to one. How then can the painter ever hope to depict more than the aspect of a studio-lighted object?

There comes to his rescue that part of physics which studies the methods of response of measuring instruments. The eye is affected by the surroundings of the object measured, and its performance varies with the level of its excitation. By placing contrasting areas together we get an enhancement of their difference. By decreasing the differences of color and tone we simulate the effects of bright illumination, which dulls the discrimination of the eye, and so whitens and flattens. A picture can thus be made to sing with sunlight even when under the subdued light of the gallery.

Although it originates in representation, art embraces much more. Its life is in selection, arrangement, composition, and design. What can physics offer in this field? We need only recall such critical terms as "unbalanced" and "top-heavy" to recognize that our basic ideas of harmonious design come from physics. Da Vinci treated the human figure as a system of weights and levers. The forms of architectural elements are dictated by the physical stresses to which they are subjected. The graceful shapes of Greek vases are closely connected with the physical laws of rotational equilibrium.

What of the future? Can physics do still more for art? The flat surface has possibly been stretched in space and in light as much as it can well be. We may have to look to other arts, as in the application of the newest forms of lighting to the theater stage. The future may well adjudge the greatest contribution of physics to art in our time to be the motion picture, with its command of lighting, motion, and color, and, in the imaginative field, the animated cartoon which, in an earlier form as the zootrope, was a plaything of the physical laboratory. These mediums are still new and, doubtless, have years of development still ahead, throughout which art and physics will continue to work hand in hand.

Mathematics and the Laws of Nature

By Hermann Weyl

Dr. Hermann Weyl is a member of the Institute for Advanced Study
at Princeton, New Jersey.

KNOWLEDGE in all physical sciences—astronomy, physics, chemistry —is based on observation. But observation can only ascertain what is. How can we predict what will be? To that end observation must be combined with mathematics.

One of the ancient Greek philosophers, Anaxagoras, first explained solar and lunar eclipses by means of the shadows of moon and earth intercepting the rays of the sun. You may say that he applied the idea of perspective to the heavenly bodies. Just a few years before, perspective had begun to be used for the stage decorations in the Athenian theater. Anaxagoras had the imagination to see something in common between stage decorations and eclipses. What made his approach possible? First this: that the Greeks had developed geometry as a mathematical science proceeding by pure reasoning from a few basic laws or axioms. "Through two distinct points there goes one and only one straight line" is one of these axioms that everybody takes for granted. Geometry had made the behavior of straight lines predictable. The second prerequisite for Anaxagoras' achievement is the conception of light rays as the agents that carry messages from the object to our eyes and thus give rise to our visual image of the object. This conception is purely hypothetical—a flash of genius as it were.

Third: a mathematical theory of light rays, namely that they are straight lines. That theory is suggested by experience. By combining these three ingredients—geometry, the conception of light rays, and the theory that they are straight—one can account for all the familiar facts of shadows and perspective.

It is on the same theoretical foundation that a surveyor determines the distance of a remote object: he measures his base and certain angles and then draws his conclusions by means of the geometry of light rays. In very much the same way Anaxagoras made his indirect measurement of the moon's distance from us.

That distance is certainly not directly measurable by tapeline. With this example in mind you will understand the following general statements: All indirect measurements, like that of the distance of the moon, are ultimately anchored in direct measurements. The link between the indirect and the direct measurements must be furnished by theory—in this case by the theory of perspective. A theory makes good when all indirect measurements based on it check. This is a methodic principle of paramount importance.

Anaxagoras could have carried out his construction with pencil on paper, or rather with a reed on papyrus. But diagrams thus drawn are far too inaccurate for the purposes of astronomy.

Numbers, on the other hand, are capable of truly unlimited accuracy; and the use of numbers instead of geometric diagrams becomes indispensable anyhow as soon as time and such entities as mass, electrical charge, force, temperature have to be dealt with. The latter are all measurable quantities, though accessible to indirect measurement only. It was Galileo who said: "Measure what is measurable, and make measurable what is not so."

Mathematicians got along with geometry all right, but with the numbers they really come into their own. For the sequence of the natural numbers, 1, 2, 3, * * * is our minds" own free creation. It starts with 1, and any number is followed by the next one. That is all. According to this simple procedure the numbers march on towards infinity. 2 is the number that follows 1, 3 the number that follows 2, etc. Nothing else. You know very little about Henry VIII when you know that he followed Henry VII on the English throne. But you know all about 8 when you know that it follows 7. Man has his substantial existence; the words of our language have meanings with shifting subtle nuances; the tones of our musical compositions have their sensuous qualities. But numbers have neither substance, nor meaning, nor qualities. They are nothing but marks, and all that is in them we have put into them by the simple rule of straight succession.

It is therefore no wonder that we can predict what they do: for instance, that 7 plus 5 makes 12, or that an even number is always followed by an odd one. But do not imagine that all arithmetical laws are that trivial. As a matter of fact the mathematicians have been busy for many generations to discover more and more profound and universal laws, and they find that every progress raises new problems. I think the difficulty of their task is mainly due to the fact that the sequence of numbers is infinite.

After this digression about mathematics I resume my story. Passing on from Anaxagoras, and skipping 2000 years, I come to Kepler. He established his famous three laws about the motion of the planets. The only one that concerns us here is his first law: The planetary orbits are ellipses with the sun as their common focus. The Greek mathematicians had come upon the ellipses as the simplest curves after the straight lines and circles. Kepler had first tried circles; they did not fit the observations. He then turned to the only slightly more complicated ellipses and they fitted; they did so to an extraordinary degree of accuracy, and have not ceased to do so up to this date. Three remarks are here in order.

First: Kepler could not derive his laws from observation; for observation indicates merely the varying direction of the line joining our planet the earth, with the planet under observation.

Second: his idea of the elliptic orbit depended on the preliminary discovery of the ellipses by the Greek mathematicians.

Third: whatever the observations are, they could always have been fitted by a suitable curve; the point is that a vast number of detailed observations fit with such a simple curve as the ellipse. Kepler shared with Pythagoras and his followers a deep belief in the harmony of the universe. But for the Pythagoreans this was a sort of mystic creed. With Kepler it became a fact, in my opinion the most important fact we know about the universe. I formulate it this way: There is inherent in nature a hidden harmony that reflects itself in our minds under the image of simple mathematical laws. That then is the reason why events in nature are predictable by a combination of observation and mathematical analysis. Again and again in the history of physics this conviction, or should I say this dream, of harmony in nature has found fulfillments beyond expectation.

Now I can be brief. The conceptual basis of Kepler's theory was still the same as with Anaxagoras. Galileo, the father of modern science, brought in a new conception: he visualized motion as a struggle between inertia and force. A moving body has mass and momentum, and is acted upon by forces. This conception has remained the firm foundation of our physical understanding to this day, unshaken even by atomic and quantum physics.

And so has his basic law: Force changes momentum at a rate equal to the force. Rate of change is a mathematical notion that is defined in calculus. Newton added the idea of a universal force of gravitation acting between any two mass particles. His dynamical law of gravitation, the simplest that algebra can devise, is essentially simpler than the medley of Kepler's three kinematical laws, but covers and predicts a far wider range of phenomena with the minutest accuracy. Again we find the three characteristic features: the necessary mathematics, here calculus and algebra, developed beforehand by the mathematicians; a basic conception about the nature of things; and a theory expressed in terms of both. Many more illustrations could be adduced from modern physics. Digging for the roots of the phenomena we drive the spade deeper and deeper. Galileo and Newton reached a deeper layer than their predecessor Kepler, and we continue their labors. But thereby the gap between theory and observation becomes ever wider. Mathematics has to work harder and harder to bridge this gap. Newton himself was held up by a mathematical difficulty of this sort for twenty years.

A peculiar situation prevails in quantum physics: The mathematical apparatus, in terms of which Schrödinger expressed the basic law of quantum physics, had indeed been developed by the mathematicians beforehand—as in the other cases we discussed.

But the stimulus to this mathematical development had originally come from a ground where music and physics meet, the acoustics of vibrating bodies. Studies undertaken to understand musical harmony have thus finally enabled us to understand the richest harmony in the visible world—that of the spectral lines emitted by radiating atoms.

CHAPTER 8

CHEMISTRY AND LIVING THINGS

THE BEST way to get large and high-grade yields of corn, as we will see in the next chapter, is to make hybrid crosses. Great productivity may also result from joining together two lines of science.

Physical chemistry and chemical engineering are two of these scientific hybrids which have long been established and have fully demonstrated their value. Biophysics, chemical physics, and astrophysics are relatively recent crosses. The present chapter is devoted to still another scientific hybrid, biochemistry, the offspring of chemistry and biology.

Much significant biological research of the last half century has been concerned with studying out the detailed chemistry of the processes which take place inside living creatures. Some of this work has involved patient years of experimenting with worms, insects, and bacteria. At other times the research has dealt with our own bodies and the normal or abnormal processes within them. But whether through mice or men, biochemistry has built up a precious store of knowledge of the chemistry of life. All of this knowledge fits together, and gradually but surely increases our power to maintain health and to cope with disease and accident.

This chapter shows how modern chemistry is applied to biological and medical problems. The reader will discover that the men who make these applications are not necessarily labeled as biochemists. Three of the scientists whose work appears here are physical chemists, and others originally specialized in organic chemistry. Indeed, the interest of this chapter is not strictly limited to biochemistry at all. Catalysts, which are described here, are of great importance in all fields of chemistry, especially in industrial work, as well as directly in biochemistry.

When we read about biochemistry, the word "protein" recurs frequently and inevitably. These complex chemical compounds are essential constituents in every individual cell of every living plant or animal. It is not strange that scientists picked out for these compounds a name which in the original Greek meant "of primary importance."

Certain proteins, in fact, provide the best possible evidence for the close relationship between chemistry and life. For among the proteins are viruses, those strange and tiny objects which sometimes act as though they were alive, and which at other times are pure chemical substances, as inert in a bottle as so much sugar or salt. So great is the biochemist's interest in viruses that three of the sections in this chapter are devoted to them.

W. W.

The Golden Age of Biochemistry*

By Robert R. Williams and Roger J. Williams

Dr. Robert R. Williams, for many years chemical director of research, Bell Telephone Laboratories, is director of grants, Research Corporation. His younger brother, Dr. Roger J. Williams, is director of the Biochemical Institute at the University of Texas.

ROGER:—Bob, why do you call this the Golden Age of Biochemistry?

BOB:—Roger, it is a Golden Age because of the rapid succession of important biochemical discoveries. Specific chemical substances have been found to be the keys to the nongerm diseases. Goitre, diabetes and the diseases caused by incomplete diets have yielded to the biochemical approach.

ROGER:—The diseases have been known a long time. What were we waiting for?

BOB:—Increased attention to science and the scientific way of doing things for one thing. Also, the special tools had to be developed —such as ways of making chemical analyses of tiny specks of material.

ROGERS—Yes, I wonder what you could have done with vitamin B_1 crystals if you had obtained them when you first began working with vitamins back in 1911.

BOB:—Not much. For methods of analysis did not then exist to handle tiny amounts. In a way it was fortunate that it took many years to obtain the vitamin—but it didn't seem fortunate at the time.

ROGER:—Yes, we owe a lot to two Austrian scientists, Pregl and Emich, who first devised ways to analyze mere pin point samples. Vitamins occur in minute amounts and to get even a little is a tremendous chore.

BOB:—Not only vitamins. Progress with hormones and antibiotics, such as penicillin, has also been tremendously helped by the

---

*In the planning of the radio talks which resulted in the present volume, the experiment was tried on two occasions of having these talks occur in dialogue form, as a conversation between two scientists closely related in their work and interests. The following paper is one of these dialogues, and has been left in its orginal radio form.

same methods. You had to devise some new methods yourself in the study of another B vitamin which you discovered. I mean pantothenic acid.

ROGER:—Yes, we found we had quite a detective job on our hands—we learned enough about pantothenic acid while it was in impure solutions so we could guess its identity without ever isolating it.

BOB:—I believe that was never done before. It was like Sherlock Holmes describing a criminal having nothing more to go on than his footprints and the ash from his cigar.

ROGER:—Bacteria and other tiny organisms have been wonderful helpers in our work too. By watching them grow in trial solutions, we can determine the presence or absence of any one of nine vitamins. Even the amounts of each vitamin present can be determined with accuracy.

BOB:—Little did we realize years back that a tiny snip of tissue could ever be assayed for vitamins. In Manila, years ago, we had to use pigeons and chickens for testing and they ate up a lot of our vitamin before they told the answer.

ROGER:—You were after something pretty definite. Beriberi is a serious disease in the Philippines and you were hunting the cure.

BOB:—Yes, my inclinations are toward the practical. I remember feeling rather sorry for you when you were messing around with substances that only made yeast grow, while I was dealing with pressing human needs.

ROGER:—Yes, maybe my bump of sheer curiosity is more developed than yours, Bob. However, I thought the stuff I was after would turn out to be a vitamin—and it did.

BOB:—It's fortunate that men do have different bents because it often happens that the most entrancing discoveries lie at the end of some lane which seems uninviting to many. The most marvelous discovery in which we have had a share is that the things which make our bodies tick are pretty much the same things which have made all living things tick, presumably since life's dawn.

ROGER:—Yes, you worked with pigeons, rats and humans while I dealt with yeasts, bacilli and alfalfa, but in the end we found ourselves converging on the same objectives.

BOB:—Together we have seen the accumulation of more knowledge of vital biochemical substances than all previous history had gathered. We are lucky to have lived in such a thrilling period.

ROGER:—We surely are; but where do we go from here? I can visualize a continuation of biochemical research bringing us progressively a mastery of many degenerative diseases, perhaps within the lifetimes of those now living.

BOB:—Yes, that seems quite credible. Just think of what we have ourselves witnessed in the field of infectious disease. You don't remember it but when you and I were first vaccinated in India, it was done with a pocket knife and the heifer which supplied the scab was in a stall at the back of the vaccination station. Asepsis was then in its infancy. We can reach back and touch the hand of the brilliant French chemist, Pasteur, who was also the father of practical bacteriology. He was still living at that time.

ROGER:—Yet we have far to go to link our knowledge of the simpler substances which chemists could understand with the complexities of the biological systems. Only within the past five years have we realized the possibility of dealing with the huge molecules of the proteins which make up the great bulk of our tissues and our blood. Within the individual molecule, there are features which, for example, distinguish each species from every other and the modification of such features without breakdown of the molecule is now becoming possible. Chemical production of antibodies is already beginning.

BOB:—Curiously a good deal of our ability to deal with these macromolecules comes from the study of man-made rubber and plastics.

ROGER:—I think with the aid of biochemistry we will one day be able to understand the personality characteristics of human beings much better than we do. As a result we will learn to get along together more peaceably.

BOB:—Yet while we are exploring the unknown we must concern ourselves also about the intelligent application of what is known. For example, our habits and even our laws should reflect the growing knowledge of nutrition in our own day. There is no reason why we need to have rickets, pellagra or beriberi any longer, but we do.

ROGER:—But is that not a job primarily for others than those who have been specially trained for research?

BOB:—Insofar as others can do it, yes. However, I feel that scientists should have a better wisdom about what can be safely attempted, what must be left till further knowledge accumulates and how to go about what we do undertake.

ROGER:—Probably one's choice will be determined partly by his temperament. Each will obey his inner urges whether still to seek the unknown or try to use the known.

BOB:—Concern about the second appeals to me because our present era of notable scientific advance has latterly been one of conspicuous social unrest or even retrogression. We deal more successfully with our environment than with ourselves. Life has on the whole been advancing through millions of years. Should not science, if worthy of the name, derive some wisdom from nature as to how man himself should behave? What's your opinion, Roger?

ROGER:—I agree, but sometimes I wonder if we know enough about man to venture to predict. It is difficult to experiment with man, and he lives too long to give us a quick answer.

BOB:—Yet Darwin's conception of evolution, now so universally accepted, was based originally on observation rather than experiment. By tracing the course of life's development, one can see in some degree what forms of social organization led to progress and which to decay and deterioration of the individual.

ROGER:—Bob, do you mean that a congress of biological science could contribute wisdom to our choice of political ideologies?

BOB:—Yes, Roger, for I believe that our very love of liberty is rooted in the long past which made us men. Much of the charm of biochemistry is that while it deals with very tangible details which can be explored experimentally, its ultimate concern must extend to the mystery of human consciousness and aspiration, to the spirit of man itself.

Protein Chemistry and Medicine

By Vincent du Vigneaud

Dr. Vincent du Vigneaud is head of the Department of Biochemistry
at the Cornell University Medical College in New York City.

WE HAVE heard over and over again of the great contributions that the chemist has made to the well-being of our people through his contributions to medicine. These are gratifying successes and the chemist has a right to be proud of them.

However, not all the attempts of the chemist to contribute to medicine have been crowned with success. There are many problems which are badly in need of solution, and upon which the chemist has worked but to date has not entirely succeeded.

I should like to take one sector of the field of biochemistry in relation to medicine and devote a few paragraphs to discussing an example or two of the unsolved problems. For isn't it essential for us to evaluate our failures as well as our successes? In considering chemistry's effort to help medicine, we can best appreciate the need of highly trained chemists—and more chemists—to continue the attack on such problems.

When a field such as chemistry has not been able to provide medicine with a necessary drug, or an understanding of a particular biological process, or the fate of a substance in the body, or the structure of a certain compound, or a method of analysis for a particular constituent of the body, it usually means that somewhere along the line some piece of fundamental knowledge has been lacking. In order to obtain this knowledge more fundamental research is absolutely necessary.

Now, then, what are some of these unsolved problems to which I am referring? Well, let us consider a very important hormone which we have all heard about. I am thinking of insulin, the hormone which is essential for the utilization of sugar by the body, and which, as you know, is used medically in the control of diabetes.

The chemist has done a creditable job of getting this hormone out in pure form and has contributed greatly to many aspects of the chemistry of this important compound; but chemists the world over for twenty years have tried to solve the riddle of insulin. Still we don't know why it possesses its remarkable physiological properties and how it brings about its miraculous effect.

We know that it is a protein, that is to say, that it is a very complex structure made up of many small building blocks, called the amino acids. But somehow the clue has eluded us as to how and why this substance can regulate the amount of sugar in the blood. Furthermore, it has defied synthesis! Why is this? Some will say, of course, that it is impossible to synthesize a protein and therefore it is impossible to synthesize insulin.

Are we going to accept that? Of course not! But, if there is to be any hope of ever accomplishing the synthesis of insulin and of truly understanding its chemistry, we must start much further back, and must seek to understand more fully the fundamental chemistry of proteins. For this is the type of problem in which no one knows what the answer might be, nor from what direction the answer might come.

Just as insulin is elaborated by the pancreas to regulate sugar utilization in the body, a series of other proteins are elaborated by the pituitary gland to control various physiological mechanisms. For example, one of these proteins influences the mammary gland, another stimulates the thyroid, another affects the sex glands, and still another is vital for growth. These as well as other protein hormones all present problems similar to those mentioned in connection with insulin.

Akin in some respects to the problem of the chemistry of insulin and the other protein hormones is another problem, that is the chemistry of viruses, some of which have been shown to be a type of especially huge protein molecule. The solution of this problem is of particular importance to the advancement of medicine because viruses are causative agents of many diseases. Problems still more baffling than those posed by the protein hormones are here encountered. How does this particular type of protein multiply in the body? Furthermore, how can this multiplication be hindered? Perhaps in this way, some of the virus diseases might be counteracted. Even though brilliant contributions have already been made by virus chemists, many vitally important questions are yet to be answered.

There are still other proteins which possess remarkable properties, the understanding of which is of importance to medicine. For instance, there is a protein of the blood which forms the blood clot, but just what change takes place in the protein during the formation of the clot, and exactly how the transformation takes place, remain to be worked out. There are other proteins in the blood likewise playing vital roles. It is the proteins of the blood, such as the albumin and globulin, that counteract the shock resulting from wounds. It is the need for these proteins that made collection of human blood so important in the war effort. Other proteins in the blood, present in much smaller amounts, afford the body protection against many diseases such as measles and influenza. These are the so-called antibodies which confer on an individual immunity towards certain diseases. These intricate immunological processes abound in problems challenging the chemist and demand more fundamental knowledge of proteins. The same could well be said for enzyme chemistry, which involves an almost countless number of proteins which, at times in conjunction with the vitamins, possess remarkable catalytic powers.

Finally, I might point out that the whole process of the formation and breakdown of the host of proteins in the tissues within the body is still to be worked out. I need not point out that our skin and flesh and internal organs consist mainly of proteins to have you realize how important protein chemistry becomes to the comprehension of the nature of the repair of tissues, of the healing of wounds, and of the many disease processes, and even to the understanding of cancer.

I think that it is evident that more chemists—and even more highly trained chemists—will be needed in the years to come to carry on with these and other problems with their brother scientists in other fields, in order to afford the fundamental basis for still further advances in medicine and thus to help the doctor in his conquest of disease.

As we plan for the future, we must realize that it is easier to appreciate the need of scientific research directly connected with a practical application. It is harder to grasp the need of true fundamental, pioneering research. The type of research I mean is that required to solve the kind of problem which we have been considering, where no one knows what the answer may be or from what direction the answer may come.

In whatever planning and organization we may carry out in the post-war years, we must make very sure that we provide to scientists not only the facilities for fundamental research, but we must be very careful to preserve that type of environment which provides the complete freedom for the "playing" of his "hunches" and which allows him to travel without hindrance the pioneer trails that his curiosity beckons him to follow.

In thinking specifically of medicine, I might point out that medicine does need chemistry and chemists for the building of the medicine of tomorrow. The field of medicine today has assimilated the biochemistry and physiology of yesterday; and the biochemistry and physiology of today must be encouraged along fundamental lines to build the medicine of tomorrow. We can see in retrospect what chemistry has done for medicine but it is so much harder for the human mind to grasp that the chemistry of today and tomorrow will likewise yield discoveries that will be of aid to the medicine of the future.

Blood and Blood Derivatives

By Edwin Joseph Cohn

Dr. Edwin Joseph Cohn is professor of biological chemistry and head of the Department of Physical Chemistry of the Harvard Medical School.

BLOOD has been related to life in the minds of men since the earliest times. Savage tribes have celebrated symbolic blood brotherhoods and blood sacrifices. In Biblical times and in the middle ages blood was regarded with superstition and awe, and often associated with the spirit of man. In the recent war, also, blood symbolized the spirit relating a civilian population to its sons in distant parts. The blood collected by the American Red Cross not only brought relief but also evidence of social coherence to the most distant corners of the world to which it was sent.

What is the scientific knowledge regarding blood, as a result of which superstition and awe are receding and are slowly being replaced by an understanding of the chemical nature of the sub- stances of which blood is composed and of their value in medicine and surgery?

Blood is a tissue, composed of many of the same kinds of sub- stances as the other tissues of the body, of water and salts, sugars and fats and proteins, but fluid, since it must circulate and main- tain equilibrium within the body. Its circulation was discovered by Harvey in the early seventeenth century, and the first step in unraveling its complexity followed the development later in that century of powerful lenses which revealed the presence of cells suspended in this circulating fluid. The cells are readily separated from the fluid in which they are suspended by centrifuga- tion, the same process used to separate cream from milk. The lighter layer is called the plasma. The heavy layer contains all of the cells of the blood stream. These cells are of more than one kind, but one type of cell, red in color, occupies nearly half the volume of the blood.

The primary function of the red cells is to provide for the respiration of the body. Every time you breathe you bring a fresh supply of oxygen from the air to your lungs where it is combined with a special agent, the hemoglobin of the red cell, which carries it to the tissues. This special agent, hemoglobin, is a protein which contains iron in the state responsible both for the color and the great affinity of blood for oxygen.

Red blood cells are needed when there has been severe loss of blood, when major operations are to be performed, and to com- bat the anemia which frequently occurs in convalescence from wounds. Whole blood is, therefore, made available whenever these conditions obtain. However, many of the functions of the whole blood are performed not by the red cells but by the plasma pro- teins. In these conditions plasma, or the special plasma proteins that are needed, may be used.

The plasma can be dried by methods that had been developed just before this war. Dry plasma was prepared from the blood of many millions of Red Cross donors and proved effective in the prevention and treatment of shock.

Shock, as observed in military medicine, generally results from a rapid decrease in the volume of the blood due to the loss of blood and plasma proteins. Reduced in volume and often thickened by the loss of more fluid than red cells, the circulation of the blood becomes inadequate. Restoration of the volume of the blood so that its circulation by the heart again approaches normal may be brought about by administration of plasma proteins.

Proteins are very large molecules, and are the highly specialized substances which are most responsible for the structure and the complex functions of the body. The proteins of the plasma, as of other tissues, differ in size and shape. The smallest dimension of all plasma protein molecules—their diameter—is roughly the same. This diameter is five times that of sugar molecules. Small molecules, indeed all the molecules that have been studied which are appreciably smaller than the plasma proteins, are readily lost from the blood stream into the tissues or through the kidney. They are, therefore, of less value in the prevention and treatment of shock than the plasma proteins which are normally retained in the blood stream.

Two out of every three of the protein molecules of plasma are of one kind, called albumin. Albumin is the protein in plasma largely responsible for the maintenance of blood volume. Albumin molecules are the smallest in size, the most nearly spherical in shape, the most soluble and the most stable of the plasma proteins. Albumin can therefore be prepared as a concentrated solution which is as fluid as whole blood, and is effective in the treatment of shock. Large amounts of this very compact derivative of plasma were prepared and used by our Navy.

The separation of albumin from plasma by the large-scale methods which have been developed, releases the other plasma proteins for uses in medicine and surgery closely related to their functions in the body. How do we separate the plasma proteins from each other? Even closely related proteins can be separated because of their different solubilities in water or in alcohol-water mixtures, at different acidities and at different temperatures. As conditions are attained in which a fraction of the plasma proteins becomes insoluble, it is separated as a precipitate in the centrifuge and dried as a stable white powder. These purified dried products can be stored indefinitely and redissolved when needed as specific concentrated therapeutic agents.

Let us consider the physical properties of another derivative of plasma, fibrinogen, which is concentrated in another plasma fraction. Only one in every hundred of the protein molecules in plasma is fibrinogen. Fibrinogen is far less soluble than albumin. Its molecules are of roughly the same diameter but six times as long as albumin. Indeed fibrinogen molecules are like needles, twenty times as long as they are thick. This shape is closely related to the fibrous structure of the clot formed of fibrinogen which stops the flow of blood from a cut or wound.

The chemical nature of the fibrinogen molecule endows products made from this protein with remarkable elastic and mechanical properties not unlike those of certain synthetic fibres such as nylon. Films of fibrinogen have been used as substitutes for the dura, the lining membrane of the brain. Fibrinogen can also be formed into plastics.

The transformation of the fibrinogen dissolved in the plasma into the insoluble blood clot involves a series of reactions in which a protein we call thrombin is liberated. To stop the flow of blood in many surgical procedures thrombin is the only component which must be supplied. Thrombin is best applied, however, with a matrix which can hold the thrombin in the bleeding area until clotting is completed. Such a matrix, formed of human fibrin and called fibrin foam, has been used in military and other neurosurgery.

If the properties of hemoglobin, of albumin, and of the fibrinogen of the blood stream are so different, how are we to understand the functions of the variety of other plasma proteins which have been called globulins? Globulins are of many kinds. One group holds fats in solution and transports them in the plasma. Another small group agglutinates the red cells of different blood types. These may be used as reagents for the typing of whole blood. The most important globulins from the point of view of the public health are, however, the gamma globulins which are the antibodies to infectious diseases.

Not all of the antibodies concentrated from human plasma will be of value in the control of disease. However, in the case of measles, the concentrated antibodies have been employed with great success, either to assure protection or to modify the severity of the disease. Gamma globulins were supplied to the Armed Forces and through the American Red Cross to public health agencies for protection against measles. Their value in the control of infectious jaundice has also recently been demonstrated.

All of these products may be separated, purified and concentrated from the same blood. The chemist is fulfilling his function in making available derivatives which are more concentrated, stable, and specific agents than the blood from which they are derived. Starting with the assumption that every part of human blood performs an important natural function, we must make available in the post-war world, as we did in the recent war, as many as possible of its diverse cellular, protein and fatty components, separated and concentrated as specific therapeutic agents, of value in different conditions, in the interests of the most effective and economical use by a society of the blood which it contributes.

Some Acids Which Are Necessary for Life

By WILLIAM CUMMING ROSE

Dr. William Cumming Rose has for many years been professor of biochemistry at the University of Illinois.

EXPERIENCE has shown that the diet of man must contain a number of components in order to keep him alive. In general terms, these components may be classified into four groups, namely: carbohydrates and fats which serve primarily as fuels; minerals, which are necessary for the formation of bones and teeth; vitamins, which indirectly regulate the speed of chemical changes in the body; and proteins, which are the raw materials out of which most of the soft tissues are manufactured. It is this fourth group, the proteins, to which your attention is directed here.

Proteins occur in greatest abundance in meats, eggs, milk, cheese, and such vegetables as beans and peas. There are many different kinds of proteins, but it is characteristic of all proteins that their molecules are huge structures, and that these structures are in turn built up of various combinations of relatively simple crystalline compounds known as amino acids.

Twenty-two different amino acids have been identified. Some proteins contain all twenty-two, others not so many, and the amounts and order of combination of the amino acids vary widely in proteins of different sources. Indeed, no two proteins are exactly alike. This remarkable fact may be comprehended more clearly by reference to an analogy suggested by Professor Kossel of Heidelberg. The amino acids, said Kossel, are almost as numerous as the letters of the alphabet. There are twenty-six letters and we know twenty-two amino acids. Just as the letters can be built into thousands of words and be made to express an infinite number of thoughts, so the amino acids can be combined into an infinite number of different proteins.

In the progress of digestion, proteins are broken down into their constituent amino acids, and the acids pass into the blood stream. Thence, they are distributed throughout the body, and are available to serve as "building stones" in the construction of the many characteristic proteins which enter into the formation of muscles, nerves, blood, and many other tissues of the body. The unerring accuracy with which the living system manufactures specific tissue proteins out of the variable mixture of amino acids circulating in the blood is truly astounding.

One is warranted in asking: Is it necessary that man's diet contain all the amino acids, or is the body itself able to make—or synthesize as the chemist says—some of them out of other materials? This question was raised by biochemists almost half a century ago, but only in recent months has it been possible to obtain a reasonably definite answer. The first studies used animals as the experimental subjects; and one could not be sure that the results were applicable to man.

The method that brought an answer to our question made use of diets which were well balanced in carbohydrates, fats, minerals, and vitamins, but contained amino acids instead of proteins. The experiment was not an easy task, because amino acids in pure form are not readily available, and to isolate them from proteins or to make them is laborious and costly. Nevertheless, after several years of preliminary work, such feeding experiments were undertaken with human subjects in the biochemical laboratories of the University of Illinois.

Healthy young men served as the experimental subjects. The diets were not what one would select of his own volition. Meats, fish, most vegetables and most of the other natural foods contain significant quantities of proteins, and hence of amino acids, therefore they were ruled out. The natural foods that remained available for the experiment were narrowly limited in number.

Each day the young men ate mixtures of highly purified amino acids, starch, sugar, butter, fats, minerals, vitamins, and water. With the exception of water, each article was taken in weighed amounts. The daily ration of amino acids was dissolved in water, flavored with a little lemon juice and sugar, and taken as a drink three times each day. It was a rather costly lemonade—worth approximately 20 dollars per man per day. The daily ration of vitamins was taken in the form of tablets. The remaining components of the diet were mixed with water, worked into a dough, and baked into wafers. Part of the butter was used as a spread for the wafers.

Naturally, such a diet became exceedingly monotonous. However, health and well being were maintained so long as the correct amino acids were furnished in sufficient amounts. Several young men followed this regimen for fifty to seventy days without losing weight or showing any ill effects. This was *expected* since the diets had been planned to furnish an abundance of each component.

A criterion for such studies is a condition known as nitrogen equilibrium. It is well known that when adults receive a properly balanced diet they excrete an amount of nitrogen which is equal to the intake. On the other hand, if the diet is insufficient in its protein or amino acid content, the output of nitrogen exceeds the intake. By watching the nitrogen balance we were able to know when the diet was adequate and when it began to fail.

Prior to these experiments with the young men, similar studies had been made with animals. The earlier studies had demonstrated that only ten of the twenty-two amino acids are essential for growing animals. So, at the start of our human experiments, we included these ten amino acids in the lemonade—omitting the other twelve—and immediately the young men came into nitrogen equilibrium. This demonstrated that the twelve amino acids which were omitted from the food are not needed.

In subsequent tests each of the ten amino acids in turn was left out of the diet. The complete results showed that only eight of them are necessary for the maintenance of nitrogen equilibrium in adult man. Whether the growing child, like the growing animal, requires more than eight must await the results of further investigation. Moreover, one cannot yet exclude the possibility that certain amino acids, which are not essential for the maintenance of nitrogen equilibrium in normal adults, may become necessary for special functions, or during disease.

It appears, therefore, that the body system of the normal adult can synthesize fourteen of the twenty-two amino acids. But the other eight are indispensable, for the tests disclosed that the absence from the diet of any one of them leads to a tremendous loss of nitrogen, a decline in body weight, a profound failure in appetite, and a marked increase in irritability.

Although the absence of any one of the eight essentials causes these drastic effects, the quantities necessary for health are quite small in certain cases. For example, 250 milligrams, or about 4 grains, appear to be a safe daily intake of the amino acid known as tryptophane. A pint of milk will supply this amount.

Mixtures of amino acids, in correct proportions, may prove to be valuable in the treatment of patients who temporarily are unable to consume food in the normal way. Unlike proteins, amino acids can be safely introduced into the blood stream. Their usefulness for intravenous feeding is being explored in a number of laboratories. Reports appear to indicate that this method of administration is beneficial in the treatment of severe burns, as an aid in promoting the healing of wounds, and as a means of reducing the surgical risk in patients who enter the clinic in poor nutritive condition.

Further research is needed to evaluate thoroughly the medical uses of amino acids. Meanwhile, experiments are being conducted to determine just how much of the eight essentials is required by man. When this has been accomplished, a mixture can be prepared in which the composition is adjusted to the needs of the body for each component. Such a preparation should be particularly valuable as a source of amino acids for intravenous feeding.

The Quick and the Dead

By John Howard Northrop

Dr. John Howard Northrop, recent Nobel Prize winner, is a research biochemist in the Rockefeller Institute for Medical Research.

THE world of living things used to be considered as entirely distinct from the world of inanimate things. In the days before the development of the experimental method, when research was carried out by debate, the existence of two such classes was taken for granted. The discoveries of the early anatomists, physiologists and chemists seemed only to strengthen the distinction, since each succeeding discovery revealed greater and greater complexity in the living organism.

Thus Harvey's discovery of the circulation of the blood showed how complicated and extensive was the mechanism of blood supply. Schwann's cell theory gave evidence of the most intricate and delicate arrangement of the minute units of which we are made. Other discoveries indicated that the chemical reactions which take place in the living body were quite different from those which occurred in inanimate systems. The compounds found in the living were different and distinct from those found outside of living cells. A separate branch of chemistry was developed, which dealt with the compounds formed by living organisms. It was called "organic chemistry" and was considered to be a separate science, quite distinct from the chemistry of inanimate objects. Thus right up to the 18th century, each new discovery raised and strengthened the barrier which separated the quick and the dead. However, beginning in the eighteenth century, the tide changed. From then on, one after another of the activities within living organisms have been shown to agree with the general theories of the chemistry and physics of all matter.

The optical properties of the eye proved to be in accord with the theory of physics. The mysterious humors which were considered to be the cause of disease turned out to be bacteria in many cases and viruses in others. The viruses, themselves, at first as mysterious as the humors had been, turned out to be proteins. It was found that eggs could be made to grow and develop by treatment with salt solution in place of spermatozoa. Even the behavior of some animals under certain conditions could be predicted as accurately as is the flight of a bullet. Today the division between organic and inorganic chemistry has completely disappeared, and the mechanisms of a great many of the chemical reactions which occur in living matter are now thoroughly understood.

The progress in this interpretation of a vital activity as a chemical reaction is well illustrated by the history of man's theories of the process of digestion. In the middle ages the digestion of food was considered to be an inherent peculiarity of living things and, as such, was quite outside the realm of science. The first intimation that digestive reactions might after all be related to ordinary chemical reactions came from some experiments performed by the Italian, Spallanzani, about a century and a half ago. Spallanzani found that meat could be digested just as well in a test tube as in the stomach of an animal, provided a little juice from the animal's stomach were added. It thus appeared that the whole animal was not necessary for this reaction, but only some of its secretion. The German physiologist, Schwann, then suggested that some peculiar substance must be present in the stomach which caused these reactions to take place. This explanation would be considered obvious today, but in Schwann's time it was an entirely new idea. Meanwhile, somewhat similar effects of small amounts of various substances had been observed in certain inorganic reactions, and the great Swedish chemist, Berzelius, made a very shrewd guess. Berzelius said these substances which are present in animals, and which cause these peculiar and characteristic vital reactions, act in the same way as do certain other substances which have such curious effects on some inorganic reactions.

Berzelius' idea was far ahead of his time and, as is usual in such cases, the idea was violently attacked. Great pains were taken to argue that vital reactions did not occur, even in the test tube, in the same way as typical inorganic reactions; and hence, it was urged, vital reactions did not obey the laws of chemistry. In the next generation, however, another great Swede, Arrhenius, disposed of most of the objections, and gradually the view became accepted that these peculiar reactions did not differ in principle from other chemical reactions, but that they required special and mysterious agents which could be made only by the living cells.

The controversy over these reactions was now renewed, the dispute this time relating to the nature of the peculiar agents which caused them. Attempts to isolate and identify the special agents were carried out by chemists and physiologists for nearly a century with little or no success. It was stated by eminent workers that the special agents—which came to be called enzymes—could not belong to any known class of chemical compounds. It was even suggested that they really did not exist but were simply "properties conferred upon matter." In 1926, however, one of the enzymes was finally purified and crystallized by Sumner. It appeared to be a protein, but the results were received with great skepticism by most workers in the field. Several other enzymes, including pepsin which digests meat, were isolated and crystallized in my laboratory. They also were found to be proteins. Since then many other enzymes have been isolated and also found to be proteins. It is now pretty generally accepted that most, if not all, chemical reactions which occur in living cells are controlled and directed by enzymes. The actual chemical structure of these peculiar proteins is still unknown and they have not been produced in the laboratory. The difficulties are practical rather than theoretical, however, and few would now say that chemical synthesis of enzymes is impossible.

The enzymes are exceedingly powerful agents and only a minute amount is necessary to accomplish their purpose. A pound of pepsin, which is the agent responsible for digestion in the stomach, would digest thirty tons of meat in a couple of hours. The same amount of pepsin would clot a million gallons of milk in a few minutes.

The amount of enzymes actually present in body cells or secretions is therefore very small, and this fact, together with their very perishable nature, is responsible for the great difficulties encountered in the earlier attempts at purification.

Two of the enzymes, pepsin and trypsin, possess the extraordinary property of causing their own formation. These enzymes are not present as such in the body tissues. Instead there is present a peculiar protein, which has no effect on any reaction. Unless one were suspicious, this inert protein would be considered simply a "normal" tissue protein. However, if the inert protein is dissolved under certain conditions and a trace of either pepsin or trypsin added, all the inert protein present changes to pepsin or trypsin. These enzymes can therefore reproduce themselves, a property which has frequently been considered a distinguishing characteristic of living things.

The growth of pepsin and trypsin differs from the growth of cells, however, because the growth of cells requires the addition of energy, whereas the growth of these proteins does not. The virus proteins which cause disease also grow, but whether they require energy for the process is not yet known.

Thus, the criterion of reproduction, which has long been used to distinguish the quick from the dead, has failed, and the problem of defining a living thing, always a difficult one, has become even more difficult. It begins to look as though this difficulty is inherent in the subject, and may be due to the fact that there exists no fundamental distinction between living things and inanimate things. Thus the modern biochemist finds that in some cases it is very difficult to make any very fundamental distinction, these days, between the quick and the dead.

At the Twilight Zone of Life

By Wendell M. Stanley

Dr. Wendell M. Stanley, recently granted the Nobel Prize for his work on viruses, is a member of the Rockefeller Institute for Medical Research.

As you look about, you may see a dog, a gold fish, or a flowering plant, all of which we surely think of as alive. You may also see a glass vessel, a metal plate, or a piece of stone—objects which we call inanimate or nonliving. Have you ever wondered what makes the essential difference between living things and nonliving things? More than 2,000 years ago the Greek philosopher Aristotle pondered over this question and decided that Nature had made such a gradual transition from the nonliving to the living that the boundary line was doubtful, perhaps nonexistent. In Aristotle's time there was little or no scientific evidence by which to evaluate his conclusion but, recently, a great deal of information has been obtained, thanks to research on certain agents of infectious disease.

It was generally believed until about a half-century ago that infectious or "catching" diseases were caused by living microbes, of which the smallest were bacteria. Then, in the early 1890's, came the discovery of still smaller disease producers, the viruses. Many of the diseases which afflict human beings—for example, smallpox, yellow fever, poliomyelitis, influenza, and the common cold—are virus diseases. Among animal infections we recognize hog cholera, fowl pox, certain tumors of rabbits, and the foot-and-mouth disease of cattle as of virus origin.

Tobacco mosaic and curly top of sugar beets are examples of virus diseases of plants. The viruses of most of these diseases are so small that it is impossible to see them with even the best of the optical microscopes. With the recent development of the electron microscope, which is able to magnify a hundred thousand times or more, it became possible at last to observe and photograph the viruses. The results obtained have served to confirm earlier estimates of sizes obtained by indirect methods.

Now, it so happened that chemists had found certain huge molecules which were about one millionth of an inch in size. Biologists, working with living microbes, had found certain bacteria to be about ten times the size of the huge molecules. Therefore, between the molecules of the chemist and bacteria of the biologist, there was a gap, a no-man's land, unexplored by either chemists or biologists. But in recent years, as the sizes of different viruses began to be determined, it was found that the viruses closed this gap between the molecules and the bacteria. Even more surprising, some viruses proved to be larger than certain accepted living bacteria, whereas other viruses proved smaller than certain accepted chemical molecules.

This discovery of the overlapping sizes served to heighten discussion of the nature of viruses. For viruses have remarkable peculiarities. For example, you cannot grow viruses in a test tube, although bacteria lend themselves quite readily to cultivation in a glass vessel and, so long as nutrients are supplied, bacteria will multiply until the vessel is choked with them. But viruses held in a test tube are as inert as a lump of coal. They neither grow nor reproduce until they are placed within the cells of living tissues— then, immediately, they spring into action, multiply and cause disease. But each virus is specific to certain kinds of living tissue. Influenza virus will grow only within certain cells of man and a few other animals; tobacco mosaic virus will grow only within the cells of certain plants, such as the tobacco and the tomato plant. And so with all the viruses—each has its special likes and dislikes. Still another characteristic is the ability of a virus to change its nature and suddenly become more virulent or less virulent. These dramatic changes are called mutations, and when a mutation occurs it produces a new strain of virus which can cause a slightly different disease.

After these properties were discovered, some scientists argued that because viruses could grow, reproduce, and change or mutate, they must be alive. Other scientists disagreed, pointing out that the complicated internal processes of respiration, digestion and other metabolic functions of life could hardly be contained within structures as small as those of certain viruses.

I am a chemist and it occurred to me to see what might be learned through certain techniques of chemical research. I selected the first known of the viruses, that of the tobacco mosaic disease and, after pressing the sap out of some diseased tobacco plants, and filtering it, I subjected the clear liquid to methods of precipitation. As a result of these experiments, in 1935 I succeeded in isolating a crystalline material, and tests showed that the crystallized substance was a member of the chemical group known as nucleoproteins. When applied to healthy tobacco plants, a solution of these nucleoprotein crystals transmitted the mosaic disease.

Through various stratagems it was found that the molecules of this crystalline substance were larger than anything studied up to that time. They weighed about forty million times the weight of the hydrogen atom.

This means that a molecule of this substance weighed nearly seven times as much as any previously known molecule; and on many sides doubt was expressed that this giant nucleoprotein could actually be the tobacco mosaic virus. But a long series of tests has demonstrated beyond a reasonable doubt that this substance, which can be cyrstallized out of infected fluid like any crystalline chemical, is indeed the virus of this disease.

Further experiments showed that the same nucleoprotein could be isolated from different kinds of plants with mosaic disease. Moreover, when there were tobacco plants diseased with different strains of the virus, each yielded a somewhat similar and yet slightly different nucleoprotein. The nature of some of the chemical distinctions between these nucleoproteins of different virus strains has been established. This work is of great importance because it provides a basis for relating differences in chemical structure to differences in disease-producing properties. Eventually it may prove possible to manufacture, in the chemical laboratory, new virus strains which may prove useful as vaccines against virus diseases.

Since the time when the tobacco mosaic virus was crystallized in 1935, about a dozen other viruses have been concentrated and obtained in essentially pure form. Some of these viruses are crystalline nucleoproteins, whereas others appear to be large structures somewhat similar to bacteria in composition and organization. Yet all of them possess the characteristic properties of viruses— that is, they are able to grow and reproduce only within the living cells of certain specific hosts and, also, in the course of this reproduction they are able to change or mutate. The ability to reproduce and to mutate has long been regarded as characteristic of living things, yet we see it is possessed by these molecules of a crystalline nucleoprotein. If the virus nucleoproteins did not possess this ability to reproduce and to mutate, they would be regarded as ordinary chemical molecules, such as the molecules of sugar or salt on your dinner table.

Viruses thus present a perplexing problem to one who attempts to classify them as living or nonliving. Perhaps the analogy of distinguishing between blackness and whiteness may be helpful. Some objects are obviously white, others are obviously black; but in examining things which are progressively less black, one reaches a range in which it is difficult, if not impossible, to decide whether the thing is white or black.

The new work on viruses has provided us with a series of struc-

tures of gradually increasing complexity, overlapping at one extreme with the molecules of the chemist and at the other extreme
with the organisms of the biologist. These new scientific discoveries,
which are of present importance in many fields of science and
medicine, provide support for Aristotle's idea of 2,000 years ago.
Perhaps it is true, as Aristotle suggested, that Nature makes so
gradual a transition from the nonliving to the living that the
boundary line is doubtful, possibly nonexistent.

Viruses—Master Parasites

By George Packer Berry

Dr. George Packer Berry is professor of bacteriology and head of that
department, associate professor of medicine and associate dean at
the University of Rochester School of Medicine and Dentistry.

Mankind is afflicted with a wide variety of parasites which cause
disease. Some of these parasites are microscopic animals, like the
amoeba of dysentery and other protozoa. Some parasites are tiny
plants, like the bacillus of tuberculosis and other bacteria. But, to
my mind, the master parasites are the viruses. Viruses are the cause
of some forty different maladies in man, ranging from influenza
and mumps to infantile paralysis and sleeping sickness. The long list
of human ills caused by viruses has grown rapidly of late, and will
doubtless continue to grow.

But it isn't only man that is subject to attack by viruses, Cattle,
horses, sheep, pigs, chickens, dogs, and cats—all these have virus
diseases which are destructive and costly. Among the lower animals,
frogs and fishes have their virus infections; even the insects are
not free.

Among plants there are nearly two hundred known virus
disorders, and most of the cultivated crop plants suffer, with huge
losses annually to agriculture. Corn, potatoes, tomatoes, beans, beets,
and lettuce are severely afflicted with mosaic diseases. These disorders are called mosaic diseases because the virus produces a
peculiar mosaic-like mottling of the leaves.

The sugar-beet disease, "curly-top," may reduce the crop by a quarter or more. When virus-resistant types of beets were introduced into California, the yield was increased by three tons per acre. Similarly in Louisiana, the introduction of virus-resistant sugar cane raised the yield of sugar by fifty per cent. In a war-ridden world, suffering from food shortages, the plant virus diseases constitute a serious problem.

Even the lowly bacteria, which themselves are often parasites, suffer from attacks by viruses of a special kind known as bacteriophages. Almost every species of bacteria is susceptible—and thus we have the picture of a parasite attacking a parasite. It reminds us of those famous lines of Jonathan Swift, written more than two centuries ago, in which he remarked:

> *So, naturalists observe, a flea*
> *Has smaller fleas that on him prey;*
> *And these have smaller still to bite 'em;*
> *And so proceed* ad infinitum!

Chapter 12 of this volume will indicate the dramatic story of man's progress toward understanding infectious disease. Contagious maladies had been recognized since antiquity, but it was only seventy or eighty years ago that bacteria, fungi, and protozoa— living agents—were found to be the causes of contagion.

Though microscopic in size, all these first-known agents of disease were alive, and they were recognized as parasites preying upon the host which they infected.

Then, just before 1900, came the discovery of a new group of disease agents, which seemed so different from the known parasites that their discovery created an upheaval in biological thought. For these new agents, the viruses, were not only invisible through the most powerful microscope, and so small that they passed readily through porcelain filters, but they had very peculiar growth characteristics. Unlike the bacteria which Pasteur, Koch, and their successors had grown in broths and other culture media, the viruses were inert in such nutrients. They would grow only in the living cells of plants, animals, and men.

The previous paper, by Dr. Stanley, tells how viruses were chemically isolated, purified, measured, and analyzed. It is twelve years since Dr. Stanley announced that he had succeeded in crystallizing one species of virus, thus demonstrating that its structure was molecular and not cellular.

And so we come to this curious concept, this idea that the virus, which is an infectious agent and therefore a parasite, is a molecule. The idea that a molecule can be a parasite is startling to biologists, but true.

Viruses vary in complexity and size. Although all viruses apparently are organized on a level below that of the living cell, the largest viruses are comparable in dimensions and complexity to the smaller bacteria; while the smallest viruses, at least some of them, compare with molecules in size and structure. Yet, no matter how minute they are, all viruses grow and reproduce their kind. We don't know how, but one thing is sure: only within the living cells of a susceptible human being, animal, or plant can viruses exhibit the basic living attributes of growth and reproduction. Removed from their host's cells, they are inert. Completely dependent on their hosts, viruses are highly specialized sorts of parasites, and constitute the only group of parasites which exert all of their influence through activity carried out within cells.

Within the host's cell, the virus leads a stolen life. It insinuates itself into the cell's living machinery, and perverts the cell's activities to its own advantage.

The virus induces the cell to make more virus, using the cell's own energy in the process. This, we believe, is how the virus grows. This perversion of the cell's normal function results in damage to the cell, and when enough cells have been injured or killed, the host becomes diseased. Clearly, viruses are master parasites.

The fundamental struggle to survive resolves into a struggle for food and a search for the easiest way to obtain it. One of the easiest ways is that of the parasite, which lives at the expense of its host. Evolution has affected parasites as it has all living things, and as the parasites adjusted themselves more and more to dependence on a host, they gradually lost the functions which the host supplied. Just as one who has a permanent room in your house can safely discard his own washing machine, his own refrigerator, etc., because he can count on always using yours, the virus which lives within a cell may, during long evolutionary changes, have discarded various bits of the machinery which a living thing ordinarily possesses for itself. Following this basic concept, one can speculate on the development of viruses, as Dr. Robert G. Green, Professor of Bacteriology at the University of Minnesota, did some years ago.

For if a parasite, through slow evolutionary changes, tends to lose those functions which are supplied free, so to speak, by his host, then the larger and more complex viruses are presumably those which have progressed the least along the evolutionary road of parasitism. These large viruses may be regarded as living organisms which have lost the power to synthesize some factor essential for their growth. As we pass down the scale to smaller and still smaller viruses, we are dealing with agents which have lost more and more of their synthesizing abilities. Finally, we reach the smallest viruses, and find that they are without enzymes, ferments, any agents which normally permit a living organism to synthesize the chemical substance it needs. As a result, these viruses are unable to function at all apart from the cells they infect. But once within the correct cell, where the cell has at hand all substances needed for growth, the viruses unite with the requisite system of the host cell, and so, by a completely borrowed life, they grow, reproduce, and finally possess their host. These smallest viruses, it would seem, occupy the summit of parasitism.

There are many aspects of this subject, and no discoveries in the new field of molecular biology are more profoundly significant than those that concern viruses. Perhaps man's greatest victory over nature would be deliverance from the heavy burden of parasitism with which all life is encumbered. Recent work with viruses opens bright vistas for the future.

The Time Factor in Chemistry *

By Hugh Stott Taylor and Henry Eyring

Dr. Hugh Stott Taylor and Dr. Henry Eyring are both physical
chemists. Dr. Taylor is chairman of the Chemistry Department and
dean of the Graduate School at Princeton University. Dr. Eyring is
dean of the Graduate School at the University of Utah.

TAYLOR:—Since we are going to discuss chemical reactions, perhaps,
Eyring, we ought first to make clear what our understanding
of chemcial reaction is?

EYRING:—All right, Taylor. Suppose we set off a chemical reaction
right here and now. I'm going to light this match. The friction
of scratching the match on the box generated heat, the heat agitated the molecules in the tip of the match which then combined
with the oxygen in the air, and the match burst into flame. The
bursting of the match into flame is a chemical reaction.

TAYLOR:—But lighting a match is a rather commonplace performance. Most people, when they think of a chemical reaction, doubtless picture something dramatic—like exploding a stick of dynamite. Fundamentally, of course, they are the same sort of thing.
I believe it was Sir Humphrey Davy who said that a flame is a
tethered explosion. In the flaming match the chemicals unite
with oxygen more slowly than do the chemicals in the exploding
dynamite.

EYRING:—The utilization of sugar and other nutrients in the human
body is another example of burning in which oxygen unites with
carbohydrates and other substances to produce a release of energy
with various by-products—just as happens in the flaming match
and the exploding dynamite.

TAYLOR:—I imagine, Eyring, that you have been fascinated, as I
have, by the wide range of speeds at which chemical reactions
occur.

* In the planning of the radio talks which resulted in the present volume, the
experiment was tried on two occasions of having these talks occur in dialogue form,
as a conversation between two scientists closely related in their work and interests.
The following paper is one of these dialogues, and has been left in its original
radio form.

EYRING:—Yes, I have. And, I think, that our readers would be interested, too, if we gave them an example or two of the speeds at which chemical reactions occur.

TAYLOR:—All right. Let's start with the vibrational speeds of the atoms themselves and of the molecules which are made up of atoms. A molecule of sugar, for example, is composed of atoms of hydrogen, oxygen, and carbon. Each of these constituent atoms is continually vibrating back and forth, and the molecules are vibrating in the sugar crystal at the rate of a thousand billion times a second.

EYRING:—That will seem an incredible speed to most of our readers, who know that the human eye is unable to detect the flicker of a movie film when the picture is changed only 16 times a second. It is remarkable that the sugar molecules, for example, vibrating at a thousand billion times a second, are able to hold together at all!

TAYLOR:—True—and as we've discovered, sometimes a molecule *does* break. That happens when it is bumped so hard that a pair of its constituent atoms vibrate with enough violence to overcome the electrical bond that holds them together. In the split-up— I almost said fission, but probably we should leave the term fission to the nuclear physicists whose studies of uranium fission have brought us to the threshold of the atomic age—in the split-up, whenever the vibrational strain reaches the breaking point the molecule splits into two fragments.

EYRING:—At this point, Taylor, it seems essential for the reader to know that each of the two fragments carries an electron, which held the two pieces together. And it is these unsatisfied electrons that constitute what we know as chemical affinity—the attraction of one element for another. This is important to know because it is the unsatisfied electrical force or charge of each fragment that causes it to combine with some part of another molecule to form a new chemical compound.

TAYLOR:—Let me give an example. If a fragment of a sugar molecule darting through the solution in the blood stream or in the stomach juices crashes into a passing molecule, a part of the sugar may chip off and combine with the collision partner. The remaining fragment of the sugar molecule is left with its unsatisfied electrical charge, and this fragment may continue the process, chipping off and combining with a particle of another molecule. This repeated process is a chain reaction—just as the burning of a match and the explosion of dynamite are chain reactions. Now, Eyring, why don't you go on to explain that chemists are able to speed up or slow down the rate of chemical reactions. Our knowledge of how to control the velocity at which chemical changes occur is one of the triumphs of chemistry, and you have contributed importantly toward our understanding of these phenomena.

EYRING:—Let me point out first, Taylor, that heat is a form of motion. Heat stirs up the molecular animals, so to speak, and so produces a greater number of catastrophic collisions. For if the temperature goes up the agitation of the molecules is increased. Then the exceptionally rapid vibration loosens the powerful electrical bonds which hold the atoms of the molecule together.

TAYLOR:—So raising the temperature speeds up the rate of reaction. And what about lowering the temperature?

EYRING:—The rule is that if you decrease the temperature from 98° Fahrenheit to 32° Fahrenheit, only about one-eighth as many molecules will be split apart by vibrations. Consequently the reactions will proceed only about one-eighth as fast.

TAYLOR:—The rule is true for many chemical reactions in the laboratory but what about reactions in the body?

EYRING:—In some substances the chemical reactivity is retarded by a temperature of 32 degrees Fahrenheit so that the disruptive vibrations are brought almost to a standstill. This is true of the human body. If it is cooled too much, its system of chemical reactions gets hopelessly slowed down and out of step, and death may ensue. Loss of consciousness is associated with a slowing down of the chain reactions by which the brain uses oxygen. A similar slowing down occurs when a patient is anesthetized. The drowsiness of the freezing victim is similarly a consequence of this slowing down.

TAYLOR:—Now perhaps I can antipicate a question from some of our readers. Do cold-blooded animals, such as fishes and snakes, have a different kind of body chemistry?

EYRING:—They can certainly endure considerable reduction of temperature without fatality. I've seen a gold fish superficially frozen in liquid air, at a temperature hundreds of degrees below zero. The surface of the frozen fish became as brittle as glass—and yet, with careful warming, it thawed out, revived its faculties, and swam away. A variety of microorganisms can be frozen in liquid air without fatal damage. But there are agencies other than heat that are used to control the rate of chemical change. You, Taylor, have spent much of your time at Princeton studying catalysts. I think the readers would be very much interested in an explanation of catalysts.

TAYLOR:—A catalyst is an accelerator of chemical change. A catalyst will start a chemical union between substances that seem entirely indifferent to one another. It is used to change other molecules in a reaction though it itself is not changed. Apparently what happens is that the catalyst provides a path by which the molecules can come together more easily. It affords them an opportunity to collide more efficiently.

EYRING:—And many probably know that much of our chemical industry is dependent upon this action of catalysts.

TAYLOR:—That's right. Germany was able to wage World War I for four years because she had learned how to make ammonia for explosives out of air and steam in presence of iron at high pressures. She used catalysts in World War II to make synthetic rubber and gasoline. But in the last 25 years the United States outstripped all others in the study of catalysts and their use, for example, in the cracking of petroleum to yield high-octane gasoline, in making toluene, rubber, nylon, and plastics from her abundant raw materials, oil, coal and grain. One important branch of catalysis is really surface chemistry—and we are constantly making greater use of surfaces to speed up the processes of chemical change.

EYRING:—And, as you have often remarked in our discussions, Taylor, nature can still give us many lessons in the way she uses catalysis in living systems.

TAYLOR:—True, Eyring. The use of catalysis in our laboratories has been known to us for about a hundred years, but the human body has employed this scheme of surface chemistry through countless ages. The human body catalysts are the vitamins, hormones, and enzymes that circulate in the blood stream to initiate and promote the innumerable chemical reactions without which breathing, thinking, consciousness, digestion, and life itself would cease. When we see a diabetic, unable to assimilate the small amounts of sugar that get into his system, and observe how quickly this defect is corrected by a dose of insulin, we comprehend the power and function of a catalyst. So much for catalysis and surface chemistry. There's still a chance for you to mention some other promoters of chemical change.

EYRING:—Yes, before we conclude this discussion I want to emphasize that the most fundamental of all promoters of chemical reactions is sunlight. We have learned how to use sunlight in a score of ways in industrial chemistry. Sunlight is basic, of course, in the chemistry of photography. But the grand demonstration of the power and effectiveness of light as a chemical instigator and accelerator is all about us, in the forests, fields, and gardens. The daily magic by which the green leaf converts inorganic elements into organic foodstuffs and other substances is the fundamental process of the world—at least the world of life— and the green leaf performs its chemistry only in the presence of light.

CHAPTER 9

PLANTS AND ANIMALS

THE WAY to learn about life is by studying living things. So closely interrelated is the whole pattern of nature that the biologist cannot afford to consider any kind of living creature as too remote, too small, or too special to be of interest. It is from microscopic forms of life—molds and microbes—that we get the drugs penicillin and streptomycin. The tiny fruit fly is the most widely useful of all subjects for experiments in genetics. The mouse helps us learn about cancer, and the rat about nutrition. The great apes help us understand the rudiments of thinking and social behavior.

An old, but still basic, part of biology is the first-hand, out-of-doors examination of life by the naturalist. The present chapter opens with an illustration of this sort of activity—the account by a distinguished ornothologist of those fascinating birds, the penguins.

Twenty-five years ago essentially all that was known of the chimpanzee would have come under this label of natural history; but Dr. Yerkes, the author of the second essay in this chapter, brought this uniquely important animal out of the jungle and the zoo and into the laboratory.

In the other sections of this chapter we find instance after instance of the valuable things we can learn from studying plants and animals. Who would have guessed, for example, that scientists could learn fundamental facts about our own bodies by studying plant roots?

The variety and ingenuity of nature is a constant source of surprise, interest, and inspiration to the scientist. Nature can be a helpful friend or a subtle enemy, as is illustrated by both bacteria and fungi. Scientific understanding is essential in order that we may capitalize fully on the help or avoid the danger. If our scientific knowledge is deep enough, we can modify nature to our great advantage, as in the breeding of improved crop plants. If the reader ever hears doubts expressed concerning the support of scientific research, it would be well for him to remember as one example among hundreds that the money value of the increased corn yield due to new hybrids was, during the four war years 1942-1945 alone, more than two billion dollars.

We have made progress in exploring and analyzing nature, but we should be very humble. All that we have learned is only a tiny fraction of what there is yet to know. We pride ourselves on our science of illumination, but the firefly, discussed by Dr. Harvey, still knows better than we how to transform energy into light without wasteful heat. And the plants, as Dr. Sinnott points out, still hold many deep secrets which we have yet to learn.

W. W.

Ambassador to the Penguins

BY ROBERT CUSHMAN MURPHY

Dr. Robert Cushman Murphy, a zoologist and ornithologist who has been in charge of numerous expeditions to South America, the Antarctic, and elsewhere, is chairman of the Department of Birds of the American Museum of Natural History.

IT IS many years—although it seems but yesterday—since I landed on a beach between the high fronts of glaciers at South Georgia, an island near the bottom of the map, where the Atlantic merges with the Antarctic Ocean. The time was November which, as you will recall, is spring in the Far South. Penguins were gathering on their nesting grounds and, in the absence of human residents, they made me think of the Eskimos who would have greeted me if I had been coming ashore at the other end of the earth.

They were not the giant emperor penguins, nor the roly-poly Adelie penguins, which have had their triumph in motion pictures presented by Admiral Byrd. My penguin friends were a less familiar kind, know as the gentoo. They had blue backs, breasts like starched shirts, coral-red bills and orange feet, and across the crown of the head they wore white fillets resembling the caps of trained nurses.

More than 4,000 of these fascinating birds inhabited the largest of several communities that I kept under my eye for four months. Few if any of them had ever before seen a man. This gave me the hope that I might be able to observe their absolutely unaffected responses to my presence.

The point of view of birds toward other creatures is based in the long run upon past experience. In the Antarctic there are neither native men nor four-footed flesh-eaters such as the polar bears, wolves and foxes of the Arctic. It was therefore interesting to find that the general attitude of the penguins toward such a strange visitor as myself was one of indifference or of curiosity unmixed with fear.

On the first day of my ambassadorship to the penguins, I sat quietly for an hour while the gentoos went about their business.

Then I pulled on leather mittens for safety's sake, seized a passing penguin, lifted it off the ground, and tried with all my might to prevent it from struggling. The outraged bird screeched, beat a tattoo with its flippers that stung even through thick polar garments, bit, squirmed, kicked, and fought like a demon. The tussle continued for about a minute, and I was just about to give up and drop the furious armful when it abruptly quieted down. There it rested in the crook of my elbow, unhurt, bright-eyed, and as contented as a well-fed baby. I stroked it from head to tail and it acted as though hypnotized. I placed it gently on the ground, whereupon it looked up serenely, as though nothing unpleasant had ever occurred between us.

Later observations confirmed my conclusion that the penguins were creatures of the moment, not readily holding one mood after the novelty of the stimulus had worn off. A gentoo that was at first hugely excited by my appearance in the colony was quite likely to lapse into a yawn, shut its eyes, and fall asleep.

On land or ice, the gentoos were unprepared for danger because they had never had experience with an enemy able to harm them out of water. By this I mean that on shore there was no animal to attack a full-grown, healthy penguin. The flesh-eating skua, which is a gull with the plumage and habits of a hawk, was an ogre in their colonies because it stole and devoured penguin eggs and chicks. The gentoos fully appreciated the role of this foe. They guarded their nests solicitously, rushed at every skua that landed near by, and swore vainly at those that flew overhead. But, although concerned for their offspring, they had no fear for the safety of their own persons unless they became too ill to strike back. When a penguin died ashore, the skuas promptly devoured the body, and the absence of commotion apparently fooled the neighboring penguins into believing that nothing was happening.

But the ocean was different. Along the coasts lurked the sea-leopard, a slender, spotted seal, with jaws full of terrible, three-pronged teeth, and a hearty appetite for penguins.

There was always the danger that a sea-leopard might be floating just under the penguins' jumping-off place. The gentoos hesitated at the water's edge and jostled each other like boys on a pier, as though each hoped that some other penguin would brave the first plunge. After that momentous move, the rest poured in like shot out of a bottle. But always a fatal chance had to be taken; a sea-leopard might be waiting to doom one of their number.

The fixed association of peril in the ocean and safety ashore seemed to have had a strange effect upon gentoo character. It meant, for example, that the birds often made an instinctive, rather than what we would call a rational, reaction. If you started in hot pursuit of penguins at the brink of the sea, they would deliberately run *away* from the water. If they had dived in, they would have been instantly out of your reach, but that obvious deduction never entered their heads.

Such behavior of the penguins was sufficient to cast doubt upon the "intelligence" with which they are often credited. The real basis of their human resemblance lay rather in their upright carriage and inability to fly, their strong bump of curiosity, their peering nearsightedness (due to eyes adapted for clear vision under water), the readiness with which captive birds became tame and companionable, and the fact that everlastingly, even if unconsciously, they played the clown. Devoid of the convolutions in the brain and of the "gray matter" by which man sets so much store, they relied, like bees or ants, upon their heritage of instinctive behavior, and were certainly capable of very little thinking.

The gentoos fed upon shrimps, captured far from shore and fathoms deep. They swam with their flipper-like wings, which worked with amazing rapidity and power. Beneath the surface they moved incredibly fast—about thirty feet a second, as I determined by stopwatch timings—but periodically they leaped out, giving a gasp for air, to be gone again within a twinkling. Toward evening, we would see countless penguins "porpoising" back from distant feeding areas to their regular landings. The habit was so dependable that whenever we were overtaken in our whaleboats by blinding afternoon fog we could rely upon the homing penguins to point us toward a smooth shore.

The season of my arrival among the gentoos corresponded with May in the northern hemisphere. The courting penguins had begun to give up eating and to remain ashore hungry, but too much in love to realize it, for periods of at least two weeks. Furthermore, they had the odd custom of making the situation harder than necessary by clambering as far as possible from their only source of food, the sea. Steep ridges a half mile or more from the water were favorite nesting places. Some of the birds bred on small islets in the bays, where they evolved a ridiculous method of satisfying their urge to go "inland." They would come ashore on one side of an islet, toddle across its whole diameter, and nest close to the waves on the opposite coast. By always traveling the long route, and ignoring the water at their back door, they deceived themselves if nobody else.

Lady gentoos first selected nesting sites, after which they awaited the attentions of suitors bearing gifts in the form of pebbles or ancestral bones, which made the foundation of the nests. The hen was the builder of the home, the cock the bearer of bricks, and the acceptance of the first pebble the symbol of success in wooing.

Two eggs were laid at intervals of three or four days, and about a month later they hatched in the same order. Consequently the first young gentoo had a big start in life over his brother or sister, and for many days there was a marked discrepancy in size.

The chicks were alternately guarded and fed by father and mother penguin until an age of six or seven weeks, at which time the adults abandoned family life and went communistic. The fledglings were herded into nurseries under charge of a few guards, and the number of parents thus released to catch and carry food was nearly doubled. Particular offspring seemed no longer to be recognized by the old birds, which merely pumped up shrimps from their stomachs for any or all chicks in one nursery.

We often remarked upon the extraordinarily few dead penguins encountered in these populous colonies. The accidental discovery of a gentoo "graveyard" therefore proved one of the most romantic episodes within the whole range of my natural history experience. Near the summit of a coastal hill I came upon a lonely pond in a hollow of ice-cracked stones. Several sick and drooping penguins were standing at the edge of this pool of snow-water, which was ten or twelve feet deep. Then, with a tingling of my spine, I perceived that the bottom was strewn, layer upon layer, with gentoo penguins that had outlived the perils of the sea to accomplish the rare feat among wild animals of dying a natural death. By hundreds, possibly by thousands, they lay all over the bed of the cold tarn, flippers outstretched and breasts reflecting blurred gleams of white. Safe at last from sea-leopards in the ocean and from skuas ashore, they took their endless rest; for decades, perhaps for centuries, the slumberers would undergo no bodily change in their frigid tomb.

Chimpanzees as Servants of Science

By Robert M. Yerkes

Dr. Robert M. Yerkes was for many years professor of psychobiology at Yale University. He was the organizer and first director of the Yale Laboratories of Primate Biology at Orange Park, Florida. Since Dr. Yerkes' retirement this laboratory has been renamed the Yerkes Laboratories of Primate Biology.

It may be a good precaution to make sure that we are all thinking of the same creature when we say the word chimpanzee. First let us be clear that we do not mean any one of the smaller, long-tailed monkeys, which one finds in every small zoo, but rather one of the great anthropoid apes which are usually found only in the larger and more complete zoos. There are three types of anthropoid apes: the orangutan, the gorilla and the chimpanzee. All three are roughly man-size. The orang, native only in Borneo and Sumatra, is red-haired; while by contrast the gorilla and the chimpanzee, both natives of Africa, are black-haired. The association of red with Asia and black with Africa should aid our memories. Throughout its life span the chimpanzee is smaller, larger-eared, more agile, alert, emotionally responsive, and more friendly with man than either orangutan or gorilla.

Early and late, chimpanzees are natural actors, and of all the subhuman primates they are the most readily trained as performers for human entertainment, the most gifted, and the most versatile. One often feels that the ape is enjoying his act quite as much as does his audience! On the stage and in films, the naturally histrionic and acrobatic chimpanzees serve us remarkably well. This the reader doubtless knows, but perhaps he does not know that young chimpanzees have high value as experimental animals, and that in at least one biological laboratory they are being bred and reared especially as servants of science to promote human welfare. A few examples of their scientific usefulness may be cited.

In physique, chimpanzees seem a caricature of man; and in bodily functions and behavior also they are strikingly like us. They differ importantly from such laboratory animals as mice, rats, rabbits and guinea pigs in that they are liable to most human diseases. This suggests special values for medical research. The famous Russian bacteriologist, Ilya Mechnikov, some fifty years ago discovered that both chimpanzees and monkeys are invaluable subjects for the study of many infectious diseases. Incidentally, I may remark that among the hundreds of chimpanzees which I have met or used in experiments I have seen not one with a malignant growth and none insane. Why this remarkable difference between them and us in the incidence of such dreadful disorders? Have they immunity, or a better way of life than ours?

To give point to these general statements about the medical usefulness of chimpanzees I quote the words of a friend and fellow investigator. "Yerkes, the young chimpanzees you helped us to get have paid for themselves a thousandfold!" My eyes must have popped, for at that moment I recalled that the first young chimpanzee I owned cost me $2,000 and it flashed through my mind that a thousand times two thousand dollars is two million. That is considerably more than the current market price of the apes!

I knew that the infant chimpanzees referred to had served as test animals in a study of the sources of infantile paralysis infection. My expression must have indicated that I assumed that they had been sacrificed to human need. Sensing my unspoken question, my medical friend asked if I would like to have a look at the animals. Imagine my surprise when I saw before me a pair of healthy, active and seemingly happy infant apes. For although recipients of the poliomyelitis virus, and for a time its "carriers," they had not developed acute symptoms of the disease, and appeared to be in perfect health.

Medical uses of these apes may outrank their entertainment value, but in my opinion they in turn are outranked by the services which the animals can render as subjects of psychological and related experiments. I have especially in mind studies, of which many are in progress, planned to extend and perfect our knowledge of normal human growth and development and of our skills in the use of educational and other methods of guidance.

To cure disabilities which we never should have permitted to develop is a necessity. To prevent deficiencies, abnormalities and disease liability is eminently desirable. But still more important is such wise and skillful control of the conditions of life, growth, and development, and of educational processes that each of us as a person may fully achieve his potentialities for normal physical and mental self-realization, social usefulness, and happiness. It is, in fact, a case of substituting positive for negative values, prevention and improvement for cure.

Chimpanzees happen to be almost ideal subjects for experimental studies of behavior and of the conditions which affect it; for inquiry into the role of heredity versus that of environment and education; for studies of learning or of ability to profit by experience; or for studies of social relations and intimations of culture. In all of these desirable sorts of striving for wisdom and skill in the control of life, the chimpanzee can be made to serve mankind valuably, and perhaps also uniquely, because of its essential similarity to us. But once more, I must take account of the question which is in the reader's mind. "Just how can the chimpanzee help us learn useful lessons about human behavior?"

We humans are talking animals, but the chimpanzee is not. Its linguistic abilities—vocal, postural, gestural—are meager, whereas ours are exceedingly complex and correspondingly important. Speech, indeed, seems to be man's most nearly distinctive ability. It is an inborn capacity; and any group of normal children, reared apart from adult influence, may be expected to invent and use some sort of spoken language. Experiments with chimpanzees prove that they have only the rudiments of those brain functions which in man make possible an elaborate spoken or written language. Hence, in our search for the origins of speech we turn to the ape as our willing subject.

If one is to speak, an object or an event must be represented by something which, although entitrely different from it, serves as its sign. For example, for us the color red may be symbolized either by a combination of sounds, namely the spoken word red, or by the sight of the letters—*r-e-d*. But whether the sign is the word red, either as heard or seen, the sign is clearly an entirely different thing from our actual experience of the color sensation.

I wish now to report an illustrative experiment whose results take us a step nearer to the discovery of the process by which such signs are associated with things. If a man and a chimpanzee see some much-desired object—a delicious-looking meal, for example, —placed in one of several boxes which differ only in color, and if then the boxes are removed from view and after an hour re-presented, one may safely predict that both man and chimpanzee will immediately, and seemingly with ease, select the food-containing box—"Ah!", the inexperienced observer exclaims, "the chimpanzee, like the man, perceived and was able to remember the color of the box in which the food had been hidden away." But that this is not fact but instead only appearance, is proved by the following simple variation of the experiment. Let the boxes be shifted during the interval when they are out of sight so that their spatial relations to one another and to surrounding objects shall be changed before they are re-presented to view. Now one will see the unexpectedly surprising and significant! For whereas the man will select the food-containing box without apparent effort or delay, the chimpanzee, after some hesitation, will go to the place where the food-containing box was first seen and will select and attempt to open the box which happens to be there, whatever its color. Failing, however, to find the expected food in its original location and relations, the animal is likely to express surprise, incredulity and finally resentment, as though suspecting that the experimenter had deceived or tricked it!

Our inference from observations such as these is that in man the color of the food box is represented by an event in the brain which we may call a symbolic process and may think of as counterpart of the word *red*. The chimpanzee, by contrast, has no comparable way of holding the color experience *red* in mind during the interval between the experience of seeing food placed in a box and the subsequent re-presentation of the box. For it, in this case, out of sight is definitely out of mind, unless perchance, it can depend on the spatial relations of the food-containing box.

This type of experiment suggests some of the reasons why we are hopeful of discovering, by patient study of the functions of the nervous system and behavioral responses in chimpanzees, the hypothetical nerve and brain processes which are essential for language. Without symbolic processes our thinking, as well as our talking, would be impossible. Only with extreme difficulty can a chimpanzee be taught and trained to act as though it, like a man, can make a sign or symbol really stand for an experience.

Space permitting, I might similarly describe experimental studies of the ways in which behavior can be modified; of the ways in which one can discover, factor by factor, the motives lying behind any certain behavior; of the role of heredity versus individual experience in chimpanzee development; of the nature and significance of social dominance and of the traits of masculinity and femininity in the life of individual and species. These are, indeed, fascinating quests in which, surprisingly enough, chimpanzee subjects are helping us immeasurably as servants of science.

I have written of our hopeful search for the beginnings of language in these apes. There are intimations in their behavior of the dawn of conscience as a response to social expectancy, of foresight and of cultural expressions. It has been suggested that by appropriate, systematic selection of mates, training and other varieties of experimental treatment, it may be possible to produce chimpanzees of model temperament—eminently constructive, dependable, unselfish, co-operative—which might even be exhibited as object-lessons for man! Already studies of anthropoid apes and other experimental animals have gone far towards shattering the prevalent assumption or supposition that human nature can not or should not be changed and improved.

Plant Roots and Human Problems

By Philip R. White

Dr. Philip R. White, a plant physiologist, is head of the Division of
General Physiology in the Institute for Cancer Research in Philadelphia,
Pennsylvania.

THREE basic facts about roots are doubtless familiar to us all. We
all know that they serve as anchors by which plants are held firmly
in their allotted places; that they provide the means by which
the various elements of soil fertility are introduced into the interior
of plants; and that they serve as water pipes by which the tree-tops
are supplied with this most necessary of all fluids. I wonder, however, if you have ever considered just what machinery Nature has
provided for hoisting hundreds of gallons of water each day to the
top of an elm tree, 200 feet high. I should like to consider this
problem and to picture for you some of the less obvious ways in
which the scientist can make use of roots, in obtaining answers
to questions closely bound up with human welfare. I shall concentrate on two such problems, vitamin nutrition and secretory
function.

You have all heard of vitamin B_1, whose technical name is
thiamin. It is a recently discovered substance which food processors
now put into baked goods, breakfast foods, soups, or wherever a
real or fancied place can be found for it. It is supposed to have
some ill-defined but important role in general well-being. More
specifically, it is presumed to play an important part in the welfare
of the nervous system. All sorts of annoying nervous disorders are
attributed to lack of thiamin.

But how do we know these things? Only by indirect means.
No one has yet isolated a nerve from the body and grown it,
deprived it of thiamin, observed the resultant degeneration, then
provided the vitamin and watched it recover. We have as yet no
means of doing that. We cannot *prove* that nerves require or
use thiamin.

But we can do exactly that with roots. A seed can be allowed
to sprout and the tip of the root cut off when it reaches a length

of half an inch. This tip, when placed in a bottle containing a suitable liquid nutrient, will continue to grow. Roots of tomato isolated in this fashion twelve years ago are still growing in bottles in the laboratory. They do not form stems or leaves or flowers, but they lengthen, branch and apparently perform all the vital functions characteristic of normal roots. One of those functions, of course, is nutrition.

The nutrient in which we grow such roots is not like a seven-course dinner, containing a pinch of this and a sprinkling of that washed down with some delectable but unidentifiable fluid. Every ingredient is known exactly both as to kind and as to quantity—the purest of water, sugar (which is one of our purest, least contaminated chemical substances), highly purified salts, and last but not least, vitamins.

If, from an otherwise complete nutrient, we omit thiamin, the roots become thin, branching decreases, and the roots eventually die. Add a trace of thiamin, only one part in a thousand million, and the roots resume growth. If to sugar, salts, and thiamin is added a little of the simplest of all the building blocks out of which proteins are made, the amino-acid glycine, the roots will grow still more rapidly. If two more vitamins which you have surely seen mentioned on your flour-bag label, pyridoxine and niacin, are further added, the growth rate again increases. Tomato roots in such a solution will grow a half inch a day, day in and day out, for years. In practice we cut them back once a week so as not to be overrun.

It is clear from studies carried out in this way that plant roots, whose comparatively restricted variety of cells have a physiology similar in many ways to that of human cells, require for normal growth and function thiamin, niacin, pyridoxine, and amino acids just as do the molds discussed in previous chapters, and as we believe do human tissues. They themselves do not make these substances, or at least do not make them in quantities sufficient to satisfy their needs.

Moreover, and what is of great importance, many of the conditions which restrict our experiments with human tissues are here lacking, so that we can study the way by which these vitamins influence the welfare of root tissues under strictly controlled conditions. Here is a potential means of examining in detail the chemical processes involved.

We hope by applying the methods worked out with plant tissues, to be able, some day, to do the same sort of thing with animal and human cells. If and when that day comes, we will be able to study a nerve cell in a controlled nutrient and answer the question, "Is thiamin directly involved in nerve-cell welfare and function, or is the nerve degeneration observed in thiamin deficiency only an indirect and secondary result of imbalance in some other co-ordinated body tissue or function?" And our work with plant roots will have contributed to that answer.

So much for nutrition. Secretory processes may seem still more remote from roots. One of the major problems of the body is the constant repurification of the blood. This purification is carried out in two stages. The first stage is that of a passive filtration. Water is squeezed out of the blood under the pressure created by the heart, carrying with it substances such as salts, acids, and other small-moleculed unwanted substances.

The red blood cells and the large-moleculed proteins are held back as are the grounds in your drip coffee pot. But the amount of water which must pass through this filtering mechanism is enormous. Fortunately very little is actually lost because a second much more obscure but equally important function is performed, that of taking this filtered water and pumping it back into the blood stream so that it can be used over and over again. This second task must be carried out against the pressure of the blood. It involves real *work*, and work requires energy which must come from the burning of fuel, in this case sugar. In this respect the body is functioning as a pump. The pressure in the spinal fluid is maintained by just such a glandular pumping process.

How are these tasks accomplished? Again, we simply do not know.

It is very difficult to study such mechanisms in the body, with one of several by means of which water is raised in the plant roots can come to our aid as models. Roots take in water, containing salts, from the soil. It can be demonstrated by suitable means that some as yet unidentified mechanism drives this water through the root, from tip to base, with great force. This process, which is one of several by means of which water is raised in the plant against the pressure of a water column sometimes hundreds of feet high, appears to be comparable to the process by which water is driven back into the circulatory system or into the spinal column, against the pressure of the blood. That is to say, it is an active, pumping action, involving the performance of work.

The details of such processes cannot be studied in the animal body. Their apparent counterpart, however, can be investigated in tiny roots grown in artificial culture similar to those used in studying vitamin nutrition. If a bit of root tip a few inches long and the size of a piece of store twine is attached by means of a suitable gauge, the force with which the root tip drives water into this gauge can be measured. This force is truly astonishing, sometimes exceeding a hundred pounds per square inch, more than the pressure in many locomotive boilers. It can be shown that in roots this pumping action involves the utilization of energy developed through the respiratory burning of sugar.

Poisons which affect respiration, as does carbon monoxide, will stop the flow of water. Flow will be resumed when the poison is removed, if it has not been permitted to act too long. Here it is possible to study the process of water secretion in plants, which is probably the prototype of all gland action, in a greatly simplified system, under conditions which can be controlled in every respect and manipulated pretty much at will.

Thus it is that plant roots, which might at first glance seem to offer little to interest a medical physiologist, can serve as experimental material for the study of two general problems of fundamental importance, cell nutrition, and gland function, neither of which can be studied with the same degree of precision in any animal or human material now available.

Pure research, as has proved to be the case time and again, is in the very best sense of the word, practical research.

Bacteria—Friends or Foes

By Edwin Broun Fred

Dr. Edwin Broun Fred is a bacteriologist who, at the University of Wisconsin, has served successively as professor, dean of the Graduate School, dean of the College of Agriculture, and now president of the University.

IF YOU should step outside your home, after reading this, and pick up a lump of earth, you would hold in your hand millions of living bacteria.

In that piece of soil, plus the bacteria, you would hold some of the secrets of the world's most important process—the production of food, upon which our lives depend. Crumble that lump of soil and let it slip through your fingers, or toss it away as just a piece of dirt—and you'll be missing a chance to explore a wonderful mystery. But, study that soil and examine the bacteria under a powerful microscope—and you'll begin to understand something of the tiny but powerful forces at work in the ground beneath our feet.

It was nearly 300 years ago that the Dutch scientist, Leeuwenhoek, first saw those tiny organisms—actually microscopic plants—which we call bacteria. From the beginning of time they had remained hidden from view because they cannot be seen with the naked eye. Then, about a hundred years ago came Pasteur, and, a little later, Koch, two great European scientists who carried the discovery of bacteria over into the stage of experimentation and control. They applied their findings in the fields of chemistry and medicine to the study of diseases in human beings and animals, and, in the case of Pasteur, to overcoming defects in the then current processes of wine making and in the cultivation of silk worms.

But agricultural bacteriology—that is, the direct application of the study of bacteria to farming and food growing and processing —began even later, just about 50 years ago. So when you make a study of those millions of microorganisms in that piece of soil you pick up, you are entering a relatively new branch of science, but one that's fundamental to all life on the earth.

Of course, the real agricultural bacteriologist is the intelligent farmer. He is the man who puts into practice the findings of the laboratory. He manages the soil and controls the bacteria. He makes the friendly bacteria work for him and he kills off or holds back the harmful ones. He knows he must grow two crops—a crop of green plants above the surface and the crop of bacteria below. Those green plants which the farmer grows take materials from the soil and the air and energy from the sun, and convert them into food for man and the animals. But it's those tiny organisms in the soil which regulate the kind and size of the crop of green plants. They determine in large part whether we, the people of this world, are well fed or hungry.

The harvest of plants each year may vary in total amount, but there's one fact we all ought to remember, and it's this: the world's supply of materials upon which the plants themselves feed is fixed and unchangeable.

Nothing we can do will add to the world's total supply of nitrogen, phosphorus, sulfur, carbon and water. However, we can control the forms available to plants, if we make use of our bacterial friends in the soil.

Suppose we take an example—the story of nitrogen. Nitrogen in soluble form is easily lost from the soil. In the form of nitrates it is carried away by rain, washed down with streams and rivers, swept out to sea, and is hidden away in the accumulated sediments deposited on the ocean floor. This all goes to show how important it is for men to conserve the soil in which so much nitrogen may be stored. But a much brighter picture may be painted. And here our friends, the bacteria in the soil back on the farm, enter the story. Ordinary green plants alone cannot obtain nitrogen from the air. But there's one group of green plants which, in association with a group of bacteria, can take nitrogen from the air. These are the leguminous plants. They are pod-bearing plants, such as alfalfa, clover, peas, and soybeans. When they put down their roots, a friendly invasion takes place. Perhaps the roots give off something that attracts the bacteria. In any event, certain bacteria enter the roots and begin to grow, causing a swelling or nodule to form. And then the partnership begins to operate.

Free nitrogen, as the chemist uses the phrase, does not mean nitrogen without cost. It means nitrogen existing freely, by itself; that is to say, not combined with other elements. When nitrogen is combined in a usable form with other elements, it is called fixed nitrogen.

No one knows just how, but the combination of nodule bacteria with its particular plant host takes the free nitrogen from the air and changes it into a usable form of nitrogen. Likewise, no one has yet explained why the nodule bacteria alone, of all the thousands of kinds of soil bacteria, are able to use air nitrogen when growing in association with legumes. Nor do we know why they cannot do the same thing with other plants.

That's an unsolved mystery, but the bacteriologist and the farmer working together have learned how to benefit from this fact that the leguminous plant and the nodule bacteria also work together. The discovery of that relationship in the 1880's was a really great discovery. Sir William Crookes, a distinguished scientist, had predicted the ultimate starvation of the world because of a lack of fixed nitrogen. But now we know this need not happen if the farmer uses the tool nature has provided, this strange association of lower and higher plants.

Many of the true and astounding stories told in Russell Conwell's book, "Acres of Diamonds," are no more remarkable than the thrilling accounts of the operations of friendly bacteria.

Take legume bacteria, for example. These tiny organisms have the power to take from the air above every acre of land, vast stores of free nitrogen and put it to work growing food and feed for man and beast. It would be hard, indeed, to estimate the dollars and cents value of the stocks of nitrogen which float about in space above every field and farm. It almost outruns imagination. Yet the farmer can have that nitrogen for nothing, if he cooperates with the bacteria.

There are still other kinds of nitrogen-fixing bacteria which are usually present in soil. Namely, bacteria which possess the unique power of fixing nitrogen without the host plant. These organisms live in the soil, feed upon the sugars and starchy substances of the soil and, in exchange for their food, they fix the nitrogen which later changes to nitrates.

Or let us turn to an example more familiar and more directly associated with our everyday lives—the processing of food. For no matter what the processing may be—dehydrating, canning, fast freezing, cold curing or what not—bacteria play an important role.

They must be held in check if food is to be preserved and be ready for man. It's no wonder, indeed, that bacteriology and bacteriologists are quite generally credited with laying the foundations for the canning industry.

The men who practice agriculture today go far beyond the mere growing of crops. They, or those who handle their wares, engage in industrialized activities dealing with the processing of farm products—as in the preservation of foods by dehydration, canning, and quick freezing—or the making of butter, cheese and similar foods. And in all these processes, as we have already said, bacteria play an important part. Canning fruit, for example, is chiefly a matter of killing or controlling bacteria. Otherwise, a can of peaches on your pantry shelf might explode with a loud report and splatter spoiled fruit all over the ceiling.

The quality and flavor of your favorite cheese are the result of bacterial action. And the concentrated foods—the K rations and other forms—which sustained our fighting men overseas when they were beyond the reach of fresh foods—all these were possible only because we have learned to control certain forms of bacteria.

But we have really just begun. There are still countless hidden mysteries to be solved in the field of bacteriology; there is still a great deal more to be learned about these microorganisms which are all about us and which touch our lives so deeply.

The war gave us a graphic lesson in the importance of science and research. May we never forget that lesson. May we remember always that the world is engaged in a race between education and chaos. Education must win.

Fungi—Friends and Foes

By Elvin Charles Stakman

Dr. Elvin Charles Stakman is professor of plant pathology at the University of Minnesota, and has also for many years been a special agent of the United States Department of Agriculture.

Fungi are among man's best friends and worst enemies. Just what do we mean by fungi? The word fungus—or its plural form fungi —designates a group of plant forms which range from the microscopic cells of yeast, through the molds and mildew familiar to the housewife, the rusts and smuts all too familiar to the farmer, up to mushrooms and to giant puffballs that may weigh as much as 50 pounds. For long periods in the past, molds, mushrooms and toadstools were among men's deepest mysteries. But it is only during the last hundred years that scientists have really begun to understand this interesting and important group of plants.

The ancients regarded the fungi as of miraculous origin. Today we regard some of the fungi as of miraculous power—*Penicillium notatum,* for example. It is this lowly fungus of the blue and green mold group that produces the wonderful drug penicillin. Does it not seem a strange irony that these familiar molds which we have known for centuries, which have been cursed thousands of times for rotting our apples and molding our breads and cheeses, should all the time have locked within themselves this secret for combatting deadly disease and saving human lives? Of course, *Penicillium notatum* produces penicillin to serve its own interests. It has long been known that some fungi exude toxic substances which kill hostile bacteria and other fungi—and apparently penicillin is one of these substances.

Fortunately it is poisonous only to the bacteria, and not to man, and thus the chemical which this mold produces to protect itself against germs becomes a powerful agent to protect human life against the same germs. This discovery will surely lead to other discoveries. It marks the beginning of a new era in the history of medicine and of mycology.

Mycology is the name of that branch of science which deals with fungi. Even the primitive mycology of the ancients taught people to know that some mushrooms were delicious and others deadly. But the ancients never dreamed that fungi could be both so highly beneficial and so terribly destructive. Fungi rot wood and other plant remains, and build them into soil. Thus they make it possible to grow the plants we use for food, clothing, and shelter; but they also cause destructive diseases of those plants. Some fungi raise the bread we eat—other fungi mold the bread we don't eat. Fungi mold the cheese that we don't want to get moldy—and they put the flavor into cheeses that we want to be moldy. They ferment beers and wines—and they spoil them. They cause human diseases and they cure them.

There are myriads of fungi. Almost 100,000 distinct kinds or species have been scientifically described. They are everywhere: they grow in soil, on dead and living plants of all kinds, on foods and food products, in the birds of the air, and even on fish in the water.

All fungi are plants, either primitive or degenerate, but plants nevertheless. But nature did not give them the basic chemical, called chlorophyll, of the green leaf plants, or else she gave it to them and then took it away again. Chlorophyll enables higher plants to use the sun's energy to make their own food from water and chemicals that the roots take from the soil, and from gases that the leaves take from the air. Fungi cannot do this. They, therefore, grow on some higher plant or animal, alive or dead, or even on the product of some plant or animal, borrowing their food as a parasite. Fungi are without roots, stems, or leaves. They consist of single cells, such as many yeasts, or of branched networks of small tubes, such as those that give the molds their appearance of a cottony or felty mass. Even the mushrooms are made up of filaments, woven together by the master hand of nature into beautiful forms.

The fungi digest their food, as we do, by means of digestive ferments or enzymes. But we put the food into our stomachs, and our enzymes do their work there. The fungi, on the other hand, digest their food outside of themselves, merely by producing and discharging the enzymes that make the food soluble so that it can be absorbed into the fungus cells. When a fungus rots an apple, it is only digesting the apple. But here it comes into conflict with man because he wants to eat the apple and digest it himself.

Therefore man uses his intelligence in devising ways of preventing the fungus from growing on the apple. But man purposely grows the fungus which we commonly call bread yeast; he imprisons large numbers of yeast cells in yeast cakes and then puts them into dough where the yeast feeds, grows, and produces gas that raises the bread. Man likewise grows pure cultures of the kinds he wants to use for making drugs, for fermenting beer and wines, and for producing enzymes and chemical substances of various kinds. He even breeds fungi, the way an expert farmer breeds his cattle, to get better strains.

Fungi do not produce seeds. They propagate themselves by means of simpler structures known as spores. Even a fairly large spore is only about one-thousandth of an inch long, and many are much smaller. A spore can be seen only with the aid of a microscope, but many are of characteristic size and shape so that the different kinds can be distinguished just as different kinds of seeds can be distinguished. The number of spores produced is almost beyond comprehension. A large bracket fungus, one of those commonly seen growing on trees, may produce more than five thousand billion spores. And these spores are discharged at the rate of thirty billion a day for six months. In a small smut gall on corn, there are about six billion spores. Many of these spores remain alive for months or even years.

They have been found in the air at altitudes of more than ten thousand feet and are carried hundreds of miles by the wind, by insects, and other animals. Spores, like seeds, germinate and grow when moisture and temperature are favorable.

Some fungi are marvels of architectural symmetry and form. The ordinary mushroom is an example. A mushroom is only the fruit body of a fungus, but the beautifully precise arrangement of the gills on the lower surface of its cap is a thing to admire. These gills bear the spores, usually four on each of millions of little club-shaped structures that stand at right angles to the surface of the gills. The spores are catapulted off and are then ready for a trip on the wings of the wind. Other fungi bear their spores in tiny sac-like organs packed together in cups, such as the scarlet-cup fungus. It is hard not to rhapsodize about the marvels of fungi. The longer one studies them the more marvelous they seem.

But thousands of species are enemies of man. Some mushrooms, like the death angel, contain fatal poisons. Many molds and other fungi are allergenic, causing asthmatic and hay-fever-like disturbances. Others cause human and animal diseases. And thousands of them inflict such destructive diseases on crop plants that they continually threaten man's food supply.

More than 3000 kinds of plant rusts alone are known, each with its characteristic appearance, host preference, and life habits. Powdery mildews are found on more than 1500 kinds of plants. Stem rust of wheat alone destroyed 200 million bushels of wheat in the United States in a single year. Man must continually fight these enemies of his food supply. Seed treatment, or spraying and dusting plants with appropriate chemicals, prevents some diseases. Others can be combatted by crop rotation. There are also practices that encourage the development of other fungi and bacteria which in turn oppose the development of the disease fungi. Many of these plant diseases can be controlled only by discovering or developing varieties of plants which are disease resistant.

And this is not always easy because it sometimes is necessary to combine, in the same variety, resistance to several fungi. Moreover, many fungi that cause plant disease, such as the cereal rusts, comprise numerous parasitic strains that look alike but behave differently. A cereal variety may be resistant to some strains and completely susceptible to others. And new strains of disease fungi are being produced continually as a result of mutation and hybridization. Plant pathologists and plant breeders study the complexities of these changes and try to forecast what may happen in their attempts to produce and maintain resistant crop plant varieties.

Thus, through the microscope and by many experiments and observations, science studies the fungi, learns how to make use of the good ones and how to fight the bad ones.

Hybrid Corn

By L. J. Stadler

Dr. Lewis J. Stadler is professor of field crops at the University of Missouri, and principal geneticist of the Bureau of Plant Industry of the U. S. Department of Agriculture.

For every man, woman, and child in the United States, we grow each year about two-thirds of an acre of corn. In normal times we consume it all in this country. Your individual share is about 1300 pounds of ear corn. You do not eat all this as corn flakes, or corn bread, or corn-on-the-cob; most of it comes to you as beef and pork and other meats, and also as milk and butter and starch.

During the war years we needed greatly increased food production, in spite of sharply decreased man power and equipment. In the first three crop years of the recent war, we grew the three largest corn crops in our history, 15 per cent larger than in the three years 1917 to 1919. The significant thing is that American farmers grew these record crops on an acreage 10 per cent less than was used in 1917 to 1919. This means not merely the saving in land; it means a proportionate saving in man power and equipment badly needed elsewhere during the war years.

By and large, the size of the corn crop determines the size of the meat crop. Meat has recently been scarce. The ration points we received in 1945, for example, represented an allotment of 115 pounds of meat per person for the year. The increased yield of corn per acre, which I have mentioned, was equivalent to 38 pounds of meat per person, or one-third of the 1945 ration. Without this improvement in corn production we should have had to make a corresponding increase in the man power and resources allotted to food production, or we should have had to get along with that much less food.

The big factor in this improvement is hybrid corn. Hybrid corn is a new kind of corn which farmers are now growing. The great improvement in corn production which it has brought about has occurred during the last ten years. In 1934 hybrid corn was still a curiosity. By 1944 more than three-quarters of our total corn harvest was hybrid. Accurate yield tests show that adapted hybrids consistently outyield the varieties formerly grown by 25 to 30 per cent. What the farmer calls "40-bushel corn land" is now 50-bushel corn land, if planted to a good hybrid.

Hybrid corn was not a wartime discovery. It is the product of 25 years of intensive research by plant breeders, based upon scientific studies of heredity in the early years of this century. It is a fortunate circumstance that hybrid corn was ready for large-scale production when the emergency came, but its value is in no way limited to war periods.

Everyone is familiar with the truism "Like begets like," and with its application in the breeding of better animals. Our highly improved race horses and milk cows are the result of careful selection of breeding stock, generation after generation. The same principles are applied in the breeding of better crop plants. Each plant, like each animal, has a mother and father, and the principles of heredity are essentially the same in plants as in animals.

The plant breeder works, as the animal breeder does, by selecting the best individuals as parents of the next generation. Working with inexpensive individuals, he can grow thousands to find the plant he wants, and can grow large progenies to test the plants selected. In a sense, he produces nothing new; he can only re-shuffle the elements of heredity, as the chemist re-shuffles the elements of matter. But, like the chemist, he can bring these elements into new combinations which have qualities never seen before. Often he scours the world to find a plant with some desirable quality lacking in our native stocks. Among plants which interbreed, these qualities may be recombined almost at will.

For example, the spring wheat grown in the Northwest and in Canada, which makes up half our bread crop, is grown under constant threat of a devastating disease, called black stem rust. In some years, this disease has almost wiped out the crop. Among the poor relations of our good bread wheats, there are some forms much more resistant to rust. Plant breeders in both Canada and the United States have intercrossed these wheats, and have extracted from the hybrids new varieties combining rust resistance with good bread-making quality and yield.

Hybrid corn is the product of a different kind of plant breeding.

The varieties which it is now replacing were produced by repeated selection of the best plants as seed parents of the next generations, beginning about one hundred years ago. These varieties were remarkable products of the practical breeder's art. Technical plant breeders started to work on them in earnest in the 1890's, and they worked them hard for thirty years or more. They tried every method known in scientific selection, and they devised special methods as they went along. They could readily modify the varieties in certain special traits, for example, in protein content or ear type. But they couldn't make any material improvement in the yield. Apparently selection on the "Like-begets-like" principle had gone about as far as it could go.

The break came with the application of new discoveries in heredity. Mendel's laws of heredity were rediscovered in 1900, and all over the world, botanists and zoologists were re-examining their theories of heredity in new experiments with plants and animals. Corn is a favorite plant for such experiments because of its technical advantages, quite aside from its economic value. Two young American geneticists, Shull at the Carnegie Institution, and East, at the Connecticut Experiment Station, were using corn in such experiments between 1905 and 1910. They weren't interested in improving corn production; they were interested in the mechanism of heredity, and particularly in the effect of close inbreeding. A corn plant is both male and female; it produces male germ cells in the tassel and female germ cells in the ear. Under natural conditions practically no self-fertilization occurs. But it is a simple matter to apply the pollen by hand to the ear of the same plant. This produces a family of seeds whose mother and father are the same individual—a family representing the closest possible inbreeding. Shull and East were interested in learning how such close inbreeding, followed generation after generation, would affect the plant.

The first inbred generation was distinctly poorer and weaker than the parents. The best plants were self-fertilized again. With continued inbreeding, they grew steadily worse. Many of the strains became so poor that it was impossible to maintain them. Even the best of the inbred strains were extremely weakened, and their yield of grain was only a fraction of that of the original corn. Years later, in carrying on similar studies at our experiment station, we

used to grow the inbred strains of corn on plots well off the beaten
path, hoping that no visiting farmer would see them. It would have
seemed a crackpot experiment to any practical corn grower.

But when these scrubs and runts of inbred corn are crossed with
one another, the result is astonishing. The hybrid vigor they have
lost is suddenly regained. Many of the combinations are as good
as the original corn before inbreeding began. Some are better, and
a few are much better. The progeny of these hybrids again revert
to mediocrity, but the excellent first generation hybrid, once it has
been found, can be produced again each year by crossing the same
two inbred strains.

This is the foundation of modern corn breeding. Hybrid corn,
in the technical terms of the plant breeder, is the first generation
cross between two inbred strains, or more frequently in practice a
cross between two such crosses. There are many different hybrids
now in use, differing widely in adaptation and in value. Each hybrid
is the product of crossing certain inbred strains, and its value depends upon what those strains brought into the cross. A hybrid is
not good just because it is a hybrid—it is possible to produce bad
hybrids as well as good ones.

During the last 20 years, corn breeders have produced thousands
of inbred strains, and have studied them in detail to find what
qualities each strain can transmit to its hybrids. Some are remarkable for stiffness of stalk, some for quality of grain, some for resistance to one disease and some to another. Some make high yielding
hybrids in almost any combination, others in certain combinations
only. A hybrid built for Minnesota is useless in southern Illinois,
and vice versa; a hybrid excellent today may fail 5 years from now
before a new enemy like leaf blight or the European corn borer.
But lines resistant to the blight or the borer are also found, and
the breeder makes ready for these enemies before they reach his
borders. His job is to build more efficient crop plants, as an engineer builds more efficient machines.

Living Light

By Edmund Newton Harvey

Dr. Edmund Newton Harvey, a physiologist who has worked in many fields of experimental biology, holds the Henry Fairfield Osborn professorship at Princeton University.

SOME of my readers have lived through two revolutions in lighting, first, the change from oil lamp to gas and then from gas to electricity. A third revolution is now in progress—replacement of the incandescent filament by the modern fluorescent tube. By this change we have turned to the mode of illumination adopted by living things —the firefly, the glowworm and the host of minute animals whose light gives phosphorescence to the sea. As contrasted with the electric bulb this living light is a cold light or a luminescence. Its study is a fascinating field of pure science.

Who has not thrilled at the sight of a June meadow, at dusk, dotted with the myriad flashes of fireflies, as they rise from daytime hiding places? In the tropics are even more brilliant displays, with flashing of many fireflies in unison. A traveller in Siam writes: "They have their favorite trees, round which they sport in countless multitudes, and produce a magnificent and living illumination: their light blazes and is extinguished by a common sympathy. At one moment every leaf and branch appears decorated with diamond-like fire; and soon there is darkness, to be again succeeded by flashes from innumerable lamps which whirl about in rapid agitation."

Each variety of firefly has a characteristic method of flashing, distinguished by length and rapidity of flashes. By these differences the male and female recognize and signal to each other.

As the flashing beam of an air beacon guides the aviator to his landing field, so the series of flashes guides the firefly to his mate. It is with truth that the poet remarks:—

"Before, beside us and above
The firefly lights his torch of love."

Many other animals are luminous. Some are amazingly different in the nature of their light.

For example, a squid or cuttlefish, from Mediterranean depths off Sicily, surrounds itself with a brilliant, luminous liquid when disturbed. While the common squid ejects a black cloud of ink to conceal its position, this deep-sea cousin, living in perpetual darkness, shoots out a liquid fire.

One unusual insect from South America, called the "railroad worm," has lights of two colors, red and yellow. Like a train at night, there is a row of yellow lights along its sides and a red light at one end. This lighting system is under the control of nerves so that the two colors can be turned on together or separately.

Another startling form is a fish from the Dutch East Indies. These fish swim in schools, flashing large luminous spots at regular intervals, in a series of winks. The light glows continuously and winking is accomplished by drawing a black fold of skin, like an eyelid, over the light.

Unlike most light-giving animals, these fish are not self-luminous. The light comes from a colony of luminous bacteria growing in the organ. The bacteria derive their food from the fish. In turn, the fish obtain the benefit of their light, an example of one of the strangest partnerships in the living world.

Many other kinds of luminous bacteria are known. You may have read a newspaper report from Texas of "mystery meat," which became luminous in the icebox. This light was due to harmless luminous bacteria growing on the meat. Many billions of these minute bacteria would be necessary to produce a light of one candle.

Nearly 300 years ago the great English chemist and philosopher, Robert Boyle, placed some "shining wood" from decaying stumps of trees under his newly invented air pump. When he exhausted the air he found that the light disappeared but again returned when air was readmitted. This phosphorescent wood derives its light from a luminous fungus growth. By this experiment Boyle proved that oxygen is necessary for living light, just as it is for life itself.

Life and light are intimately connected. They both depend on a combustion or on an oxidation. Painstaking research has shown that animal light comes from definite chemical compounds whose properties are largely known. Some day they will be made synthetically. By slow oxidation they produce light without the large amount of heat characteristic of ordinary combustion processes. The lighting efficiency is very high.

It is evident that living light supplies a common ground of interest for the student in various branches of biology, with additional problems for the chemist, the physicist, and the illuminating engineer.

My own interest has been largely in the borderline fields of biochemistry and biophysics—a study of the intimate mechanism by which the light is produced. Many of the chemical details are known, but one unsolved problem has to do with the setting off of the firefly flash.

What is the trigger mechanism that starts this light shining? It is difficult to imagine a more impractical problem or one more remote from current affairs. Here is a subject for pure research which is nevertheless related to a universal problem of great medical import. What sets off the contraction of a muscle when we will to move our arm or leg?

It is known that a nerve impulse starting in the brain speeds along nerves at 100 yards a second, and, reaching the muscle, starts a movement. Detailed knowledge remains to be filled in. So long as our activity is unimpaired, this subject may not be of particular interest. When the ability to move muscles ceases, as in paralysis, then the details become of great practical importance. The setting off of a firefly flash is similar to a muscle movement. Study of the flash can help us understand the muscle.

The history of science has shown that no sharp distinction can be drawn between pure and applied research. Pure research is merely research in which no practical application can be seen at the time it is undertaken. The motive is curiosity and I, for one, hope that the direction of research will never suppress the innate desire to explore the unknown, no matter how impractical the search may seem.

To arouse your own curiosity, I should like to suggest an experiment. When you retire tonight, take a roll of adhesive tape or tire tape with you. Turn out all lights in the room and when your eyes are well accustomed to the dark, strip the tape quickly from the roll. A beautiful line of greenish light will appear. It is light similar to that of the firefly. Here is something unusual, something to be studied further. Try stripping the tape under water or at high and low temperatures. Only by finding out all about an unusual observation will facts appear that may lead to an important discovery.

What is the future of commercial lighting? Will it be possible to illuminate dwellings with firefly light? The answer is that fluorescent lamps developed within the last few years are already similar in principle to that of the firefly and approach it in efficiency. They both emit much light and little heat; they both utilize a substance which is "excited," as we say, to luminesce—the fluorescent lamp by the energy of ultraviolet radiation, the firefly by the energy of a chemical reaction.

No chemical luminescence has yet been devised for general lighting. Nevertheless, such a process involves a principle of great importance for the light of the future. This is the principle of reversibility, whereby the luminous material may be used over and over again. This is what is done in the fluorescent lamp—and the fluorescent lamp is a step toward man's attainment of light with little heat. Let's turn back to the living thing—the firefly—and continue to strive for its perfection in producing light without any heat.

Plants Hold the Basic Patents

By Edmund W. Sinnott

Dr. Edmund W. Sinnott is Sterling professor of botany at Yale University and director of the Sheffield Scientific School at Yale.

CAN you imagine a marvelous liquid pumped into the tank of your car which would not only give it motive power but would service it, repair it, and provide the means for transforming it into next year's model? If you can imagine this, then you will have a fair picture of what food does for your own body and for that of every living thing. These bodies are complex organic machines, and food is the stuff which provides the fuel to keep them running and the material from which they are built and repaired. The problems of what food is, whence it comes and how it is used in the growth and activity of living things are therefore among the most fundamental ones in biology; and are particularly important in a world where millions of people still go hungry.

One of the most important facts about food, but one which fails too often to be recognized, is that all food is made by plants. In plants alone are produced those basic chemical compounds from which every kind of food must come. Out of the relatively simple compounds produced in plants there are then built, in the bodies of animals which eat the plants, a host of more complex substances; but these simple compounds themselves are made only by plants. Plants hold, so to speak, the basic patents upon which not only the food supply of the world, but also all other products of living things, are manufactured. There is solid scientific truth in the familiar remark that all flesh is grass.

Notable among these patents is the one which plants use for making sugar out of water and the carbon dioxide gas of the air. This union is brought about only through the agency of the all-important substance called chlorophyll—the pigment which makes plants green—and by the energy of light. Glucose, the simple sugar formed in this way, is the basic material from which starch, cellulose and the other carbohydrate substances are made, so that from green plants come most of the staple energy foods of mankind. The practice of agriculture is primarily the exploitation of this fundamental food-making ability of green plants. The process itself, which yet we are unable to duplicate in the laboratory, is also of the utmost scientific interest and is being studied intensively by botanists, biochemists, and biophysicists.

Another basic patent held by plants is used in the making of proteins. These substances, produced by the union of nitrogen compounds with carbohydrate, are important since they are necessary for the growth and repair of living tissues, which themselves are mostly made of proteins. Proteins are extremely complex but they are all built from a score or so of relatively simple nitrogen-containing substances called amino acids. Those essential for human nutrition are made only by plants. All the milk, meat, eggs and other such protein foods which we obtain from animals have their original source in the plants which these animals eat.

Many colorless plants as well as green ones can make proteins, and light is not necessary in the process. Yeasts (which are plants), have, for example, come to be used in the last two or three years for the production of great amounts of proteins from molasses, distillery wastes and other materials. A whole new industry and source of food for men and domestic animals is thus being developed which will be of great importance in regions like the West Indies, where these materials can be produced so cheaply.

Other tiny plants, the bacteria, some living free in the soil and others in the root nodules of beans, soys and similar crops, hold a third basic patent, that for taking nitrogen directly from the immense supplies of it in the atmosphere and converting it into protein, something that higher plants cannot do since they must get their nitrogen only from compounds in the soil. This is what makes members of the legume family, which harbor these bacterial guests, so important to man and the economy of nature generally; and their proteins thus made from sugar and air are of increasing importance in our diet. Here also is a hopeful source of other raw materials. Soys alone already yield almost everything from meat substitutes to door knobs!

In recent years still another group of substances essential in nutrition have been found to owe their origin to plants—the vitamins. Vitamin A is related to the yellow pigments associated with chlorophyll. The B vitamins, some of the names of which are now household words, cannot be made in the bodies of animals or man, but in nature have their source entirely in plants. So does much of our supply of vitamins C, D, E and K. An understanding of these facts holds great promise for better health of the human race through a wiser choice of foods. It has recently been found that plants as well as animals use vitamins in their metabolic machinery, and a study of their formation in plant cells and their role in nutrition has led to important discoveries in some of the fundamental bodily processes which are common to all living things.

Finally, plants are notable for the healing substances which they alone can make. Herb doctors were the first botanists. Drugs of all sorts have long been obtained from the vegetable kingdom. In recent months this curative power of plant products has been emphasized by the discovery of the wonderful new drug penicillin, formed by a simple plant mold. This is only a beginning, for streptomycin, streptothrycin and other substances from lowly plants may prove even more important in the control of infections and disease.

These unique abilities of plant tissues to bring about the basic chemical unions which underly all organic compounds are important in the production not only of food and healing agents but of many other things. Wood, fibers, rubber and hosts of other products have long been the concern of agriculture and forestry, and will continue to be. In recent years, however, a new and significant field for the use of plant products has opened through the immense progress made in synthetic chemistry. We have learned that rubber can be produced in a factory as well as in a rubber tree. Fibers, plastics, and a host of similar things are now the products of industry as well as of agriculture, and in the years which lie ahead this fact promises great changes in our economic life. The postwar world may be largely built of new synthetic materials. Give a chemist sugar or cellulose or the simple compounds formed from them and he can make almost anything under the sun. But—and here is the significant fact—he must have one of these simple plant-made compounds to begin with. The cleverest chemist is not yet able to perform these basic syntheses on which all else depends, nor does it seem likely that he will do so for a long time, at least on a commercial scale. We must still depend on the cheap labor of sun and soil and leaf for many of the raw materials of industry.

We shall probably have to turn to this same source in the future for another great need, as well—the power to run our mechanized civilization. Coal and petroleum, derived from plants of ages past, will not last forever, and as they become scarce the products of plant life today, rich in energy locked up in them from the sun, will be invaluable. Alcohol, already an important fuel, can now be made from sawdust and other plant wastes at the rate of about 50 gallons per ton, and petroleum-like compounds are produced from the same source.

All this means a new direction, in the near future, for the development of agriculture and forestry. We shall more and more use the synthetic ability of plants, not simply for foods or for specific industrial materials but for those simple and really basic raw materials like sugar, starch, cellulose and proteins from which the industrial chemist can, in turn, make so much. Here the whole plant can be used, including much material which is wasted today. In this new program forestry will have increased significance for an acre of trees makes considerably more actual plant product per year, on the average, than an acre of cultivated crops. The tropics, with their high temperatures and other favorable conditions for plant growth, will more and more attract the attention of producers for agriculture and industry. The immense reservoir of plant life in the sea, still untouched by man save in the use of fish and other animals which live on marine plants, is destined to be of ever greater economic importance.

All these sources present many problems to the student of plants, for they all depend on the unique productive capacity of members of the plant kingdom. Surely there are few places where fundamental research is likely to yield richer returns than on this question of the ability of those tiny laboratories, the cells of plants, to perform the basic chemical unions on which life and civilization so depend. We still have far to go in knowledge of biochemistry and biophysics before we shall understand some of the simplest activities of living things. In this fertile field, plant scientists and their collaborators have already made good progress, but the biggest problems are still unsolved. In finding answers to them we shall not only contribute to man's economic welfare but—what is perhaps more important—we shall gain a clearer insight into the mysterious processes of life itself. There is good hunting ahead.

CHAPTER 10

FUNDAMENTAL BIOLOGY

BIOLOGY, AS we saw in the preceding chapter, begins with the direct examination of nature. In earlier days, for example, the botanist was a naturalist. That is, he was largely concerned with collecting plants, observing their forms and habits, and arranging them systematically in carefully described classes.

The modern botanist is no less of a naturalist, but in addition he brings to his studies of plants the powerful methods of modern chemistry and physics. Using precisely controlled experiments, and all the quantitative apparatus of the physical sciences, he describes the details of the structure of plants, discovers the secrets of their inheritance, determines the mechanisms involved in their development, and analyzes the chemical changes which take place as they grow.

This application of the physical sciences to the study of plants and animals has played an important role in the development of a basic structure of knowledge, both experimental and theoretical, which can be characterized roughly as *fundamental biology*. The fields which make up this fundamental biology deal not so much with a particular plant or animal, but rather with general questions, the answers to which can be applied to all plants and animals.

This chapter, then, devotes two essays to one of these general fields, genetics, which analyzes the way in which all living things inherit their characteristics. The preceding chapter was also concerned with genetics, but in the present chapter the emphasis is upon the broader and more general aspects of the subject.

Since every form of life is composed of *cells,* and since every living thing *grows,* studies of general properties of cells and studies of the biochemistry of growth clearly have universal application, and thus these subjects also qualify as fundamental biology.

On a still more basic level, every cell which biologists study is in turn composed of molecules. One of the most significant and exciting of the newer fields of fundamental biology is the one which is just beginning to be called *molecular biology*. Here the biologist, like the physicist and chemist before him, must probe far beyond the power of the ordinary microscope and follow his problems into the unbelievably tiny world of molecular structure.

Calling studies like these fundamental biology is admittedly a little unfortunate, for it would be wrong to conclude that these modern developments have made unimportant and unnecessary the older interests of biology. All aspects of nature are closely interrelated; and are of vital interest and importance. None can be neglected if we are to get a complete picture of the world about us.

W. W.

The Science of Heredity

By T. S. Painter

Dr. T. S. Painter, long known for his research in cytogenetics, is
president of the University of Texas.

As we turn our minds to the planning of a better world in which
to live, many different groups of thoughtful people are seeking
scientifically sound answers to questions of immediate human
concern. One field of knowledge that may help us is genetics, the
science of heredity.

Biologists have long realized that they must know the laws of
heredity before they can hope to understand how new species of
animals and plants arise in nature, or how the different human
races came into existence.

Agricultural experts are using genetics to develop plants and animals of improved strains, better adapted to serve the needs of a
rapidly growing world population. Sociologists, psychologists, medical men, and other specialists in social problems recognize that
many of mankind's physical and mental ills, as well as special
talents, have a hereditary basis. The science of genetics assists us
to understand the relative value of heredity and environment in
the life of the individual, and thus indicates the extent to which
we can hope to improve the race through better education or
through better living conditions.

Genetics, like other branches of science, is a complex technical
study, but the underlying principles are not difficult to understand.
The whole science is based on the fact that the hundreds and thousands of characteristics which constitute the individual man, animal, plant, or other organism are controlled by tiny units built
into the living cells. These units of heredity are known as genes,
and hence the derivation of our word genetics, meaning quite
literally the study of the genes.

In the cells of a man's body there are certain genes which determine the color of his eyes, other genes which determine the color
of his hair, still others which determine the shape of his nose
or mouth, the texture of his skin, and so on for each individual

characteristic. Every cell of his body contains the same pattern of genes, there are thousands of them in each cell, linked together in chains like the beads of a necklace, and so there are plenty of genes to account for, determine, and control every aspect of our body's form and other characteristics.

Having said this, I must tell you that no one has ever isolated and examined a gene. They are too small for our present microscopes. But we judge the nature of the genes by the ways in which they behave and by the effects which they produce, just as chemists earlier learned the structure and properties of the invisible molecules by observing their chemical behavior.

Genes behave, in fact, as if they were themselves large molecules. They seem to be independent of one another, and, generally speaking, are not affected by the physical or chemical agents found in their surroundings. On the other hand, the extent to which a gene actually succeeds in expressing itself in the body is often determined by the environment. For example, a baby's sex, the color of its eyes, the color of its hair, and the potential limits for capacities of many sorts are determined before birth by the genes which the baby inherits from its parents; but thereafter, from infancy to adulthood, the size and physical configuration of the body, as well as mental and spiritual qualities, may be greatly affected by improper food, disease, and a variety of other factors which we may describe as environmental. Inadequate nutrition, illness, or other hardships may make the baby's eyes weak, or its hair scant, or its body stunted. These adverse environmental conditions are able to distort development because they interfere with the body's chemistry; and, since it is by control of chemical reactions within the body that the genes act, the final result is a certain impairment of or interference with this control.

Thus, what we inherit are genes. Whether or not our genes express themselves fully depends on the environment in which we are reared.

I have described genes as molecules. They are quite stable structures as a rule, but every now and then a gene will suddenly undergo a spontaneous change. This change we call a mutation. Once a gene mutates, it is as stable in its new form as it was before, but it may now dictate an entirely different line of development. In studies of insects, for example, we find that a gene which normally produces red eyes, may suddenly mutate, and thereafter, instead of red eyes, white eyes will be produced. In foxes, one of the genes controlling the color of the fur may mutate, and thereafter instead of a red fox, a silver fox results. It often happens that the same gene will mutate several times. This has been observed in some flowers, for example, and a whole series of color changes in blossoms is traceable to a sequence of mutations of a single gene.

Certain genes undergo the same mutation repeatedly. For example, in mammals there is a single gene on which coloring or pigmentation depends, but every now and then this gene changes to such an extent that it is no longer able to control pigmentation. The result is an albino. There are albinos in human races and in many other species. There are even albino crows. Another common mutation is that of a gene, one of many, which controls body size. As a result of this mutation we have dwarfs. There are dwarf races of men, pigmy elephants, pigmy hippopotami; and in the seed catalog you have the choice of plants of dwarfs or normal size.

You may wonder how frequently genes mutate. There is no simple answer to that question, because some genes are more stable than others. We know of a relatively unstable gene in the fruit fly which changes once in 1,200 generations, on the average. In terms of human life this would mean one mutation in about 300 years. Whether or not such relatively unstable genes exist in man is unknown, but this example from insect life gives some idea of what we mean by the stability of genes.

Even though gene mutations are rare, most of the known species of animals and plants have existed so many thousands of years that every gene capable of mutating has probably done so a number of times. As a result wild species are reservoirs of mutant genes, and man is learning to tap this reservoir in his search for new varieties of food and other useful plants. Ordinarily, the mutant genes do not manifest themselves. The reason for this lies in the fact that, with rare exceptions, there are always two genes of every kind in the cells of our bodies. The genes occur in pairs, of which one gene is contributed by our father, the other by our mother. Let us suppose that in a child a certain gene contributed by the mother is normal, while the corresponding gene contributed by the father is a mutant. Which will prevail? The answer is that almost invariably the normal gene will be dominant. Thus, a black rabbit carrying one albino gene is just as black as a rabbit which has two genes for normal pigmentation. But when a baby rabbit is conceived with two albino genes, then you can confidently look for an individual with white fur, light eyes, and all the other characteristic of an albino, though both its parents may be jet black.

The fact that normal genes usually take dominance over mutant genes is of extreme importance. Many undesirable gene mutations are known to occur in humans. As long as one of these occurs paired with a normal gene, the individual is in no way affected. But when two of the same kind of "bad" genes occur together, a defective, or at least a handicapped, individual is the usual result. It is therefore clear that if "bad" genes exist in one's ancestry, it is wise to avoid marriage with a mate whose family has shown the same defective gene. Whether or not a gene will find expression depends on whether it is dominant or recessive to its companion gene. If it is recession it will not assert itself, neither will it be destroyed, but will remain hidden, maybe for hundreds or thousands of generations, until the chance occurs when it is paired with a like gene. Then its effect will appear.

These are some of the basic principles on which genetics rests. Our science is comparatively young, yet its influence in some areas is profound. More than one industry has been saved by the isolation of disease-resistant varieties of plants. It is said that the increased yield from hybrid corn has given farmers, within the last ten years, more profit than the cost of the atomic bomb. Human genetics is perhaps the field of greatest promise. The application of the science of heredity to human problems will be slow, but we may confidently predict that as we learn more, and intelligently apply what we have learned, the world will become freerer of preventable human misery and a better place in which our children may live.

Genes, Vitamins, and Nutrition

By George W. Beadle

Dr. George W. Beadle is professor of biology and chairman of the
Division of Biology at the California Institute of Technology.

Our bodies are largely composed of exceedingly tiny units called
cells. There are almost a million times as many cells in a man's
body as there are human inhabitants on earth. Inside each one of
these cells are certain threadlike wisps of matter which, if they were
straightened out and examined under a very powerful microscope,
could be compared very roughly with strings of kindergarten beads.
The individual beads in these strings correspond to what the
geneticist calls genes.

These genes are the units of inheritance. Part of our genes we
inherit from our mother, part from our father; and we in turn pass
on genes to our offspring. The genes we carry determine not only
our physical characteristics, but our physiological properties as well.
What goes on inside our bodies chemically, how and what we
think, our nutritional requirements—all these are directly related
to the genes we receive from our parents.

As an example, we are all vitally interested in vitamins because
without them we cannot exist. The reason we must have these
substances in our diets, while certain other organisms get along
without them, is that these other organisms are able to manufacture
vitamins within their bodies; in contrast our genes are present in
such a condition that our bodies are incapable of making them.

Many plants are able to make vitamins and this is so because of
the genes they have. How do we know that genes are concerned
with the ability of an organism to make its own vitamins? We
know because it is possible to inactivate certain genes experimentally in organisms that normally make vitamins and show that,
following such inactivation, the organism is no longer able to
build up certain substances. In order to understand how this is
done it is necessary to consider briefly how genes are related to the
chemical process of the organism.

Genes function by controlling particular chemical transforma-

218

tions. For example, the pigment that gives color to our hair, skin and eyes is formed chemically under the direction of certain genes. If one particular type of gene is received in defective form from each parent, an individual cannot form this pigment and becomes a white-haired, light-skinned, pink-eyed individual known as an albino. Albinos are like pink-eyed white rabbits in pigmentation. Another specific gene controls a chemical reaction which is necessary for normal functioning of the brain. If a defective gene of this type is received from each parent, the individual is hopelessly feeble-minded.

If we are to understand what genes have to do with our needs for vitamins and other dietary essentials, we must study some organism other than man. This is so both because man is not a favorable organism for experimental study, and because he cannot normally make these substances. If we are to find out how they are made, it is obvious that we must study some organism that makes them. Studies of this kind have been made on a very simple living organism—a particular fungus known as red bread mold. While at first thought a mold seems very different from a man, actually in its basic metabolism it is remarkably similar.

The red bread mold is found to be a clever chemist, able to make all the vitamins of the B group, except biotin. The remaining ones, B-1, B-2, B-6, niacin, and five others, it makes from sugar and a mixture of salts like those contained in the medium on which the mold is grown. We grow the mold in a pure culture, that is, in the absence of bacteria and other organisms and we can, therefore, be sure it makes vitamins from the medium on which is grows.

It is shown that genes are essential to the manufacture of vitamins by the mold in the following way: We can make genes defective by treating the cells in which they are carried with ultraviolet light, with X rays, or with rays from a cyclotron. We cannot aim beams of radiation at particular genes, but by treating all the genes in a sufficiently large number of cells, it is possible to select those in which one particular gene has been modified. It is then found that the mold arising from a cell in which a particular gene has been inactivated is no longer able to make vitamin B-1 and is now dependent on a dietary supply of it just as we are. This inability

of the new type of mold to make vitamins B-1 is inherited according to the same principles by which albinism is inherited in man.

If another particular gene is changed by the irradiation, the
mold loses the ability to synthesize vitamin B-2. By this we know
that the original unchanged gene of this kind must play some
essential part in the control of the chemical reactions by which
the mold builds up vitamin B-2 from the materials supplied in
the medium in which it is grown. In the same way it has been
shown that still other genes are concerned with the capacity of
the mold to make other vitamins of the B group.

It is a general rule that each particular gene is concerned with
one particular chemical reaction. When one gene is destroyed or
inactivated, the ability to make one particular chemical substance
is lost. This may be a particular vitamin, but this is not always the
case. In addition to vitamins, there are many other chemical substances essential to the living organism. Each of these must either
be made by the organism directly, or furnished ready made in the
diet. Actually there are other chemicals that are just as important
as vitamins. These include the amino acids which are the building
blocks from which proteins, like muscle fibers, are constructed.
Their formation from simpler chemical materials is likewise controlled by genes. This can be shown in the same way in which it
was shown for vitamins. Still other vital chemicals are likewise
built under the guidance of genes. If a gene is defective some one
of these will be absent and the organism will be defective.

But being defective is a relative term. Thus it is almost embar-
rassing to note that, as compared with the elementary bread mold,
we are very defective indeed—we cannot make our own vitamins
and we cannot construct amino acids.

There are other important substances as well that we cannot
make and must, therefore, obtain from other organisms through
our diets. So long as we obtain a sufficient supply of food containing these essential materials that we cannot make, we get along
quite satisfactorily. This illustrates the important point that in the
welfare of any organism both heredity and environmental factors
are important. In the absence of vitamin B-1, our hereditary inability to make this component which is essential to all living beings

would be disastrous. But in a world in which our diets contain plenty of it, we do not in any way suffer.

Our studies on the bread mold not only show that genes control the ability of the organism to make substances essential to life, but they help us to understand how these substances are made. For example, we know that vitamin B-1 is made of two parts and that it is the gene that directs the chemical union of these parts. It is obvious that such knowledge is necessary as a basis for a sound application of biological sciences to human welfare. An understanding of the nature and function of the gene should underlie an enlightened science of nutrition. The study of genes, which attempts scientifically to analyze inherited traits, has a direct bearing on many problems of medicine and will certainly continue to contribute to their solution.

Living Cells in Action

BY CARL CASKEY SPEIDEL

Dr. Carl Caskey Speidel, a cellular physiologist, is professor of anatomy, Department of Medicine, University of Virginia.

OUR own bodies, and the bodies of all the lower animals and plants are made of cells. Every living thing starts as a single cell. There are simple forms of life which never get beyond the single cell stage. Usually cells are very small. Nevertheless, the complicated processes of growth, respiration, nutrition, reproduction and aging are all, ultimately, functions of cells.

Some years ago I became deeply engrossed in watching living cells in action. In order to watch them, it was necessary to select animals small enough to see through, and yet large enough to present some complexity. The most suitable animal for the purpose appeared to be the frog tadpole and my studies were focused on this small creature.

By a suitable technique it is possible to place a tadpole in a small glass vessel, lightly anesthetize the animal so that it will not wiggle, and then focus a microscope on some part of its body. The tail fin is particularly appropriate for study, because its tissues are transparent. The same cells may be watched for hours, the tad-pole then replaced in pond water to be returned to the microscope next day for further observation. In this way the seqence of slow changes of cells can be watched, extending over periods of days, weeks, or even months.

At first sight, living tissues seem motionless except for the cir-culating blood and an occasional twitching of a muscle fiber. Close scrutiny, however, reveals that cells undergo slow, almost imperceptible, movements. It occurred to me that such movements could be brought out vividly in moving pictures by taking the pictures at slow speeds and projecting them on the screen at fast speeds. One minute on the screen might thus represent as much as two hours of actual life.

In 1932 I obtained, in this way, speeded-up movies of growing nerves. These pictures show: first, how the moving tips of growing fibers probe and explore their way through the tissues; second, how the sheath cells, on the outer surface of nerves, glide outward along the primitive nerves and multiply; and third, how some fibers slowly become covered with a fatty insulating sheath, called myelin. This insulating sheath is formed only through the cooperative ef-forts of both sheath cell and nerve fiber. Neither one alone is able to form it.

Similar moving pictures were made of other tissues, such as the cells of the skin, muscle, connective tissue, pigment, blood and the lining of blood and lymph vessels. These pictures show how cells pulsate, move, divide and mature.

A particularly interesting thing to watch is a common bruise. The discoloration of a bruise is caused by red blood cells which have escaped from injured blood vessels and crowded into the tissues. What is the fate of such stranded red blood cells?

First, as we discover when we watch a bruise, the near-by lymph vessels get busy. These lymph vessels are like small veins only their fluid, unlike blood, is clear, almost colorless. It may take an hour or two to get into action but eventually one of the lymph vessels will send out a sprout toward the hemorrhage. After it establishes con-tact, the sprout tip begins to manipulate a red blood cell and soon draws it in. Then it pulls in other red blood cells, one by one. These rescued cells are caught up by the lymph circulation and delivered back to the blood circulation where, presumably, they resume their normal functions.

After a day or two those accumulated red blood cells which have not been salvaged by the lymph sprouts seem to deteriorate. Thereafter the lymph sprouts lose interest in the red cells, cease to reach out for them and in fact withdraw. Quite in contrast with this indifference is the behavior of the white blood cells. We call these white cells scavenger cells and as you watch the unfolding drama you see why. For now, as the stranded red blood cells begin to decay, the white blood cells move up, surround them and vigorously attack them.

As you watch you see a white cell send out a part of its protoplasm in the form of a tentacle, this outreaching arm encircles a decaying red cell, the white cell engulfs it and digests it.

Fast-motion movies give a lively portrayal of this nicely balanced economy—the early action of the lymph sprouts, the rescue team which moves to salvage the stranded red blood cells before it is too late—and the later action of the scavenger cells, the clean-up squad which rids the bruised tissue of the dead and dying red cells. Why all this happens we do not know. All we can say is that freshly extruded red blood cells attract lymph vessels, but not scavenger white blood cells. After a couple of days, when the stranded red cells have begun to spoil, the reverse is true—the spoiled cells attract the white blood cells but not the lymph vessels.

Let us turn now to certain other observations. The tadpole's tail contains a series of organs, called lateral-line organs, that look like the taste buds on the human tongue. They are sensitive to chemical variations in the water in which the tadpole lives and also to vibrations and to currents. They are innervated by the vagus nerve from the brain. In both frog and man, this vagus nerve also serves the heart, lungs, stomach, and other important structures.

By suitable operations on tadpoles, some lateral-line organs can be deprived of their nerves and be kept deprived of them. I have watched such organs over long periods of time, from a few weeks to many months. There is no question as to what happens ultimately. Organs without nerves waste away and die. Such deterioration becomes apparent after a few months, though occasionally an organ deprived of nerves may persist for more than a year.

In some experiments, organs on one side of the tadpole were kept without nerves; those on the other side were allowed to reacquire nerves. In such animals, while the nerveless organs were disappearing, the others with nerves grew and multiplied. This conspicuous difference between the two sides of the body in the same animal demonstrated the importance of the vagus nerve for the normal health and growth of these sense organs.

But the reverse is also true. That is, the sense organs exert an important influence on the health and growth of the nerve fibers. In many instances I have kept track of regenerating vagus fibers after the nerve has been cut. These fibers mature normally and develop good insulating sheaths of myelin after a few weeks. However, if a fiber fails to reach a lateral-line sense organ, the fiber will deteriorate after a time.

It will lose its insulating sheath of myelin, become thinner, and ultimately the nerve substance itself may degenerate.

In sharp contrast are the nerve fibers that do reach sense organs and establish functional connections with them. They grow large and develop thick insulating sheaths of myelin. These observations show that the sense organs markedly influence nerve health.

Cell behavior sometimes presents an element of comedy. Some time ago, I gave motion picture exhibitions at 28 universities. One movie shot, at which every audience laughed, showed a blocked lymph vessel which was not draining properly. Seven white blood cells moved steadily along in the direction of the block, like plumbers coming to fix the drain. As they traveled along in Indian file, the seven cells reminded one of the seven dwarfs in the Snow White movie going off to work.

Another shot that invariably caused laughter portrayed a large scavenger white blood cell caught in a blood vessel sprout, half in, half out. It was very sedate and leisurely. After a while, some red blood cells pressing up from below gave it a good boost in the rear, hastening its exit and quite spoiling its dignity.

All these studies have been made possible by the use of the microscope, the movie camera, and the lowly frog tadpole. I hope I have been able to convey to you something of the fascination, and at least a suggestion of the drama and excitement of watching living cells in action.

Growth

By William Jacob Robbins

Dr. William Jacob Robbins is director of the New York Botanical
Garden and professor of botany at Columbia University.

Growth is a subject of interest to all of us. It is a personal subject.
We have all grown. We may wonder at times why we have grown
no more than we have, or why we grew the way we did; but not
many persons do more than wonder. Few attempt to learn what
growth is, how it occurs, and why—or to answer any of the other
fundamental questions we might ask about this process which we
all experience.

What is growth? Most people would probably answer by saying
that when anything grows it gets bigger. But this is evidently
not all that we mean by the term growth. A dog is not merely an
enlarged puppy; a man is more than a magnified infant, and an
oak tree is much more than an expanded acorn. As an individual
grows, the body structure and its proportions and functions change.
This phase of growth is commonly called differentiation, or is referred to by the term development, and in all but the simplest living creatures it is intimately associated with increase in size.

Most living things originate as a single cell, microscopic in size
and derived from the parents. This minute bit of protoplasm, or
living material, grows—that is, it divides and multiplies, until the
mature individual—if it be one of the larger plants or animals—
contains millions on millions of cells, all descended from the original one. An averaged-sized potato, such as you may have eaten
for dinner, has between five and six billion cells. As these cells
are formed, they enlarge; and they also change in character; become organized into tissues and organs—that is, they undergo
differentiation. This phase of growth is the process that makes
our bodies develop with separate organs and parts, instead of becoming merely a shapeless mass of 160 pounds or so of quivering
jelly.

Differentiation follows a definite rule with each kind of living
thing. A frog's egg always grows into a frog, and never into a

chicken or a peony. Our nose always grows on the front of our face and not, fortunately, between our shoulder blades. What causes differentiation, and what causes it to follow a definite rule? Why do we grow hair on the top of our head instead of on the soles of our feet, and why does an orchid not produce tomatoes? Why do we stop growing? Why don't we continue to enlarge throughout our lives and reach a height of 10, 15 or 20 feet instead of 5 or 6?

A usual answer is heredity, which means in plain language that our fathers grew that way before us and we grow like them. The cell from which each individual, plant or animal, starts contains a special kind of living stuff derived from its parents. Therefore, like theirs, it carries on a predetermined series of chemical reactions and physical processes which result in the characteristic structure and life span of the individual.

To make this point of view clearer, we might use an analogy from a familiar type of fireworks. Perhaps you have seen the kind called Pharaoh's serpent, in which the tip of a small cone of mercury sulfocyanate, when lighted, burns and forms a serpent-like ash a hundred times or more the size of the original cone. The growth of Pharaoh's serpent depends on the kind of material of which the cone is made. To use charcoal, sulfur, or gunpowder will not do. It must be mercury sulfocyanate. The behavior of the ash depends also upon the chemical reactions which this stuff undergoes. Only oxidation, that is, burning, forms the snake. Also, the cone must burn from the tip. If it burns over all its surface, the ash will form a shapeless monster rather than a serpent. This shows that certain physical conditions also are necessary to get the desired result.

Thus we conceive the growth of a plant or animal to depend upon the particular kind of living stuff in the original cell. We picture this highly individualized living stuff as carrying on its own series of chemical reactions and physical processes which culminate in the characteristic mature individual. The chemical constitution of living protoplasm is, of course, exceedingly complex, and the chemical reactions and physical processes in growth are infinitely numerous and complicated.

When we say growth takes place by a process in which each cell divides into two, followed by enlargement of the resulting cells and their differentiation into permanent form, we are actually giving but the barest outline of growth. This concept is important, however, because it suggests that anything which changes the nature of the original protoplasm, the living matter in the cells, or which modifies the interrelated chemical reactions of the substance of the cells, will influence growth. And that idea is fundamental. Such substances as the sulfa drugs and penicillin are effective because they interfere with some of the chemical reactions essential for the growth of bacteria. Thus, growth is not only a problem for the biologist, it is one which concerns the physicist and chemist as well. We need to know not only the details of the way in which cells divide and how they are arranged in tissues and organs; we need knowledge also of the chemistry and physics of growth, the role played by enzyme systems and their inhibitors, information on surface tension and radiations, and many other highly technical matters.

One of the things we should like to know is how to control growth. Many of the diseases which plants and animals endure are results of the growth and multiplication of other organisms in or on their bodies. For example, athlete's foot is caused by the growth of a specific fungus in the skin of the foot; pear blight is caused by the growth of particular bacteria in the twigs of the pear tree; pneumonia is a consequence of the growth of certain bacteria in the lungs. To prevent or cure these diseases, we must prevent or stop the growth of the parasite in the host. The rotting of fruits and vegetables, the decay of lumber, and the mildewing of cloth are caused by the growth of bacteria or molds in or on the material affected.

As human beings we grow—and we grow old. What causes old age and senility? Do all living things age? Is there a fountain of youth? These are questions intimately associated with the process of growth. Even cancer is a growth problem. In cancer certain cells of the body which have matured and ceased to grow suddenly change their character and begin to grow rapidly. As a consequence they do not keep their ordered place in the community of cells but become unruly members which insist on pushing their way through and over their more orderly associates, and thus destroy the body of which they are a part. Why should some cells—and not others—change from their mature nongrowing condition to a rapidly growing form, and how can they be induced to return to their normal and harmless condition? If we knew enough about growth we could answer these questions and many others.

One of the interesting and hopeful things we have learned is that growth is fundamentally the same process in humble and simple living things, both plants and animals, as it is in man. We can experiment more easily and freely with these less complicated forms of life, though the final test, of course, is the particular organism concerned, and that may be the human body. It is important, therefore, to study growth in plants, including the bacteria, yeasts, and molds. It is important not only because such study enables us to control these living things and use them but also because it tells what may occur in our own bodies. Perhaps it seems odd to think of looking for an answer to old age or cancer in the growth of yeasts, fungi, or squashes, yet the key to these problems, so profoundly important to us, may be discerned more readily through the study of plants or some other lowly creature than in man himself.

The Structural Basis of Life

By Francis O. Schmitt

Dr. Francis O. Schmitt, who works in the very modern field known as molecular biology, is head of the Department of Biology at the Massachusetts Institute of Technology.

The unit of life is the cell, and all living things are either single cells, like the bacteria and protozoa which cause disease, or else groups of cells associated together in varying degrees of complexity. This complexity of organization of cells reaches its highest expression in the human body, which consists of many thousands of millions of cells.

Much of our present knowledge of biology and medicine rests on discoveries made during the last century by studying the structure and behavior of cells. But, although most cells are so small that they can be seen only through the microscope, the cells are in turn made up of still smaller units, the molecules. And it is to the molecules of the cells that I wish to direct your attention. These structures are beyond the power of the ordinary microscope which uses light, and to study them we have had to develop entirely new instruments and techniques.

Some idea of the nature of the problem may be gained from an analogy, in which we think of the living cell as a factory, busy receiving raw materials and turning them into finished products. We are called on to make a survey of this factory, to determine what it does and how it operates; and we wish to evaluate the efficiency and completeness of these processes.

But we are required to make this survey without entering the factory. We can only watch it at a distance, and by illuminating the factory with a searchlight and watching it through binoculars, observe from afar off what is going on. We see raw materials being brought to the factory. Through the distant windows we dimly observe men working over machines. With patience we may be able to make out the rough outlines of some of the machines. However, the manufacturing processes apparently are complex and intricate, and at best we can only guess and infer the various steps.

Roughly, this is a picture of the dilemma of the biologist, trying to understand the complicated mechanism and processes of the living cell. With the microscope as his only tool, the biologist has been in the position of the observer required to study the factory from a distance through binoculars. He has realized that somehow, by some means, he must gain access to the factory. He must visit its various rooms and observe at close range all the steps in the process by which, within the cell, raw materials are received, broken down, and fabricated into the finished products. Recent research has attained that goal. Physics and chemistry have provided instruments by which the scientist can now enter the cell and study its processes at close hand.

It is possible at last to explore the molecular machinery of cells and observe the structural basis of life.

Various instruments and techniques have proved useful in these investigations. X rays, for example, have been particularly fruitful, especially when employed in the technique known as X-ray diffraction. Dr. Linus Pauling's paper in Chapter 6 indicates how diffraction techniques are used as a means of determining the architectural pattern of molecules. This same method is employed to determine the molecular structure of various body tissues, such as muscle, nerve, tendon, bone. When a beam of X rays is passed through one of these tissues to a photographic plate, the resulting photograph shows a distinctive pattern of spots and lines disposed in a regular way. This pattern reflects the arrangement of molecules in the tissue, and by mathematical analysis of the diffraction pattern it is possible to work out the molecular pattern of which it is a sort of reflection.

Another device which has been helpful in probing into the tiny factory is the use of polarized light. Polarized light, as the reader has learned in Chapter 7, is ordinary light which has been made to vibrate in only one plane.

It has been found that when polarized light is used to examine tissue through the microscope it reveals a world of new information. This is especially true when it is used to examine fibrous protein molecules, the forms which nature has so largely employed for living things.

A more recent, and still more powerful tool of biophysical research is the electron microscope. The electron microscope is discussed in Dr. Hillier's paper in Chapter 5, and I need not give here a description of this revolutionary instrument. Suffice it to say that objects which measure only one ten-millionth of an inch across can be plainly seen. Already photographs have been taken of various biological materials at magnifications of 100,000. In this way muscle and nerve fibers, the cells of skin, and various other biological structures, have been investigated. Photographs have been made of viruses, including those which cause infantile paralysis, influenza, and encephalitis. These viruses are too small to be seen with the light microscope, but the electron microscope is powerful enough to reveal even the smallest of them.

Thus, by the use of X-ray diffraction, polarized light, and the electron microscope, science has already gained new knowledge of the structural basis of life.

Nature apparently employs the protein fiber as the chief element in the architecture of the cell. These structural proteins occur in the form of thin threads, about a millionth of an inch in thickness.

They are woven into parallel bundles to produce the fibers of such tissues as muscles and tendons. In muscle the bundles of long thin threads are able to shorten quickly when certain chemical changes take place, thus making possible muscle contraction. The muscles are attached to the bones by tendons, and when the muscles contract the force is exerted on the bones through these tendons. Studies with the electron microscope show that tendons are composed of thousands of bundles of protein threads. Each thread has an intricate molecular structure arranged in a pattern which endows it with mechanical strength that may be even greater than the strength of iron.

Among the details of molecular structure, one of the most interesting is the cell wall. Whatever passes into or out of the cell must diffuse through this thin membrane, and we know that certain materials cannot get through while other substances penetrate readily.

This selective action is determined by the structure of the cell wall. Electron microscope photographs suggest that it is a network of very thin protein threads. When the threads are closely woven only small molecules can penetrate; when loosely woven, larger molecules can get through.

Another important problem of biology is the mechanism which causes cells to divide. Without such cell division there would be no growth. But when cells divide with abnormal rapidity, tumors and cancers may result. Hence the investigation of the causes of cell division is a fundamental medical problem.

Studies of cell division show that protein fibers play an important role. When the cell divides, very thin protein threads are formed. These threads radiate from the two poles of the cell to form a spindle near the middle of the cell. The chromosomes, which are chains of hereditary genes, line up near the center of the cell, divide into two sets and attach themselves to the spindle fibers. The spindle fibers then contract, pulling the chromosomes to the two poles of the cell, and then the cell separates and forms two cells. This much we know.

But what causes the protein threads to appear and form the spindle? What causes them to contract after the chromosomes have been attached? By what process do they disappear after the cell divides? What sets off the whole process? All these details are a complete mystery, and for their investigation biophysical and biochemical techniques are now being developed and applied.

Disease and the process of aging are merely alterations of the normal behavior of cells and tissues. To understand the abnormal conditions, we must first understand the normal. To make really great advances in biology and medicine we must comprehend the detailed molecular structure and minute physiology of normal cells and tissues.

Fundamental study of the structure of the atomic nucleus has unlocked the sources of enormous energy stored within the atom. I venture to suggest that if as much intellectual effort and financial support were devoted to the investigation of the structure and chemistry of the living cell as were given that of the atomic nucleus, the results might prove highly salutary from the human point of view.

Light on the Blood Capillaries

By George W. Corner

Dr. George W. Corner, anatomist, embryologist, and endocrinologist, is director of the Department of Embryology of the Carnegie Institution of Washington, at the Johns Hopkins Medical School

Everyone knows the tale of Archimedes, the ancient Greek scientist, and how he discovered his famous law of the displacement of floating objects, while he was at the public baths. According to the story, Archimedes was so pleased and excited by his discovery that he left the baths and ran home through the streets shouting "Eureka! I have found it."

Modern scientists seldom have such violent inspirations but we do have occasional moments of sudden illumination. The other day, sitting at my microscope, I myself had the good fortune to see the answer to an old problem, more clearly I think, than anyone ever saw it before. This was no great discovery like that of Archimedes but it set my thoughts to ranging widely. I want to tell you what I saw and the train of thought it started.

I was looking at a thin section of the liver on a microscope slide. That organ is quite simple in structure, for under the microscope it is seen to consist of a network of cells, something like a sponge in arrangement. Intimately intertwined with the cells and threading among them is a second network of tiny blood vessels. Thus the liver is composed of cell cords and a labyrinth of blood channels packed jam-tight together. They are packed so closely, in fact, that the details are hard to see, even under the best microscopic conditions.

These blood vessels have been quite a puzzle. Different observers have described them differently. It has even been suggested that the finest blood vessels of the liver, unlike those of other organs, have holes in their walls, as if they were tubular sieves. This is the point that was explained by my slide. By some accident in its preparation, the liver cells of my specimen had chanced to shrink a little, enough to pull them away from the adjacent vessels and, thus for the first time, I could see the microscopic blood vessels in the clear. It was plain that they were tubes with continuous, unbroken, unperforated walls, paper-thin. No, not merely paper-thin; that is how they seemed when greatly magnified under the microscope. Actually the walls of these capillary vessels (as we call them) are a hundred times thinner than tissue paper. Whatever goes to the liver cells from the blood—salts, sugar, fatty substances, nitrogenous materials—must seep through those thin walls. Whatever goes out from the cells—waste carbon, waste nitrogenous products, glycogen—also must filter through that delicate barrier to be carried away by the blood that streams within the capillaries.

I had been working late. Darkness had fallen outside the laboratory.

Inside there was a dim light on my desk so that I could see my notes, but the only bright light before my eyes was the intensely illuminated field of the microscope, focused on that fascinating slide.

What a symbol this is of the scientist's work, I said to myself. One thing only can I see in full light, enough to comprehend it; beyond that is only dim light and outside that the dark. All one observer can do is to focus his little beam on one dark spot, and another and another, until what he and his fellow workers see blends into a broad picture of the truth.

Sitting there in the dusk I began to think of other men whose searching lights had been turned, long before mine, upon the mysteries of the blood vessels. I thought of William Harvey, physician to King Charles the First, a little man with bright eyes and a brain like steel. Before him nobody could understand why there are two sets of large blood vessels, the arteries and the veins, both going to all parts of the body, and in which, as it was thought, the blood must ebb and flow, back and forth, in two parallel tides. Harvey saw, and proved by brilliant experiment, that these two kinds of vessels are two parts of one circuit. The blood flows out through the arteries and returns through the veins.

But Harvey's view was limited. In 1628 he had no microscope and he never discovered how the circuit is closed—how the blood gets through from the tips of the ultimate arterial branches to the first twigs of the veins.

I thought too of Marcello Malpighi, the Italian, who did have a little weak microscope, with which, about the year 1660, he was the first to see the capillary blood vessels. In the delicate membranous walls of a frog's lung he saw the arteries branch and branch again until every last twig became a vessel so fine and so thin-walled that only the microscope could follow it. These finest vessels, as he saw, no longer branched like a tree, as do the arteries, but spread throughout the tissues in a rich network. Here and there the tubular meshes of this net were drained into a slightly larger vessel, a vein. Thus the missing link of Harvey's pathway of the circulation was discovered, at least as far as the lung is concerned. A few years later the famous Dutch microscopist, Leeuwenhoek, explored many other organs of the body and showed that everywhere the blood gets from arteries to veins through networks of capillary vessels.

These discoveries started a series of investigations that has continued for three centuries. In a hundred laboratories today there are men with microscopes and physiological apparatus, working away at the problems of the capillaries.

To comprehend what they are doing we must understand that the real work of the blood is done only in the capillaries. They alone are sufficiently thin-walled to permit diffusion of oxygen, salts, chemical foodstuffs and waste products between the blood and the tissues. The heart is simply a pump and the arteries merely pipe lines to carry the blood to the vast microscopic net of capillaries in the working tissues of the body. A drop of blood going, for example, to the liver or any other organ rushes down a long stretch of the arterial pipe line, until it gets at last into a capillary and there, although it flows more slowly, it has but a few seconds at most, a journey of one-twentieth of an inch during which it can yield its chemical burden to the cells outside the capillary wall before it passes into the returning pipe line, that is to say a vein, and starts back to the heart. In order to get the chemical work of the body accomplished, millions of such tiny tubular filters are always working in every organ and tissue.

The problem of our own day is, therefore, to analyze more and more exactly the work of the capillaries. We are learning, for example, that the tubular walls are selective strainers. They do not let all substances in and out at the same rate. Small molecules like those of sodium chloride pass rapidly; large ones are held back. In our own laboratory, Doctors Louis Flexner, Alfred Gellhorn, and Margaret Merrill recently made an ingenious experiment in which they injected, into the blood of an animal, water containing heavy hydrogen which they could easily trace into the tissues outside the capillaries. Their calculations show that we must visualize a very rapid oozing of water through the capillary walls from the blood into the tissues and from the tissues back into the blood.

Gases (oxygen and carbon dioxide) no doubt flow freely in and out, impeded even less than water by the filmy barrier between blood and tissues. Salts and nitrogenous substances pass more slowly and each at a different rate, whereas the large molecules of proteins may not pass at all. Upon the effective working of these innumerable microscopic filter tubes, all the functions of the body, and life itself, depend.

Among the scientists now studying these problems there may be no such geniuses as Harvey and Leeuwenhoek; and, at any rate, in this branch of science we can hardly expect, in our day, such sudden episodes as Malpighi's first sight of the capillaries.

Planned experiment and accurate measurement is now the only way to discovery, but our picture of the truth becomes ever more complete through the persistent and laborious efforts of many workers.

These were the thoughts that passed through my mind as I sat before the microscope in the dusk, thinking of all the men of science, past and present, who had given us light wherewith to see the marvelous and beautiful microscopic structure of our own bodies.

CHAPTER 11

THE SCIENCE OF OURSELVES

WHEN ALEXANDER POPE, over two hundred years ago, wrote that "the proper study of mankind is man," he was giving poetic form to a belief that natural philosophers had held for centuries. And yet we are today only beginning to lay the foundations for the science of man.

The reason for this long delay is clear. Inanimate nature can usually be closely controlled by the scientist; rocks and minerals, liquids and gases can be "taken apart" and studied, one factor at a time. But *man* is, by nature, an organic whole so that for many purposes he must be studied all at once. And man is so complicated that this study requires a whole array of specialists: the biochemist, the geneticist, the psychologist, the anatomist, the anthropologist, the endocrinologist, the embryologist, the physicist, the physiologist, the neurologist, the psychiatrist, plus their humanistic colleagues, the philosopher and the poet. All these and other workers must pool their results and integrate their resources if we are to gain a true and dependable understanding of the potentialities and behavior of men.

To be sure, one can—and must if there is to be progress—study the organs and systems of men singly, as a necessary preparation to the study of the whole. Even these separate studies cannot be accomplished rapidly, for the parts of the human body are much more precise and delicate and intricate than any of the powerful man-made machines of which we read each day.

The present chapter opens with essays about two of these amazing human mechanisms, the eye and ear. The sensitivity, the complexity, the magnificent flexibility of these devices by which man gains his visual and aural evidence from the outside world can well make us humble, even when we think of our own most advanced inventions in photography, television, or in communication engineering.

Moving to the broader fields which have more to do with man as a whole, we find an essay on the muscle machinery by which all body movement is achieved. In these days when more and more of the tremendous forces of nature are being controlled by man, it might seem that muscles are not important any more—that it is only the brain which counts. But the brain, important as it is, would function helplessly and in a vacuum, so to speak, if it were not for man's muscles. Without muscles we could not so much as operate a push-button or even express in words the ideas which our brains conceive.

Next, we find an essay concerning the liquid environment, relic of his ancient sea home, which man maintains within his body. Like all stories of how our bodies are constructed and function, it has inherent interest and importance. But in addition, it gives us a glimpse of the long orderly development of man; and thus forms parts of that larger evolutionary story which contributes so much to the significance, the beauty, and the dignity of life.

Finally, in the concluding essay, we come to the total problem of the science of the whole of man. As yet we have made only feeble beginnings: but in this direction will come some of the greatest and most useful developments in the future of science.

W. W.

The Human Eye

By Selig Hecht

Dr. Selig Hecht established the Laboratory of Biophysics at Columbia University, and has for some twenty years been professor of biophysics at Columbia. Earlier he worked as an enzyme chemist and a pharmacologist.

OUR eyes are the most sensitive instruments in existence for recording the presence of light. I state this in spite of photocells and electric eyes and amplifiers, because with our eyes alone we can see dimmer lights than any combination of gadgets so far devised. I shall come back to this later, when we have learned more about our eyes.

Three major natural sciences—physics, chemistry, and biology—have made possible our knowledge of the eye. The earliest contributions were from physics, and showed that the eye is like a camera. Actually a camera is a poor imitation of an eye, since we had eyes before we had cameras, and our eyes are more sensitive, more complex, and more flexible than the best cameras.

A camera is essentially a light-tight box with a lens at one end and a light sensitive film at the other. The lens focuses a sharp picture on the film, which is then developed and printed.

The eye is also a light-tight box, but spherical like a ball. At the front end is the lens system which focuses a real picture of objects on a sensitive film at the back. In making an image, our lens system behaves just like glass, and follows all the laws of physical optics with fine precision. Indeed when our lens system fails, as when we are near-sighted, or far-sighted or astigmatic, we wear glass lenses to make up the deficiency.

The sensitive film in the eye is called the retina. As films go, it is small, about one inch square; and it is delicate and thin, being only 1/50 of an inch in thickness. Our knowledge of this film has come from chemistry. In a camera the film must be shielded from light until the moment of exposure, after which the film is finished. If another exposure is made on it, the result is confusion, as everyone who has made a double exposure knows to his sorrow. In the eye, however, the sensitive retina is open to light all our waking hours, and it acts as if new film were continuously exposed, immediately developed, and instantly replaced by fresh film. In short, chemically, the eye is more than a camera; it is a whole photographic factory.

When an animal is kept in the dark for some time, its retina becomes pinkish purple. If we shine a bright light on it, its color immediately vanishes. Back in the dark, its color slowly returns, and in the living eye, this reversible bleaching and regeneration goes on all the time. The pinkish color is due to a pigment, known as visual purple, which can be extracted from the retina and brought into solution. The bleaching and regeneration are chemical transformations, and can take place not only in a retina removed from the eye, but even in solution in the test tube.

Chemical studies of visual purple have clarified many properties of vision. For instance, one of the final products of bleaching visual purple is vitamin A. This shows that vitamin A or something closely related to it must have been part of the visual purple molecule, and explains why a diet poor in vitamin A produces night blindness. Without vitamin A visual purple cannot be formed in the retina, and we become less sensitive to light.

Visual purple is not the only light sensitive substance in the retina. Just before the war, another pigment was found with properties different from visual purple. This is called visual violet, and its discovery gives promise of clearing up things which puzzled us for years.

Although we have learned much about the eye from physics and chemistry, our basic knowledge comes from biology. The eye may be like a camera, or a photographic factory, but it is not made of glass and metal and cardboard and black paint. It is made of living, active cells. In the retina these cells contain visual purple and visual violet, and are concerned with recognizing the form, the brightness, and the colors of objects. The retinal cells vary in size and density in different regions, so that some parts of the retina serve best for seeing detail while others are best for picking up the faintest light. The retinal cells are joined to nerve fibers which connect them with the brain. Every time a retinal cell is hit by light its visual purple or its visual violet is bleached, the cell becomes active, and sends a message along its nerve to the brain and then we see. The pattern of these nerve impulses depends on the pattern which strikes the retina. Different shapes, different colors, different contrasts are registered by different patterns of impulses which surge up the optic nerve to the brain.

Biologically, the most interesting fact is that in a twenty-four hour day we see over a tremendous range of illuminations. A landscape field in sunlight is thousands of times brighter than the same landscape field in full moonlight, and yet we see under both conditions. Starlight is even dimmer, and still we see by it. In fact, we can see light less than one thousandth as bright as moonlight.

To deal with this huge range of illuminations we have two kinds of vision, day vision and night vision. Between sunlight and moonlight we use day eyes, while below moonlight we use night eyes. With day vision we see forms sharply, we detect delicate shades and shadows, and we distinguish colors. With night vision we perceive things vaguely, we recognize only coarse shadows, and we see no colors. But to make up for these lacks, our night vision is tremendously sensitive and can pick up the faintest lights.

Many animals, like man, have both night vision and day vision. But some animals have only one kind. Moles, owls, and mice operate at night and have only night vision. Other animals are active only during the day. Chickens have only day vision and when the light fails, they go to sleep. The same is true of turtles and of many day birds like hawks who cease their activities at night.

City folks rarely use their night vision because houses and streets are well illuminated. But people in the country and in blacked-out cities have learned to use their eyes skillfully at night. One trick of night vision is to look out of the corner of your eye, because that way we see better than straight ahead. There are several other tricks, and since night vision was important for the war, R.A.F. pilots and Navy lookouts, and our own Air Force pilots, were trained to use their eyes at night.

Under the best conditions at night, our eyes are unbelievably sensitive. Provided there is no haze or mist, you can see a candle 14 miles away and if you light a match on a dark night, an aviator ten miles away can easily pick it up. The light which enters the eye under such conditions is almost the smallest amount of energy that can exist. Light comes in minimum sized little packets called quanta, nature not being willing to deal in smaller amounts than one quantum of light at a time. Well, when the eyes see a candle 14 miles away only 6 or 7 quanta actually reach the retina, where they are absorbed by the visual purple and send the nerve messages to produce a sensation of light.

The biggest unsolved riddle is how we distinguish colors. Now that the war is over, and we can again do pure science, this will be our next task. And as before it will take the combined efforts of all the sciences, chemistry, physics, and biology to reach a solution.

How Much Can We See?

BY BRIAN O'BRIEN

Dr. Brian O'Brien is research professor of physics and optics and director of the Institute of Optics at the University of Rochester, New York.

WE CARRY in our head what are really twin television cameras, our two eyes. I liken them to television cameras rather than to ordinary photographic cameras because the functioning of the human eye is a sort of television.

Each eye has a lens, just as an ordinary camera has, and at the back of the eye is a light-sensitive screen upon which the lens forms images of everything upon which we look. The light-sensitive screen responds chemically, and to this extent resembles the photographic plate. But in addition each element of the screen is connected by transmission lines to the rearmost part of the brain. There are more than a million of these communication channels in just one small head, an array that would put to shame the largest and most elaborate telephone exchange. The signals which travel along these lines, the fibers of the optic nerve, are electrical, although, more accurately, they must be described as electrochemical. These remarkable living cameras and their transmission lines are finer in many ways than any camera which man has yet made, but they have their limitations too. These limitations and the reasons for them are matters of interest to all of us.

Try to see a distant bird or airplane against an expanse of sky. Suddenly you find it, and after that following it is easy. But now try to point out the object to someone else. He, too, must search a moment before he finds it. Why is this? You can see a wide expanse of sky all at once. Why did you not see instantly the small spot, the airplane or the bird?

Obviously there is something about our eyes which requires that they be pointed in order to see fine detail. Have you a book or newspaper near at hand? Look at an ordinary printed page and find a semicolon. The dot and comma which form it are easy to distinguish. But now look fixedly at some letter three printed lines directly above, and as you do so you lose the dot and comma—they become indistinguishable blurs. Our eyes give us a broad picture, but the picture is really sharp only in the center.

Some lack of sharpness at the edges of the picture is a property common in cameras. It is a defect of most lens systems. In the case of our eyes, however, there is a more important reason for this lack of sharpness. It is to be found in the structure of the light-sensitive screen.

This screen, the retina, is made up of a large number of tiny nerve endings, each sensitive to light, and all of them packed very closely together. Some of these nerve endings are rod shaped, some are cone shaped, and they are distributed over the screen in a certain pattern. The outer edges of the screen are mostly rods. Toward the center the cones become more numerous, and in the very center of the screen is a small area called the fovea containing only cones. From these rods and cones nerve fibers lead to the area of the brain where visual sensation is affected. That is the television system. However, the hook-up is not uniform. Some of the nerve fibers are private lines, some are party lines—and it appears that the private lines serve the cones, while the rods must share party lines. Since the edges of the retina have only rods it is no wonder that there is a certain jumbling of signals from those areas. And it seems clear, too, why only in the small rod-free center of the screen, the fovea tightly packed with cones, do we secure the high resolving power, the ability to discriminate fine detail. The image there, at the center, goes to the brain over private lines.

This structure, giving sharp vision only in the fovea, may seem like a serious limitation. Actually it is not. Each eye is a ball, mounted in a cushioned orbit, and free to turn.

Its movement is controlled by six small muscles, and the control of these muscles is so perfect that we follow the objects of interest to us and are scarcely aware of the thousands of rapid eye movements which we make every waking hour. Watch the eyes of someone who is watching a tennis match if you want to see gymnastics quite the equal of anything which is happening on the court.

How much and how little light can we see? The page of a book in direct sunlight is ten thousand times as bright as the same page held one foot away from an ordinary candle, yet we can read by either light. Full moonlight is only one-fiftieth of a footcandle— that is, one-fiftieth of the illumination one foot from a candle. We can still see, but it is impossible to read fine print by moonlight; here we have passed the lower limit for keen vision.

Looking at a landscape in moonlight we still see a great deal, but fine details are lost and color is gone. Trees and grass do not look green but a sort of gray. A blue dress has become gray. With care we can drive a car under moonlight, but not with the vision we have in daytime. Pointing our eyes at something no longer sharpens the image. In fact, if we try to see an object over there in the shadows, we find it is actually clearer when we look a little above or below or to one side of it.

When the moon has set, these changes are much more pronounced. We can still see objects on the ground under the starlit sky if they are big enough and close enough, but our vision in the fovea, the central part of the retina, has gone. We are blind now in the very region where we had our keenest daylight vision. Why is this? Why is it that under the starlit sky with the illumination only one hundred millionth that of direct sunlight we can still see but in such a different way?

The key to this riddle lies in the rod and cone cells which I mentioned before. The rods cannot give us such sharp details of vision, but they are far more sensitive than the cone cells. When we step from a bright room out into the darkness at night, we find that we are quite blind temporarily. This is because the rods cannot act at once, they must have time to regain the sensitivity which they lost during exposure to the light. Usually they require twenty minutes or more to regain this to the fullest extent. It is these rods which give us our night vision, and it is because there are no rods in the fovea that the very central part of our visual field is blind at night.

Now look around the room in which you are sitting. All the details of the objects which you see are visible because they are brighter or darker than their background, or because they have a different color.

Color! What do we mean by color? You know that light consists of waves like radio waves but very much shorter, and color of light depends upon its wave length. The longest wave lengths we can see are red, the shortest violet, with the other colors lying in between. White light is a mixture of many wave lengths, and most of the colors of nature consist of several wave lengths in different proportions. Our eyes respond differently to these different wave lengths, and send different signals to the brain, and this results in the sensation of color.

Now, it was this sensation of color—you remember?—which grew dull as the light grew dim, became weak in moonlight, and was lost entirely under the moonless sky. Since only the rod cells are sufficiently sensitive to work in dim light it must follow that the rods are blind to color. And such, indeed, is true. To see color we must have enough light so that the cone cells can function. And somewhere in the structure and the mechanism of these cone cells lies the secret of color vision. In the fovea, where there are only cones, our color vision is excellent. So it is clear that only cones are necessary to provide our entire range of color sensations.

I wish that I might state why we see color, how the cones respond to different wave lengths and send their color signals to the brain. Unfortunately I do not know. It is one of the mysteries of vision. But while we do not know the mechanism of color vision, the main facts are clear. We know how much and what kind of color we can see. We can specify color by suitable numbers so that a colorist can duplicate it. And we can tell what the quality of a color photograph or color television must be in order to satisfy the eye. The requirements give us a new respect for these eyes of ours and set a high mark for the motion picture and television engineer to shoot at.

But it is never very satisfactory to set numbers and limits when the fundamental reasons are unknown. It is the scientists' job to learn the reasons. Someday, and I hope soon, we shall have a better understanding of these remaining mysteries about the wonderful mechanism by which we see.

The Science of Hearing

By Harvey Fletcher

Dr. Harvey Fletcher, who has long been concerned with the physics of speech, is the director of physical research of the Bell Telephone Laboratories.

The last time you listened to a concert over the radio, did you realize that mechanisms within your own head were playing all the melodies and harmonies over again before sending them to the brain?

The sound of the music is transmitted from the loud-speaker, through the air and into the ear. The sound waves, which of course are actual mechanical movements of the air particles, pass through the ear canal to the ear drum and cause it to vibrate. As the drum vibrates it passes the pulsations to three tiny levers attached to it. These levers amplify the sound waves about sixty-fold and pass them to the inner ear.

Up to this point the transmission and amplification of the sound waves are purely mechanical. But now, in this inner ear, the music of the concert encounters a complex mechanism which converts the mechanical movements into electrical nerve currents. It is here that the auditory nerve terminates in twenty thousand tiny nerve endings called hair cells. A tiny hair projects from each nerve ending into the fluid of the inner ear. Each of these hair cells performs a function similar to a telegraph key.

The tiny movements in the liquid of the inner ear produced by the sound cause this hair to move and thus send electrical pulses along the nerve fiber attached to it. These twenty thousand microscopic hair cells are attached to a membrane which is free to vibrate. The hair cells are arranged in five parallel rows of about four thousand each.

As the sounds of the concert reach this inner ear they are quickly sorted according to their pitch. The high pitch sounds are sent to the hair cells near the outermost end of the rows, and the low pitch sounds to the hair cells near the innermost end, while the tones of intermediate pitch are received by the hair cells in the middle part of the rows. There are several hair cells connected to each nerve fiber—perhaps as many as five—so that four thousand nerve fibers are attached to the twenty thousand hair cells. Each nerve fiber is enclosed in a sheath like an insulated conductor. The four thousand of them are enclosed in a single cable about the size of the lead in a pencil—and that cable we call the auditory nerve.

The transmission to the brain along each nerve fiber is more like the action of a telegraph than that of a telephone.

For a fiber does not transmit continuously varying signals, as does a telephone, but can only transmit pulses—that is to say, short isolated signals like the clicks of a telegraph. The number of pulses sent along each fiber depends on the degree of agitation of the hair cell to which it is attached—the greater the agitation, the greater the number of transmitted pulses.

As you listened to the concert, each of the twenty thousand inner ear hair cells was sending its impulses along its particular nerve fiber to the brain. During the loud passages, a majority of the hair cells were busy, but when the sounds were soft and low, comparatively few hair cells were sufficiently stimulated to be active.

At the other end of the auditory nerve, in the brain, the nerve endings are spread out over an area. This auditory area is, in effect, a musical map which is continually changing as the music proceeds. We recognize the pitch of the sound by the particular part of the auditory area that is stimulated. We recognize the loudness by the total number of impulses arriving at this area.

Thus there are two main parts to the apparatus with which we hear—first, the mechanical system formed by the drum, the three tiny levers in the middle ear, and related parts which transmit the sounds to the nerve endings: and second, the electrical system of the inner ear with twenty thousand hair cells and their electrical connections to the brain.

And as we have the two sets of mechanisms, so we have two kinds of deafness. If something happens to interfere with the drum, the bones of the middle ear or any of the vibrating mechanisms which transmit sound to the inner ear, then the defect is called obstructive deafness. If the trouble is with the hair cells or the nerve fibers, the defect is known as nerve deafness. These various mechanisms are so delicate that about ten persons in a hundred of the general population have some sort of hearing defect, and of the ten about four find hearing so difficult that a hearing aid becomes helpful.

The plight of a person with obstructive deafness is similar to one having normal hearing, but who is trying to listen to sounds in the next room, with doors and windows closed. Under such circumstances one can understand only with difficulty words spoken in the other room.

If the speaker raises his voice, or if a loudspeaker system amplifies the speech, then the sounds will penetrate the walls and reach the listener with sufficient loudness to be understood. If the amplifier magnifies the various parts of the speech unevenly, or if the walls transmit some sounds better than others, then the speech coming to the listener will appear strange and be difficult to understand. Such speech we call distorted.

Now a person afflicted with obstructive deafness experiences just this difficulty of hearing the sounds—that is to say, weakened and distorted. But fortunately, the human mechanism has wonderful powers of adaptation. Sounds which at first seem strange, become with repetition, more natural. Also, one ordinarily listens to speech under a variety of conditions and so can tolerate large distortions and still succeed in understanding.

Modern hearing aids are the result of scientific studies of speech and hearing, and must take into account the performance of our hearing mechanism. In general, the hearing aid should compensate for the distortion and partly compensate for the attentuation. In the case of obstructive deafness, the principal function of the hearing aid is for the latter purpose—that is, to amplify the sound so that it arrives at the inner ear with an intensity sufficient to excite the hair cells.

In the case of nerve deafness, the situation is very different. To illustrate, let us suppose that the nerve deafness is such that the person can barely hear but cannot understand ordinary conversation. In such a case the basilar membrane of the inner ear must be shaken about one thousand times the normal amplitude before any of the hair cells on it start to send pulses. Sometimes it happens that the hair cells designed by nature to receive certain ranges of pitch are completely broken down. This means that the analyzing mechanism is defective. And if the analyzing mechanism is badly damaged, no hearing aid yet devised will make it possible to get the proper sound pattern to the brain. Even when the hair cells are damaged to only a limited degree, the amplification necessary to get a normal speech pattern to the brain may be so great as to cause pain. Frequently the disease that injures the tiny hair cells of the inner ear also leaves the tissue very tender.

For the reasons just stated it is more difficult to design a hearing aid for the person afflicted with nerve deafness than it is for a person having obstructive deafness. For nerve deafness the hearing aid should be provided with a device to limit the amount of sound going into the ear. The maximum level of this sound should be just below the hurting point. It is important to recognize that both obstructive deafness and nerve deafness may occur in the same person.

Great progress has been made in improving the fidelity, portability, and convenience of hearing aids in the last two decades. One of the first sets to be built filled a large bookcase with apparatus and cost five thousand dollars. Today sets are available which weigh only a few ounces, perform better, and cost on the order of one hundred dollars. And still greater progress can be expected, for various wartime studies and recent electronic developments will undoubtedly result in sets still nearer the ideal.

The Muscle Machinery

By Wallace Osgood Fenn

Dr. Wallace Osgood Fenn is professor of physiology in the School of Medicine and Dentistry at the University of Rochester.

THE word *muscle* comes from the Latin "musculus" meaning *little mouse*. Possibly the sudden rounding up of the biceps muscle when the arm is flexed suggested to the ancients the appearance of a mouse in a sleeve.

Some muscles, like the biceps, can be brought into activity by our own volition. Others, like the heart, contract by themselves whether we wish it or not. We cannot command our hearts to stop beating any more than we can divert the stars in their courses. We cannot make the heart beat faster nor more strongly by an act of will power. Even our so-called voluntary muscles often contract without conscious effort on our part. A dancer whirls with graceful ease but gives no detailed thought to the proper sequence of contraction in the countless different muscles of the body. The supreme command is concerned only with the desire to dance, while the detailed pattern necessary to that activity originates well below the level of consciousness.

We have even less conscious concern with the mechanism of the contraction of the muscles. What marvellous power is responsible for the sudden sharp drawing in of the tissue, the abrupt shortening of the muscle fibers, the sudden beat of the heart? So familiar are these processes and so much are they a part of life itself that we seldom stop to consider seriously what the underlying mechanism really is. Wherein is the secret of this swift and silent transformation of the energy of our food into motion, and all without the aid of pistons, crankshafts or wheels?

A close-up view of a muscle under a microscope is at first exciting but in the end disappointing. There are many tiny elongated fibers and each fiber is crossed by alternating light and dark bands, some 10,000 of them to the inch, like the steps of a ladder which reaches from end to end of each fiber. All of this detailed structure is beautiful to look at but it serves no obvious purpose.

Some muscles contract even though they do not show these numerous cross striations; and for the real machinery of the contraction we must go beyond the range of the optical microscope into the world of the molecules themselves of which these fibers are composed.

A chemical analysis shows that 80 per cent of the muscle is nothing but water, but the remainder is composed of scores of different kinds of molecules. Some are small and roundish—for example, the molecules of potassium and sodium. Others, like sugar, are some five times larger, and these sugar molecules represent part of the store of fuel for the muscle machine. Still larger are the protein molecules, and here we come to the fine structure of the muscle itself. In particular, we find present a protein known as myosin, a substance which plays a fundamental role in the muscle machinery, and which accounts for nearly half of the dry weight of the muscle. A single molecule of myosin is so large that is will outweigh several thousand sugar molecules. Recently it has become evident that in this molecule of myosin we have, so to speak, combined all the necessary cylinders, pistons, crankshafts and valves which are required to make the muscle work. Even artificial strands of pure myosin in a test tube have been made to contract under suitable conditions.

The peculiar feature of the myosin molecule which fits it to play this unique role in animal life is its long and slender shape. Each molecule is a chainlike structure made up of many links. Because of these links the molecules can exist in many different patterns. They can be pulled out into a straight chain or they can fold up like an accordion. The links cannot be seen under the microscope but chemists have ways of measuring them indirectly and deducing the pattern of the molecule.

The visible pattern which we see under the microscope is due to endless bundles of these myosin fibers. When the muscle contracts, the length of the individual links becomes less, the zigzags come closer together, and the myosin molecules as a whole become shorter and wider. When this happens, the whole muscle must also become shorter and wider. The act of contraction thus requires only some chemical change in the myosin which pulls the links closer together.

Such is the essential nature of the working of the muscle machine, but it leaves much of the story untold. Two questions must certainly arise in your minds. First, how does the brain start the reaction which causes the chain molecules to shorten? Second, how does the energy of the food get transferred to the myosin chains so that they can shorten with enough force to pump the blood through the body's thousands of miles of arteries, veins, and capillaries?

To the first of these questions we have a fairly good answer which began with a famous experiment in Italy nearly 200 years ago. Perhaps you recall the episode from your history books—how Professor Galvani discovered quite by accident that a frog muscle contracted every time it was touched simultaneously by two different metals that were connected together. He had created in this way what we now call an electric battery or a galvanic cell; and the current which flowed stimulated the muscle. Ever since Galvani's famous discovery we have used the term "galvanized into action" to describe an energetic transformation of this sort. A muscle can be galvanized into action by an electric current. It is not quite correct to say that the brain stimulates a muscle by electric currents conducted to it through the nerve, but there is evidence that the activated nerve terminals cause tiny electric currents to flow through the adjacent muscle and thus bring the muscle into activity. Likewise the so-called nerve impulse which passes from the brain to the muscle progresses from point to point by a similar electrical process. Although this simple picture does not by any means exhaust our information concerning muscle excitation the existence of these electric currents is well established. They can be made audible in a loud speaker or can, like a television image, be projected on a screen and made visible.

As to the second question—how energy stored in the muscle in the form of sugar, fats, and other foodstuffs gets into the myosin machinery—we have some evidence on that, too.

The ultimate source of energy for muscle contraction must involve oxygen. To obtain this energy the muscle must burn its fuel; that is, it must oxidize its foodstuffs. And we find that this does indeed happen. With suitable apparatus it is easy to observe that immediately after a muscle contracts, clouds of oxygen molecules are pouring into the muscle, and at the same time clouds of carbon dioxide molecules are drifting out. This continues for ten minutes or more after the contraction, or until the muscle has fully recovered from the contraction. It is evident, however, that this oxygen is used after the contraction is over. In a similar way we know that it is possible for a man to swim a considerable distance under water without breathing, most of the oxygen ultimately needed for this process being taken in afterwards while the swimmer is recovering. At the moment of contraction, energy must be available from some other more immediate source. Indeed, with a suitable electrical thermometer it is possible to observe some of this energy in the form of heat. Just at the instant of contraction the muscle becomes a few thousandths of a degree warmer, and so suddenly that the process might almost be described as a miniature explosion. The source of this energy has been traced by chemists to certain phosphate compounds in the muscle, some of which compounds yield large amounts of energy when they break up. Professor Engelhardt of Russia recently discovered that one of these compounds releases its phosphate when, and only when, it is in contact with a molecule of myosin. In other words myosin acts as an enzyme or catalyst to facilitate the release of energy stored in this substance. The energy released is thus easily channeled into the myosin molecule, and temporarily the molecule is so changed chemically that it folds up and shortens. When the muscle relaxes the myosin reverts to its original pattern, the released phosphate is passed into other compounds, and eventually with the aid of energy liberated by oxygen in recovery it finds its way back to its original position and the muscle is ready for another contraction. The muscle therefore differs from a steam engine in that it burns fuel not to produce heat but to supply free energy for the resynthesis of decomposed phosphate compounds.

Such then is the basic operation of the muscle machinery whether it is used involuntarily for pumping blood or voluntarily for dancing the rhumba.

The Internal Environment

By James L. Gamble

Dr. James L. Gamble is professor of pediatrics at the Harvard Medical School. His research has been mainly in the field of the physiology and pathology of body fluids.

THIS tale of evolution takes us back to the very beginning of the experiment which we call life. The scene is an ancient sea which the geologists have named the Cambrian Ocean. There is an excellent reason why this experiment, which in its chemical terms is a rather delicate one, was first undertaken in the sea. The successful integration of chemical events within the cells of a living organism is dependent on a constancy of physical conditions in the fluid which surrounds the cells. For the earliest forms of life this fluid was sea water. In other words, the cells of these very simple organisms were directly exposed to their environment. This environment was remarkably suitable, for the physical properties of sea water are closely constant. To mention some of these properties; temperature is, of course, one of them. In the region of the equator there is almost no variation in the temperature of the sea. Then there is the property of a fluid which the physical chemist calls osmotic pressure. Osmotic pressure, which has a large biological importance, is determined simply by the sum of the concentrations of the various substances in solution in the fluid. The concentration of substances in sea water is stationary just because the ocean is so big. Therefore, its osmotic pressure is fixed. Another physical feature of a fluid we describe as acidity or alkalinity. Besides sodium chloride, which is common salt, sea water contains other inorganic salts, among them carbonates and phosphates, which provide the slight degree of alkalinity which is a fundamental biochemical requirement. The sea thus gave the cells of the early forms of life an ideally constant physical environment.

To continue our Just So story; before our extremely remote ancestors could come ashore to enjoy their Eocene Eden or their Paleozoic Palm Beach, it was necessary for them to establish, within themselves, an enclosed fluid environment which would take the place of sea water. The great French physiologist, Claude Bernard, who has been called the father of modern medicine, recognized the fluid in our bodies which lies outside the cells of the tissues of the body as our immediate environment. Bernard also taught us that, besides the obvious services of transporting nutrient and waste materials to and from the cells, this fluid provides the environmental constancy upon which the successful operation of vital processes within the cells depends. So we find that we live, as did our first forebears, in a fluid environment. This extracellular fluid circulates throughout the body by way of the blood vessels, and from the smallest vessels diffuses out into minute spaces in the tissues and directly bathes the tissue cells. The blood vessels contain about one quarter of this fluid. This portion, which we call blood, carries the red corpuscles which serve to transport oxygen and carbonic acid and which give the blood its romantic color. Our internal environment, composed of the blood and the three times larger quantity of fluid which lies between the blood vessels and the tissue cells, is quite sizeable; it amounts to about 20 per cent of body weight.

Although the animal organism has been an inveterate experimentalist along the path of evolution, it was completely conservative when it came to selection of an internal environment. It decided to carry on with the one in which its first steps were successful. We find that the chemical structure of extracellular fluid, as regards its inorganic components, is almost identical with that of sea water. The biological sanctity of this solution of several simple salts, which we call sea water, is very impressive. Apparently it not only permitted the inception of biochemical organization but remains its inviolable basis. So we can all be proud of our blood; the Cambrian Ocean was, without doubt, blue.

Now, the establishment of an enclosed fluid environment in which chemical pattern and physical properties are held closely stationary in the presence of a widely fluctuant demand for transport of many and various substances was a large undertaking and required the invention of quite a lot of apparatus. A pump was needed to sustain circulation of the extracellular fluid; and so the heart was developed. It was also necessary to arrange for the exchange of oxygen and carbonic acid with our external gaseous environment. This is accomplished with beautiful effectiveness by the lungs. Another remarkable organ of regulation, the kidney, had to be devised before the internal environment could be established. The kidney is mainly responsible for the preservation of a constant chemical pattern in extracellular fluid. One of its admirers has called the kidney the organ par excellence of evolution.

The hazards of living in a small fluid environment instead of the wide ocean are many and diverse. Indeed, much of modern medicine is devoted, directly or indirectly, to defense of the functional integrity of extracellular fluid against obstacles imposed by disease. Damage to the heart, lungs, kidney, or to other organ systems, may seriously disturb the internal environment. Various processes of disease may cause large and dangerously rapid losses. One of the simplest and also one of the most dramatically lifesaving of medical procedures is the infusion of a suitable replacement solution into a vein. For example, the mortality of the dreaded scourge of infants, cholera infantum, has been reduced from almost one hundred per cent to nearly zero since the development of fluid replacement therapy. When the loss of extracellular fluid occurs from its outermost compartment, the blood vessels, it must be replaced by blood or by blood plasma. War produces an enormous requirement for this direct support of the internal environment. Science, during the late war, made practicable for those of us at home the proud pleasure of meeting this requirement.

We will now return to the sea to consider the physiological plight of a thirsting castaway adrift on a life raft. Why should he not drink sea water which, as we have said, has the same chemical composition as extracellular fluid? The reason is a very simple one. Over the long span of time since the internal environment was established, the salinity of the sea has been gradually increased by salts carried into it by the rivers of the land. Chemical pattern has not been appreciably altered but we find that the concentrations of the individual salts in present day sea water are several times above the levels which were fixed for our internal environment by the Cambrian Sea some millions of years ago. Because of its greatly increased osmotic value, present day sea water is unsuitable for replacement of losses of extracellular fluid.

Let us now suppose that clouds gather over the sun-stricken sea, and rain falls. The castaway eagerly gathers rain water, using the equipment with which he has been supplied. By drinking this fresh water he can cover his daily expenditures of water and thus prevent further loss. But water alone will not replace the loss incurred while he was thirsting because it does not provide the salts which must be supplied along with water in order to rebuild extracellular fluid. By experiments with human subjects, who bravely volunteered to undergo periods of thirsting, it was found that by drinking a mixture of one part of sea water and two parts of fresh water, so as to provide the physiologically correct concentrations of the sea water salts, the loss of extracellular fluid caused by thirsting can be completely replaced. So, under these circumstances, the sea again sustains the experiment we call Life.

The Science of the Individual

By Earnest A. Hooton

Dr. Earnest A. Hooton is professor of anthropology at Harvard University, and a curator of the Peabody Museum.

THE maxim "Know thyself" has been repeated down through the ages from the ancient Greeks, but few of us gain that self-knowledge until we are too old to do anything with it. We learn to know ourselves only when we are no longer worth knowing. We need a science of the individual man that will teach us our physical and mental capacities and limitations early in life, so that we can profit from that knowledge. We ought to learn what we as individuals can do successfully, in order to avoid the failures and misery that result from attempting the impossible through sheer self-ignorance.

Education crams us with facts and theories and gives some of us acute indigestion rather than substantial nourishment. For education is not planned for each separate individual, but only for total groups of the young, supposedly able to thrive alike on the same mental and physical diets. Education is laid down like an artillery barrage, sometimes so faulty in its sighting that it slays its own advancing troops.

Every single person is born with an unique combination in details
of anatomical structure, peculiarities of physiological function, variations in mental capacity, and assorted temperamental traits. This
mass of inherited potentialities is then developed or stunted by all
of life's experiences from infancy to maturity—food, housing, paren-
tal care, family life, climate, human associates, formal education.
The individual is an organic unit, with each aspect of his total
personality all mixed up with every other and affected by its favorable development or its warping. None of the parts of man's organism, nor of its working, nor of his behavior in society can be
understood without a knowledge of the whole person and of his
background.

Science knows a great deal about human anatomy, physiology,
pathology, and psychology. Everyone is familiar with human behavior, of which, among others, the sociologist and the social anthropologists are expert students. Unfortunately, each specialist in
the various fields of the study of man and his behavior is likely
to make his observations and teach his students about some single
aspect of man torn out of its total organic context. So you learn
separately about human psychology, or physiology, or the structure
of the family, but nothing about your whole individual self. You
are Humpty Dumpty, all over the ground in pieces, and it is going
to take all the king's horses and all the king's men to put you
together.

A science of the total man would give each individual early in
life a complete inventory of his unique self so that he could correct,
as far as possible, his personal weaknesses, capitalize his strong
points, and seek a place in human activity that he is fitted to fill.
Such a science can be promised to you today, if you will only
demand it as your right, as the cornerstone of your education.
What is needed is a concerted attack upon the problem by the
several sciences involved, a period of investigation of the essential
relationships between different parts and functions of the whole
man, and the application of the knowledge thus gained in clinics
through which every young person may pass for study and
diagnosis.

In the individual, we are first concerned with anatomical structure or body build. This is the physical man whom we can see

and recognize. As a result of the brilliant work of William H. Sheldon, we now have a satisfactory scheme for classifying all varieties of the human physique. Apparently, variations of the form of the body give clear clues to the nature of the mind and of the total personality. Body structure does not determine mentality and disposition. But the human organism functions as a unit. Hence peculiarities of the body and its general form often reflect invisible traits that are far more important than skin, bone, muscle, cartilage, or other structural features. We are beginning to learn that the physiology of the individual also varies rather closely with his body type. Dr. George Draper, of the College of Physicians and Surgeons, Columbia University, has discovered in his medical clinic an intimate relationship between certain body builds and several constitutional or infectious diseases, such as gastric and duodenal ulcer, infantile paralysis, and the various types of arthritis or rheumatism. Students of the physiology of well persons have also demonstrated a close relationship between body build and the capacity for sustained physical exertion.

Individual psychology deals both with the measurement of correctness, speed, and originality in the performance of certain mental tasks—the so-called intelligence tests—and with the classification of traits of temperament and of the higher personality. In spite of adverse criticism, it is plain to impartial observers that some valid findings concerning the mental processes of the individual arise from intelligence tests. It is harder to invent a scientific method of determining such basic characteristics as are usually described by adjectives like "easy-going" "energetic," "sociable," "unfriendly," and so on through a long list of qualities. Psychologists differ in classification of these intangibles. However, most of these differences seem to involve definitions and choice of descriptive words rather than fundamental disagreements about the nature of the traits themselves. Nearly any straightforward scheme of classification of personality traits seems to give good results when applied by an astute and experienced psychologist.

In this field, again, William H. Sheldon has devised a scheme of temperamental rating that will serve for the present and has the unique advantage of having been related to varieties of body build. Thus such an extreme of physique as is presented by the tall, narrow, skinny person has an associated cluster of some twenty trait tendencies including "love of privacy," "emotional restraint," "hypersensitivity to pain," "need of solitude when troubled," et cetera. There is reason for believing that close enough relationships can be established between physique and personality traits so that eventually body build may be used as a short cut to personality analysis.

If you know the physical, mental, and temperamental characteristics of a person, it is possible to predict within certain limits his fitness for various tasks, his ability in performing under different conditions—in short, the quality of his behavior. The Grant Study of Harvard University, in a thorough investigation of some 268 so-called "normal" undergraduates, offered evidence of the intimate relationship of physique, physiology, mentality, and disposition both to achievement in the small academic world and to success or easy adaptation to life in the armed services (the lot of most of the men studied).

Students of the human constitution do not believe that all physical, mental and behavioral characteristics of the individual are fixed by heredity. Heredity does impose certain limitations upon change and improvement of personality. Human brass cannot be transformed into gold. Yet we are confident that most persons can be built up to a higher level of competence and self-sufficiency if they are studied individually and properly trained before they are warped and hardened by mistakes in education and bad environments. The interrelationships of personality can be studied best in the full-blown adult, but the mature human animal is rarely capable of much improvement. We have to catch our subjects young, if we hope to benefit them by personality diagnosis and corrective treatment.

Millions of young veterans have recently returned to civil life— many in doubt as to choice of career and nearly all ignorant of the full extent of their individual powers and limitations. We did not spare time, or money, or scientific effort in trying to find out the sort of military duty for which each of these young men was fitted. Is it not worth while to have science help them find themselves in a world at peace? If science can determine for a man the capacity in which he is most fit to die, it ought to be able to teach him also how best to live.

CHAPTER 12

SCIENCE AND HEALTH

HEALTH, LIKE money, seems most important to us when we don't have it. If we are sick, then medical science suddenly stops being an abstract thing, and becomes the most intimate and important kind of science we know. We want vigor and freedom from pain for ourselves, and we desire these things even more deeply for those who are near and dear to us. There is nothing vague or impersonal about the concept of health. It is vivid and clear to everyone who has had to miss going to work, to everyone who has heard a child cry in the night.

It is, therefore, natural and inevitable that every person have a direct and lively interest in medical science. But however familiar and widely approved the doctor's work is, we do not always accurately understand what makes the doctor possible. We often do not remember that his continued success in preventing and curing disease depends upon a vast and patient activity in basic medical research.

Too many people expect the doctor to have a pill for every pain. Too many assume that putting a man together is as easy as smashing an atom apart. A great many of us are willing to contribute money for research on a specific disease, but we have far too little interest in the sustained support of more fundamental long-range studies.

Yet it is to these basic long-range studies that we must look for progress on the really difficult problems of medical science. Such studies demand long-continued effort by men of the highest ability. It is not reasonable for us to expect these men to lead triple lives, spending one-third of their time teaching a new generation of doctors, one-third in earning a living by private practice, and the final, tired third in working as great creative scientists.

In other words, society must begin to support the medical sciences in a more intelligent fashion. We must provide, through federal aid if necessary, a satisfactory base of support for medical education, one which will not only provide the number and quality of doctors which our social conscience demands, but which will also adequately train the researchers we need. To this fundamental base we must add suitable recognition and support for the advanced medical researcher, not expecting him quickly to produce magical cures, but trusting him slowly and surely to drive back the frontiers of ignorance concerning the human body.

The researchers now attacking those frontiers are not only doctors of medicine but also scientists whose principal training has been in biology, chemistry, physics, or even mathematics. Often most valuable of all are the hardy souls who have trained themselves jointly in medicine and in some branch of the physical or biological sciences. Much work which forms an integral part of medical research, moreover, will always be located outside the formal program of medical schools—in departments of biology, chemistry, or physics, and in the more specialized departments of genetics, bacteriology, biochemistry, et cetera. Some of these men will be found in medical research institutes and others in the commercial laboratories such as those of the pharmaceutical industry.

It is hoped that the reader will discover a close relation between the above remarks and the essays of the present chapter. The one paper which specifically relates to a disease—the discussion of anemia—is itself a beautiful example of the power of the sustained fundamental approach. Three of the essays relate to broad aspects of health, and again illustrate that medical problems must be attacked from underneath, so to speak, and with the full armament of all the sciences. The last two essays, which relate to possible medical benefits from atomic research, are clear evidence of the way in which modern medicine has broken through old traditional boundaries.

Health is, in the language of the introductory chapter, a problem of organized complexity. To understand, and to deal with, the human body in disorder the medical scientist must patiently analyze a tangle of baffling problems. Great progress has already been made in preventing and in curing disease. If society is sensible enough to support its efforts, medical science is now in a position to develop an attack which is sufficiently broad and basic to promise a vigorous and healthy future for man.

W. W.

Agents of Infectious Disease

BY ERNEST WILLIAM GOODPASTURE

Dr. Ernest William Goodpasture is professor of pathology and dean
of the School of Medicine at Vanderbilt University.

INFECTIOUS diseases are those like diphtheria, typhoid fever, tuberculosis, and other disorders which are caused by tiny living organisms called microbes. It is only within relatively recent times that medical science has recognized these microscopically small agents as sources of disease; and the physical suffering they have brought has scarcely exceeded the mental anguish originally caused by their appalling mystery. Three centuries ago one would hardly have imagined that a reasonable solution of the mystery of infectious diseases would eventually result from the then widely debated question of spontaneous generation.

This question may be expressed quite simply as follows: Are small living creatures constantly and spontaneously arising from lifeless matter; or are these living creatures always the offspring of previous living creatures?

From time immemorial there had been much speculation concerning this question, but it was the middle of the seventeenth century before a scientific test was made. The investigator was Francesco Redi, an Italian naturalist. By carefully controlled experiments Redi showed that the grubs which developed in a piece of decaying meat were not generated spontaneously, as was commonly believed, but had hatched out of eggs deposited on the decaying meat by flies.

Redi's experiments could deal only with visible creatures, such as worms, maggots, and other larvae. For the still smaller forms of life, such as could be seen only through the microscope, the origins remained a mystery until about eighty years ago when Louis Pasteur, a French chemist, demonstrated conclusively that microbes always have ancestors, just as grubs do, and thus always descend from other microbes, each after his own kind.

Without this proof of the continuity of life in series, and the constancy of living forms, what assurance would a scientist have that microbes, already being found in association with infectious diseases, had not originated spontaneously either in his patient or in his flasks of broth? How could he keep track of them, to study their individual characteristics, if new ones were to spring into being to confuse him every time he turned his back?

Pasteur changed all this. For, in order to prove his point, Pasteur had to develop techniques by means of which pure strains of individual microbes could be cultivated and observed under controlled conditions. Robert Koch in Germany soon developed better methods; and specific microbes, as causes of particular infectious diseases, were identified.

Throughout the world, laboratories began to stir with ardent activity. Discoveries followed in rapid succession. Anthrax, it was announced, is caused by a spore-producing ribbon; child-bed fever, by microbes which look like necklaces of tiny beads; diphtheria, typhoid fever, tuberculosis, each by a characteristic microbe which appears as a colorless rod; cholera, dysentery, pneumonia—the medical journals could not publish them fast enough.

This rich fruition of the slow discovery of basic principles was of immediate benefit. It permitted man to liberate himself from hitherto unknown parasites. It also enlarged man's understanding of his relationship to the world about him, because it afforded a rational interpretation of these diseases and provided an intelligible concept to replace a sinister mysticism.

These discoveries brought man nearer to a realization of his co-partnership with life about him. He could see that while he himself subsists upon the bodies of animals and plants, many microscopic animals and plants subsist in turn at the expense of his human body. He thus learned to rationalize infectious diseases as natural rather than supernatural phenomena. He saw that what was disease in his own body could be the natural consequences of the reproductive cycle of other animals and plants.

According to the new concept thus established, infectious diseases constitute a distinct class. They are caused by living microbes whose existence is maintained by successive passage from one diseased individual to another. The disease-inducing microbes gain access to the tissues of an animal or plant and multiply in them. This is the condition of infection. In order to continue their cycle of reproduction they must get out of, as well as into, their host. The infected animal or plant is called a host because, just like a social host who invites you to dinner, it furnishes subsistence to the microbe.

This new understanding of infectious disease was indeed an advance, but scientific knowledge is only relative and partial. In the midst of their exuberant successes, the early bacteriologists were frequently stumped. For there were failures as well as frequent successes, and questions arose more rapidly than answers were found. For example: smallpox, influenza, measles, mumps, yellow fever, and infantile paralysis passed from person to person. Clearly these diseases were contagious, and yet science was unable to demonstrate the presence of any microbes. After many failures, reluctantly it had to be admitted that the methods of bacteriology were reaching their limits.

Then a discovery was made that had the significance of an enlightening principle. A Russian botanist, named Ivanovski, squeezed the juice from tobacco plants affected by a contagious spotting called mosaic disease. He forced the juice through filters of such fine porosity that no known microbe could get through. Ivanovski was not able to obtain any growth of living beings from the filtered liquid, but he found this: When he touched a healthy tobacco plant with the smallest droplet of the liquid, invariably the tobacco plant developed the mosaic disease. Something in the liquid carried the infection, but what was it? Beijerinck from Holland thought it must be an infectious "living fluid."

Soon came other developments. A German commission reported that a clear fluid, prepared from tissues of cattle with foot-and-mouth disease and filtered to free it from cultivable microbes, caused foot-and-mouth disease when inoculated into cattle. Dogs with rabies likewise carried an invisible agent that proved to be filterable; and two Italian investigators maintained that the agent of rabies was so small and of such a curious nature that it entered the filaments of nerve cells to multiply and spread throughout the nervous system. No known microbe acted like that.

Similar filterable agents, causing innumerable diseases in plants, animals, and man were soon discovered. They would not grow outside the living cells of their hosts. Nor could they be seen through the microscope. What was the secret?

If the methods of bacteriology had failed, perhaps those of chemistry and physics might succeed; and now a chemist, Dr. W. M. Stanley of the Rockefeller Institute at Princeton, took up the problem. Dr. Stanley squeezed the juice from the spotted tobacco leaves, and filtered it just as Ivanovski had done. Then, to separate out whatever might be in solution, Stanley subjected the filtered juice to the tremendous spinning force of an ultracentrifuge. He measured the size of its disease-inducing units. He examined the X-ray diffraction pattern of these units, and their ultraviolet absorption spectrum. He crystallized them from their solutions and found them still unchanged. Then he defined these infinitesimal units, not in terms of the familiar concept of biological cells, but in the measured terms of chemical molecules.

These invisible filterable agents of infantile paralysis, yellow fever, influenza, cattle plague, dog distemper, fowl pox, and a whole catalog of similar diseases are called viruses. They infect their hosts and pass from one host to the next by the same mechanisms employed by living microbes. Can they be said to live, or are they inanimate products of the bodies they injure? Can a sharp line be drawn between the living and the nonliving? The atomic physicists tell us matter and energy are one. Are we faced again with the old question of spontaneous generation, this time concerning molecular creatures of the living matter of cells instead of microbes from lifeless matter? Can a host create its own parasites?

These are only a few of the problems for scientists of the future. As basic problems are solved and new principles become established, new periods of enlightenment will surely follow to continue the liberation of man from his diseases and from the bonds of his colossal ignorance.

Epidemics

BY STANHOPE BAYNE-JONES

Dr. Stanhope Bayne-Jones is president of the Joint Administrative
Board of the New York Hospital—Cornell Medical Center. During
the recent war, he was a brigadier general in the Medical Corps.

EPIDEMICS are sometimes described as explosive. Like the detonation of a bomb, one of these mass infections may start suddenly without warning, spread widely through a community, and injure and kill many people in a short time.

It is well known that epidemics have changed the world's history. Disregarding, as they do, the boundaries of states and the spheres of political influence, epidemics are one of the oldest forms of internationalism. Through this internationalism of disease, all the people of the world are bound together in the common interest of safeguarding their health.

An element of mystery has always been associated with the rise and fall of epidemics. In Biblical times these rapidly spreading diseases were regarded as the divine visitations of punishment upon men for their sins—and perhaps that view is still held in some places. If there is any element of punishment in this mystery, it is a punishment coming as a natural consequence of ignorance, perpetuation of poverty, and suppression of peoples. Although the invisible microbes and viruses of mass infection were not discovered until the eighteenth and nineteenth centuries, ancient observers noticed that disease was often spread by contacts with sick persons or sick animals. More than 2300 years ago the Greek physician Hippocrates recognized that epidemics had natural causes, and to this liberalizing idea of ancient Greece the modern science of epidemiology can trace its origin.

The conditions of an epidemic are many. Sometimes numerous contacts between infected persons and well persons will occur without causing the disease to spread. Other times such contacts may increase the number of diseased by only a few cases. On still other occasions the spread of infection may be rapid and violent, with thousands or millions of cases. Why such differences occur is even now difficult to explain. At least three factors are involved: the seed, the sower, and the soil.

The seed of an epidemic is the germ which is specific to the disease and which has power to infect, invade, and maintain itself in the human body. The sower is the means by which the germ is transferred from an infected human body to a well body. The soil is the human population in the aggregate, but more specifically is identified as the susceptible tissues of the susceptible individual.

As each of these factors varies from time to time in quantity and in quality, the possible combinations are complex. Nevertheless, medical science knows a great deal about them in every infectious disease, from yellow fever to malaria, from poliomyelitis to pneumonia, from typhoid to typhus, from meningitis to influenza. There is also to be mentioned a general over-all remaining mystery —the seasonal rise and fall of certain diseases. The yearly rise and fall is explainable in part by weather and its effects on human association and the prevalence of certain insects. But it is not yet clear why different parts of the year seem to encourage a disease and other parts have the opposite effect. Then there is the long-term cycle of epidemic prevalence, ranging from five to twenty-five years. These long-term cycles may reflect social conditions, upgrowth of a susceptible population, or changes in the virulence of microbes.

Preventive medicine is a broad field, with areas of specialization and many achievements. With respect to epidemics it has two principal aims: first, to prevent them, if possible; and second, to stop them short if they start. When science really prevents an outbreak of disease, it is difficult to prove the fact. In this case, the evidence of success is that nothing happens—and such results are not spectacular. But the fact that disaster does not occur is one of the main criteria of peace and security.

The United States enjoys freedom from certain epidemics which in former times repeatedly ravaged the country. It is now taken as a matter of course that we do not have epidemics of cholera, plague, typhus, and yellow fever in the United States, and a large outbreak of typhoid fever is exceptional. On the other hand, epidemics of poliomyelitis, meningitis, influenza, and scarlet fever still occur, although new knowledge is showing how some of these can be prevented or stopped.

Our new knowledge concerns the three factors which I mentioned: the soil in which the epidemic seeks to take root, the seed of the disease, and the sower.

The soil, by which is meant the population of a nation, city, or other community, is made unsuitable for the growth of epidemics by increasing the number of its immune persons. It is common knowledge that smallpox can be prevented by vaccination. Typhoid fever, which was so devastating among United States troops in the Spanish-American War, was a relatively infinitesimal cause of illness among our troops in World War II—thanks to the effectiveness of vaccination. Immunization against tetanus was a main factor in preventing lockjaw in wounded American soldiers. During the recent war, there were no deaths in the American Army caused by epidemic typhus fever. The fact that there were no deaths from this disease among soldiers seems to be a result of vaccination against typhus which, although it does not always prevent contraction of typhus, makes the case a mild one with little risk of death.

At present, the public is intensely interested in vaccination against influenza, following the demonstration of its successful use by the Army in 1945. The vaccine was developed by the Commission on Influenza of the Army Epidemiological Board, an agency of the Preventive Medicine Service of the Surgeon General's Office. The vaccine consists of influenza virus of the Types A and B treated with formaldehyde. It was tested on volunteers in 1942 and 1943, and these trials indicated its value as a preventive. The vaccine appears to have been equally effective during the recent widespread epidemic of influenza. Its use marks a promising advance, and civilian health should benefit from his military development in preventive medicine.

In general it has been easier to immunize the soil of epidemics than it has been to destroy or alter the bacteria, viruses, and other invisible or microspic organisms which are the seeds of epidemics. The main advance here has been by chemical means. During the war it was shown that the administration of certain drugs, such as sulfadiazine, eliminated the bacteria of meningitis from the throats of carriers, and by means of sulfadiazine, outbreaks of meningitis were prevented or stopped. In some instances, sulfadiazine stopped scarlet fever and other streptococcal infections. Much work is being done to purify the air by treating it with chemicals or radiations which destroy microbes. Results have been obtained experimentally with ultra-violet light and vapors of aerosols or of such substances as the glycols. The problem for the future is how to use these new weapons in practice.

The third factor that we have to deal with in preventing epidemics is the sower of the seeds of disease—and the sower may be man, animal, or insect. Obviously the human sowers can be dealt with only by methods not harmful to human life—by such means as segregation, quarantine, immunization, or disinfestation. Disease spreaders among the lower animals may be inactivated by the same means, and sometimes by slaughter of infected individual animals and herds. The greatest triumphs in the fight against the sowers of epidemics have been gained by extermination of the insects which transmit such diseases as yellow fever, malaria, and typhus. Wide publicity has already been given the victories over typhus and malaria by the use during the war of new insecticides, notably the compound known as DDT. So much is now known about typhus that a typhus epidemic need never again occur anywhere if people will use the means which now exist to prevent it.

There have been no insurmountable barriers between the spirits and minds of the investigators who worked out the scientific principles of preventive medicine and those of the other research workers who developed the methods and materials for the prevention and control of epidemics. The application of these means on a world-wide scale, joining in a common effort for the public health of the world, can drastically reduce epidemics and may even prevent them entirely. With international co-operation, such an outcome may be brought to pass in the not-too-distant future.

Resistance to Infectious Disease

By Michael Heidelberger

Dr. Michael Heidelberger is a professor of biochemistry in the College of Physicians and Surgeons of Columbia University, and is also chemist to the Presbyterian Hospital.

You and I are alive today because each one of us has, within himself, the means for fighting infectious disease. Present in our surroundings, all too often, are the microscopic agents which make us ill. When the particles of a virus like influenza, or the germs of a bacterial disease, say scarlet fever, get past the natural barriers of the skin or mucous membrane, internal defense processes are speeded up. A race is then on between the invading disease particles which may multiply in the body, and these protective mechanisms which hamper and destroy the invading particles or germs. I propose to tell you something of these protective forces, what they are, how they may be stimulated, ways in which they can be measured with accuracy, and how they may be mobilized for the prevention of epidemics and for the maintenance of our public health.

Let us try to visualize what may happen when bacterial or viral agents of disease begin to multiply within our bodies. Circulating in our blood along with its characteristic red cells, and in our tissue fluids, are the active white cells which the scientist calls phagocytes. It is the function of these white cells to surround or engulf foreign particles—to pick them up and either destroy them through the active ferments contained in the white cells, or to carry off the captured particles to the liver or some other organ of the body for destruction.

Often, however, the chemical substances of which disease germs are made seem distasteful and repellent to the protective white cells of the blood and other body fluids. Or else the invading particles are encased in slimy envelopes, or they are surrounded by filaments which whip back and forth and prevent the white cells from coming close enough. Thus armored, the disease germs

271

serenely go about their business of multiplication, and as a result we get sick and call the doctor.

But at this point another important one of our natural defenses against disease comes into play to help our friend, the physician. The blood and body fluids not only contain circulating red cells and the scavenger white cells we have described, but also hold in solution a number of very complex materials. The most important of these dissolved substances are proteins, so called because they are fundamental components of living matter. One complex group of these proteins is called globulins. These globulins are very important to our story, for some of them exert a crucial influence in terminating infection.

The protein substances in our blood called globulins are important because certain of them have a way of being changed either in their shape or in the arrangement of their many parts when they are built up in the presence of materials foreign to the body —such invading enemies as virus particles, bacteria, and other disease germs.

The changes in the globulins are so slight that up to now the most delicate tests devised by chemists and physicists have failed to distinguish between the normal and the changed substances. But, though imperceptible to such tests, these changes are of such character that when the altered globulins again come into contact with the disease particles which stimulated their production, actual combination occurs. Normal globulins circulating in the blood stream just flow past the germs, but the modified globulins attach themselves directly to the germs—stick to them in actual chemical union. Because of this inherent tendency to combine with and neutralize foreign substances, these altered globulins are called "antibodies." The disease germs are called "antigens" because they stimulate the formation of these "antibodies."

The critical importance of antibodies is not so much their actual destruction of the invading disease particles. By attaching themselves to the invaders they endow these foreign particles with a more favorable exterior. Then, when the next white cell comes up, intent on carrying off the offender, it finds, not a repellent envelope or protective waving filaments, but instead it finds patches of globulin belonging to its own species, so to speak, and carrying

its own "home smell." Thus encouraged, the white cell attacks
the disease particle, engulfs it, and, if this happens over and over
again and often enough, the disease ends with dramatic sudden-
ness.

Some antibodies collaborate not with white cells, but with other
substances dissolved in the blood, to break up and destroy disease
germs. These other "helper" substances cannot act without antibodies. One of the helper substances is known as "complement,"
and it supplies important extra assistance in our immunity and
resistance to many diseases.

To summarize, the sequence of events is this: An invading substance called an antigen—it may be a germ or a virus—enters the
body. Its presence stimulates the introduction into the blood stream
of substances called antibodies, which are modified globulins. When
present in adequate amounts, these antibodies combine with and
destroy the disease-causing particles, if not directly, in collaboration with white cells or various helper substances.

Because antibodies are so decisively important, let us try to
understand something of their nature and how to produce them
and have them ready when needed. It has long been known that
antibodies and globulins exist together in the blood serum, the
clear fluid which is left when blood is allowed to clot. But there
was no way of telling how large a part of the globulin was actually
modified so as to form antibody; because antibodies could be
measured only by comparison with the curative or combining
effect of some other serum chosen as a standard. Such methods
were purely relative, and were inexact, at that.

What was needed was a rigorous, exact method, giving the answer not in pounds but in units of antibody weight a million times
smaller. No science can become exact without such methods of
quantitative analysis, and they are just as essential for the control
of foods, drugs, and all industrial processes.

The needed analytical methods were worked out by my associates and myself. With these methods it became possible for the
first time to measure antibodies with great accuracy in minute units
of weight, and so to provide rigid controls over their purification
and study. In the end, pure antibodies were separated from blood
serum, and were found actually to be typical serum globulins.

Having this measuring technique, we were now ready to go ahead with practical applications.

It is obvious that if you can stimulate your antibody defenses so as to keep you well, you will be much better off than if the defenses come into play only after disease is established. Even though we have sulfa drugs and penicillin, it is still preferable to prevent disease than to have to cure it. All of my readers, I hope, have been vaccinated against smallpox; and your children, I am sure, have received injections to protect them against diphtheria. These two highly successful and still too often neglected means of stimulating protective antibodies against a particular disease bring me to a final and recent example of vaccination against infection. This new instance of vaccination was made possible by the information given by the quantitative analytical methods which I have just mentioned.

Years ago, Dr. Oswald T. Avery and I showed that the slimy materials which envelop the pneumonia germ and which stand off the white cells of the blood, are composed of carbohydrates—complex chemical substances made up of sugars and somewhat like the familiar starch and mucilage. When these purified sugars of the pneumonia germ are injected in very small amounts into a human being—500,000 people may be vaccinated with a single ounce—the sugars cause the human system to form antibodies against the pneumonia germ. Until the new quantitative methods of analyzing antibodies were developed, there was no way even to guess whether the antibodies produced by vaccination with the sugars were sufficient to protect against pneumonia. During the war these methods were further perfected and tested, until it really seemed probable that this system of vaccination might be used to stop an epidemic of pneumonia. Through the cooperation of bacteriologists, immunologists, and chemists, such a test was made in the winter of 1944-45. Nine thousand men at the Sioux Falls, South Dakota, Army Air Force Training Camp, were each vaccinated with four different sugars of the pneumococcal germs; and after the next two weeks *no cases* of pneumonia due to these four kinds of germs developed among these vaccinated men. Among those who were not vaccinated, there were 23 cases—a really significant difference. However, in terms of the rate of infection that had prevailed up to that time, far more than 23 cases were expected. So this result showed that the protection enjoyed by the vaccinated 9,000 men had actually reduced the rate of spread among their unvaccinated comrades.

We now have, therefore, another important disease, pneumococcal pneumonia, for which a simple and effective vaccination procedure has been found.

I have tried in this short space to explain something of how the body defends itself against infectious disease and some of the ways in which science has contributed to the knowledge of these means of protection, their measurement, and their reinforcement. I have done this because the application of the scientist's contributions to health and security depends upon general understanding and full use of these measures through physicians.

Anemia

By George Richards Minot

Dr. George Richards Minot is professor of medicine at Harvard University, director of the Thorndike Memorial Laboratory, and visiting physician, Boston City Hospital. He is a Nobel Laureate in medicine for research in anemia.

Anemia is a relatively common disorder of the blood. Although the pale individual is usually anemic, pallor is not synonymous with anemia. For a person with a normal supply of good red blood may be pale simply because of circumstances which prevent the blood from coming near the surface of his body. But a person with anemia either has an actual undersupply of red blood cells, or these cells do not contain as much as they should of the red coloring matter called hemoglobin.

The patient with anemia does not exhibit outstanding symptoms until the hemoglobin is reduced by nearly one-half. Even when the red cells and hemoglobin are reduced to about one-quarter of their normal volume, patients may have little discomfort while at complete rest.

When an advanced condition exists, however, there are many

symptoms that occur with anemias of different types. These symptoms are fundamentally due to the fact that an insufficient amount of hemoglobin is present in the blood to carry the proper supply of oxygen to the tissues. Headache, faintness, palpitation, irritability, abnormal fatigue and muscular weakness and increased sensitivity to cold are common indications of this effect of anemia. Other symptoms are sometimes present, and in more advanced stages of anemia still further and more serious symptoms appear. However, modern medicine has discovered that proper doses of iron, in certain cases, or liver preparations, to patients in need of this material, often result in the dramatic transformation of a definitely sick person into a well one.

One of the numerous ways in which anemia may be produced is by loss of blood. Normally the human body is continuously producing new blood and destroying old. When a proper state of balance between these two functions does not exist, the blood ceases to contain its normal supply of red cells and of hemoglobin, and then anemia results.

One of the more common types, namely, iron deficiency anemia, is often caused by a recurrent abnormal loss of blood. The condition of iron deficiency anemia is more common in women, due to a number of causes. In the first place, women require, at least until about the age of fifty, approximately four times as much iron as the average man. The period of rapid growth and adolescence of girls makes special demands on their supply of blood. Motherhood also carries with it some risk of iron deficiency anemia; for the development of a supply of blood for the unborn child creates a real and substantial loss for the mother. Furthermore, the baby born of an anemic mother is itself liable to develop anemia within a year after birth. The answer to this situation lies in full doses of iron administered to the expectant mother, a cure which has been found to alleviate her condition and prevent the recurrence of anemia in the future infant as well. A more frequent use of iron for expectant mothers today would considerably lower the present rate of those cases of anemia which are associated with childbirth.

A well-balanced, natural diet provides a normal amount of iron, but when an iron deficit exists, it has been found that full doses of iron taken by mouth, either as pills or fluid, will correct the condition rapidly, and will return the victim of iron deficiency anemia to a full state of health.

Pernicious anemia, another of the major varieties of anemia, was first described by Thomas Addison of Guy's Hospital, London, in 1849. It has since been found to be due to a deficiency in the body of certain material which should normally be derived from food; and it manifests itself as an anemia associated with disturbances of the digestive system, and frequently of the nervous system as well. Pernicious anemia is somewhat more likely to develop in middle-aged patients with blue eyes and prematurely grey hair. In this variety of anemia the red blood cells are not pale, and average abnormally large, in contrast to iron deficiency anemia where the cells are pale and average abnormally small.

Recurrent burning and soreness of the tongue is apt to occur early in pernicious anemia, and gradually the tongue becomes smooth and shiny. Symptoms related to the nervous system sometimes develop early but usually develop later if the disease is not arrested. There may occur symmetrical numbness and tingling of the hands and feet. Eventually all degrees of limp and jerky paralyses, especially of the legs, occur and sometimes the patient cannot even walk. If untreated, the disease will progress by relapses and remissions for about four years with ultimately fatal results. But comparable to the case of iron deficiency anemia, there has been discovered a way to permanently alleviate this previously terrible disease.

Treatment for this variety of anemia requires, in fact, the application through life of adequate amounts of an appropriate preparation of liver or liver extract. Under this treatment the digestive symptoms vanish and no progress or development of the lesions of the nervous system occurs. Originally the patient was required to eat large amounts of animal liver daily. Today the effective countermeasure for pernicious anemia is supplied in an extract which may be swallowed daily in doses of several tablespoonfuls or, much better, injected into the muscles in very small quantities every one to four weeks. It is necessary, however, for this treatment to continue for life. Normally the stomach secretes a substance which is essential for the production of material, from particular sorts of

food, that eventually becomes liver extract. In pernicious anemia
this substance is virtually lacking both before and after treatment.
Thus, the patient with this disease, even though he eats the right
foods, may be said to be starving in the land of plenty. He is never
able to manufacture his own liver extract and, therefore, he must
continue to get it through his physician.

The regular treatment with liver promptly alleviates the condition of the pale, frequently grapefruit-colored, individual whose
red cells are often found to be reduced by two-thirds. Within days,
the sick individual has a return of color to his cheeks, and he develops a ravenous appetite. Young red cells are poured into the
circulation from the bone marrow where they are made. The red
cells increase about two and one-half million per cubic millimeter in
about four weeks, and the last million required cells are made more
slowly. The patient's tongue becomes normal again and the nervous symptoms of pernicious anemia are arrested.

Omission of treatment sooner or later causes the patient to feel
sick again and the neural symptoms to progress quite unneces-
sarily. The properly treated patient, however, will lose all symptoms except those caused by some nervous system changes. Thus,
contrary to its name, this disease is not to be looked upon as a
pernicious one.

You may well ask how long we have known of the use of iron
and of liver for the treatment of anemia. Iron has been used for
this purpose since an English physician, Sydenham, introduced it
about 1670 because from ancient days it had been considered a
source of strength. This was some years before iron was demonstrated in the blood. In France, Pierre Blaud in 1831 indicated
the importance of large doses of iron for the treatment of chlorosis,
a form of what today is called iron deficiency anemia. About 1890
various scientific results led to the use of only small doses of iron
with little effect on the anemia. Recently the value of large doses
of iron has been emphasized anew, indeed thirty times the amount
advised by some experts in 1900.

Liver treatment is entirely modern. The similarity of certain
symptoms and signs of pernicious anemia to those of known dietary
deficiency disease led to wondering whether pernicious might be
of this nature. Something seemed to be needed to make the primi-

tive red cells, that crowd the bone marrow, grow to normal cells and make blood. Liver had been found to promote the growth of animals and thus perhaps the growth of red cells. It was effective in certain diseases that resembled somewhat pernicious anemia. Whipple had demonstrated that liver could regenerate blood in dogs. This was proved, later on, not to be due to the factor effective in pernicious anemia, therefore liver extract should not be given indiscriminately. In 1926 a report was made of the striking effect of feeding liver to forty-five patients with pernicious anemia. Effective extracts were soon made.

The individual with a normally good digestion and a proper diet need not ordinarily fear the presence of iron deficiency or pernicious anemia as long as any blood loss is stopped and any factors which inhibit nutrition are removed. But for those of us not so fortunate, modern medicine has provided effective cures in the form of iron and liver which have brought the formerly serious effects of these anemias I have discussed, to a virtual standstill.

Medical Benefits from Atomic Energy

By James Franck

Dr. James Franck, previously director of the physical laboratory at Göttingen, left Germany in 1934, and is a professor at the University of Chicago. He was granted the Nobel Prize in physics in 1925.

Since the announcement of the first atomic bomb, a great deal has been said about the destructive power of the new explosive. But there is also a constructive aspect of the Atomic Age. Two questions present themselves. First, will our new-found ability to tap the energy within the atom promote progress in biochemistry and medicine? Second, can important beneficial results be expected in the near future? My answer to both questions is "Yes." We may look for rapid and important benefits, provided we keep scientific progress from being stifled by considerations of military security. Let me state why I take this optimistic view.

The structure of the atom is explained in several papers in this volume, notably in Chapter 6. Every atom contains a small but massive atomic kernel, the nucleus, which itself is made of heavy particles closely bound together. Revolving about this nucleus are a number of lightweight particles known as electrons. Each of these two parts of the atom may be altered. First, the arrangement of the surrounding electrons may be changed; chemical reactions belong in this class of process. Second, the particles within the nucleus may be rearranged; such rearrangements are called nuclear changes. Whenever a change occurs, energy is either absorbed or released.

If the change is such that it makes the system more stable, energy is released—just as energy is released when a stone in an unstable position on a mountainside rolls to a more stable position farther down the slope.

Chemical reactions, as already stated, involve only rearrangements of the loosely bound electrons in the outer part of the atom. Up to the advent of controlled nuclear fission, such changes have been the most important everyday source of energy. Some chemical reactions, such as the burning of coal, furnish great quantities of energy for industry. But the large amount of energy thus produced is due to the fact that countless billions of atoms react within a short time. The energy contributed by a single atom in a chemical reaction is very tiny in amount.

Nuclear changes are different. Here it is not the loosely bound electrons which are shifting their positions, but the building stones of the nucleus. These are held together by tremendous forces and, consequently, even when they rearrange only slightly, the amount of energy released may be enormous. Perhaps the most familiar example of a nuclear change is that involved in radioactivity, such as occurs when an atom of radium shoots out an alpha particle. The energy released by a single atom undergoing a radioactive change is about one million times as great as the energy released by a single atom undergoing chemical change.

Still more powerful is the nuclear change known as fission, the process utilized in the atomic bomb. Here the nucleus is profoundly altered. It splits into fragments in such a way that the energy released is a hundred times as great as the energy released by a radioactive change. Thus, radioactivity produces a million times as much energy as does chemical reaction, and fission produces a hundred million times as much per atom.

Part of the energy released by fission is in the form of powerful radiations. Moreover, the fragments of the split nucleus are not quite stable. They are therefore radioactive, and emit additional penetrating rays. These rays are dangerous. A man exposed even for a few seconds to those produced by a single unshielded nuclear power unit would surely die. That is why such a unit must be surrounded by walls several yards thick.

The destructive power of the radiations is easy to understand. When these radiations are absorbed by matter, their energy is taken up by the loosely bound electrons responsible for the structure of chemical compounds. Thus, the radiation from a single disintegrating nucleus is sufficient to change the structure of hundreds of thousands of molecules. This process plays havoc with the delicately balanced chemistry of living tissues.

The radiations produced by fission, though dangerous, may nevertheless prove to be the most important gift of the new scientific development. A knife can be used not only to kill but to cure. The radiations from radium and X rays are also dangerous, but the miraculous results achieved by using them against cancer are well known. Atomic power plants provide the means of magnifying and possibly of multiplying many times such applications in the treatment of disease.

Another by-product of an atomic power plant is an immensely increased supply of radioactive isotopes. Professor Urey explained the nature of isotopes in his essay in Chapter 6. As you know, they are atoms of the same chemical element which differ in atomic weight. Some isotopes are radioactive. That is, their nuclei are unstable, and may at any moment release radioactive energy. It is possible to produce a radioactive isotope of almost every chemical element. Carbon, iodine, phosphorus, and other elements which are natural constituents of our bodies may thus be rendered temporarily radioactive. And while they are radioactive, they may be used in the treatment of disease.

The thyroid gland, for example, selectively absorbs from the blood stream compounds containing iodine. So the attempt has been made to treat the thyroid disease known as goiter by introducing into the body compounds containing a radioactive isotope of iodine. Perhaps someday the same principle may be used to develop a successful treatment for cancer. The first step would be to find an ordinary chemical compound which is selectively absorbed by cancer cells. The next step would be to rebuild this compound, replacing some of the atoms in its molecules by radioactive isotopes. Such a project would require long and careful research, and I am certainly not suggesting that a cure for cancer lies just around the corner. All I wish to say is that we now have new and powerful tools to help in the never-ending war against disease.

Radioactive isotopes have also been used to trace the complicated sequences of chemical reactions which take place within the body. Consider, for example, the process by which sugar is used. Sugar serves as a fuel. In the body, it burns and yields energy—that chemical energy which was mentioned a few moments ago. But at body temperature, the ordinary process of combustion is too slow to maintain life. On the other hand, the body temperature cannot be increased without endangering life. So the combustion of sugar must somehow be accelerated at body temperature.

For this purpose, the body has developed a group of accelerators known as enzymes. Each enzyme molecule has a special task which it performs over and over again, like a workman on an assembly line. There are more than twenty enzymes engaged in the oxidation of sugar within the body. Some remove hydrogen atoms from the sugar molecules; others split off carbon dioxide. Thus, with enzymes serving as the activators of change, the process of breaking down the sugar and releasing its energy proceeds step by step.

It has been a long and laborious task to unravel this sequence of chemical changes by which sugar is burned in the body, but developments in this field have recently been greatly aided by the use of radioactive isotopes. The biochemists, by building radioactive carbon atoms into sugar molecules, have shown that the wrecking of these molecules is accompanied by combination of the fragments into new compounds. A similar technique has been very useful in exploring the method by which plants, under the influence of sunlight, produce sugar.

Here, then, are two benefits that we can confidently expect from the development of nuclear energy.

First, an enormously increased supply of radiation for the treatment of diseases; second, a prolific source of radioactive isotopes for use both in medical therapy and in biochemical research. And there are other possibilities. As a matter of fact, the new sources of atomic energy offer so many opportunities for advance that we are now facing the dawn of a new era in chemistry and biology.

Atomic Energy and Medicine

By Stafford L. Warren

Dr. Stafford L. Warren, the officer who was in charge of all health and protection aspects of the Manhattan District Project (atomic bomb), is professor of biophysics and dean of the School of Medicine of the University of California at Los Angeles.

Several revolutionary changes are under way in the fields of medicine as a direct outgrowth of recent advances in the application of atomic energy. I shall mention particularly three developments.

First, a whole new system of industrial hygiene has been brought into being in the plants of the Manhattan District—or as we should now say, the plants under the Atomic Energy Commission. This new system of industrial hygiene safeguards the personnel against dangerous radiations and against contamination from new toxic materials for which there was no previous experience. New safety rules have been established, following extensive preliminary experiments with animals. The unit of radiation is designated by the letter r, in honor of Roentgen, the discoverer of X rays, and our studies indicate that one-tenth of an r per day per total body exposure is a safe allowance—at least, insofar as current experience can determine. These new standards of industrial hygiene, which were developed in the plants concerned with the making of the atomic bombs, will have important application to the industrial atomic power plants which are bound to be a part of our future economy.

The second development arises from the possibility of atomic warfare. With the results demonstrated by the use of the bomb in Japan and the further information gained from the Bikini tests, it is clear that atomic warfare would bring serious hazards to civilians on a wide scale, involving areas as large as an entire county. In the case of seaports, for example, a single underwater detonation easily can result in the contamination of waters from ten to fifteen miles in width by forty or more miles in length. A widespread education program in precautionary measures must be set up, to inform not only physicians and nurses but also the population as a whole.

The third revolutionary change is the expansion of the isotope technique in research. The phrase, isotope technique, comes from the fact that physicists apply the name isotope to different atomic weights of the atoms of the same element. Some of these are unstable and thus radioactive while others are stable and not radioactive. It has long been known that certain elements can be rendered temporarily radioactive by the action of the cyclotron by neutron bombardment, but the process occurs on an enormous scale in the uranium piles where atomic energy is being released.

By isotope technique is meant the use, both in research and in medical treatment, of those isotopes, both stable and radioactive forms, of certain chemical elements which are essential to the body's nutrition—such elements, for example, as carbon, phosphorus, iodine, iron, and many others.

For some years prior to the atomic bomb development, research workers in medicine and biology had made use of radioactive isotopes as tracers to study the processes of life; for the radiation emitted by the isotopic carbon, phosphorus, iodine, or iron atom served as a tag to advertise the presence of the corresponding atom wherever it was in the body. The value of tagged atoms both for research and in certain experimental treatments of disease had been prospected before the outbreak of the war; and now, with the abundance of radioactive isotopes that are available as by-products of atomic energy production, the use of these tagged atoms has been launched on a vastly larger scale.

The three developments just mentioned will profoundly influence medical science, medical practice, and medical education. In addition, there will be need of specialists whom we may call "health physicists." The health physicists will be trained in fundamental physics and plant safety techniques, and will have responsibilities akin to the sanitary engineer's.

Medical training for the atomic age must begin in college, before the student enters medical school. As preparation for the new medical studies, the student will need a solid grounding in basic physics and chemistry, including nuclear physics and radiochemistry.

In medical schools there is gradually developing a new branch of biophysics. To a great extent, biophysics rests on the development of instruments—for example, X-ray spectrographs, electron microscopes, cyclotrons, and the like. Such devices can serve a valuable function in advancing medical research just because they are available. The applications are so promising that, in my opinion, the main emphasis in preclinical and clinical research will soon be in biophysics.

There is close relationship between the developments in biophysics and those in atomic energy. The familiar gadgets used by the atomic physicist—the geiger counter, the ionization chamber, the electroscope, and other devices for measuring radiation—will play a prominent part in medical biophysics. By use of this equipment it will be possible to carry the isotope technique to its full development, and measure the amount of the radioactive isotope, or tracer, in any specimen of biological material. For this work we need the synthetic chemist, the medical biochemist, and the physical chemist.

They must join hands with organic chemists, physicists, biologists, medical researchers, and other biological investigators—for the day of the lone wolf researcher is past, at least in most fields related to medicine. Gradually the techniques of counting tracers, determining blood volume with radioactive substances, measuring the distribution of radio-iodine in the treatment of certain thyroid diseases, and related techniques will become standard hospital procedures, cared for by specialized workers.

When it comes to a well-rounded research program in more complicated fields, it will be necessary to take atoms of radio-carbon and other tracer isotopes and to ask the chemist to build these atoms directly into the chemical compound whose action in the body is to be studied. In synthesizing these compounds, the chemist may need to handle large quantities of radioactive materials, and it is essential that he be aware of the dangerous possibilities of his work. For example, his discard material must be kept until it can be safely disposed of. Certain principles of self-protection must govern laboratories in conducting experiments with radioactive materials, because the large quantities involved may contaminate the laboratory rooms and furnishings and sewer disposal systems and make it dangerous for the personnel.

These precautions will hardly need to be as extensive as those used in the atomic bomb plants, but they are of the same type and involve the use of rubber gloves, special clothes, special ventilation, special laundering, and the like. This may sound formidable, but actually similar precautions have long been used in bacteriology and in the surgical operating room.

The possibilities which these new isotopes or tracer techniques open to medical research are truly revolutionary. Think of the many sugars and other carbohydrates which the body uses. All these contain carbon. So do the fats and many other nutrients. Previously, without the use of tracers, studies of the origin and fate of certain compounds could be accomplished only by indirect inference. Today the tracer isotope can make the pathway of a molecule through the body clear cut and definite. Think of the enzymes, vitamins, and hormones whose actions can be explored by this technique. The secret ways of insulin may be charted. It may be possible to study the physical arrangements within living cells and learn how the individual cell functions internally. It may be possible to examine the activities of the cancerous cell. We want to know why the cancerous cell is different from the normal cell from which it originated?—why the cancerous cell intoxicates the normal cells?—how the cancerous cell is able to spread to other parts of the body and take root among normal cells?

Perhaps the isotope tracer technique will illuminate some of these mysteries. It is a hope of many research workers to find some substances which cancer alone utilizes. If such a substance is found, it may be possible by synthesis or other chemical maneuvers to introduce enough of a radioactive isotope into the substance to constitute a sort of miniature time bomb so that when the cancer absorbs the substance it is destroyed by the radiations.

All in all, we can be sure that researches with radioactive iso-topes will occupy the energies and talents of an army of bio-logical and medical investigators for the next decade or two. It is safe to expect that they will return many benefits in the conquest of disease, the relief of human suffering, and the addition of useful years to the average span of life.

CHAPTER 13

THE NATURAL AND THE SOCIAL
SCIENCES

ATOMIC ENERGY has made vivid and inescapable a problem which is, in fact, very old. In its simplest terms, the problem is this: Science gives men power. Power can be used for good or for evil. How can we make sure that this power is used for the welfare of mankind and not for its complete destruction?

It should be made clear at once, however, that it would be inaccurate to single out science as the only source of this dilemma. It is spectacularly true that science gives power, but it is more generally and quite as accurately true that *all* knowledge gives power. A shrewd knowledge of propaganda, for example, may well turn out to be a sort of super-power, which will determine how physical power can be applied. If "pen" includes all modern forms of communication, then the pen is probably still mightier than the sword, even though our swords are now atomic bombs.

Society is threatened by an imbalance between physical power and social wisdom—this is all too clear. But what can we do about it?

Considering all levels of behavior ranging from individual actions to the mass activity of all society, there are undoubtedly many situations in which we already know the right thing to do, but simply do not do it. Thus we must admit, at the very base of our difficulties, a failure in our morals. What is necessary first and foremost, if we are to balance power with wisdom, is a spiritual renaissance.

It is really not too surprising that we can produce excellent physicists but are not very successful in producing unselfish and righteous individuals. It is easier to be a good physicist than it is to be good, period. The first, to be sure, requires knowledge, energy, imagination, and intellectual power. But the second requires wisdom, which is rarer than knowledge, and character, which is rarer than intelligence. The physicist, moreover, has the advantage of dealing with problems which are essentially simpler, and it is not strange that he has advanced more rapidly than the psychologist and the philosopher.

Failure to do a known right thing, however, is not all of the story. If it were, then a purely moral rebirth would be all we need to make power serve wisdom. We do need this moral rebirth, and desperately, but we also need something in addition.

For there are many situations in which we do not consciously do wrong at all, situations in which we simply do not as yet have sufficient knowledge and understanding to know what is really right. For example, what concessions of national sovereignty, what sacrifices of internal strength, is it *right* for the United States to make in the hope of thereby strengthening the United Nations? Or on a more detailed level of economics and sociology, what federal labor legislation is right? What level of personal and corporation tax best serves the interest of all the people? What kind of price control, if any, is right?

These, and hundreds like them, are questions on which intelligent and patriotic and well-intentioned persons can differ violently. Such conflicts of opinion must mean that we are trying to answer questions which are poorly defined and which involve many factors concerning which we are still ignorant.

All this, of course, adds up to a conclusion which is almost universal nowadays: It is imperative that we isolate and conquer this ignorance by great forward strides in the social sciences and great advances in our understanding of human behavior at individual and group levels.

How are these advances to be achieved? Some seem to think that the best method is to turn the social sciences over to the physical scientists and the engineers. The social sciences, however, deal with problems of organized complexity which are even more difficult and more subtle than those of the biologist or the doctor. The quantitative analytical processes developed by the physicist, chemist, and mathematician undoubtedly have some usefulness in the social sciences. But there is no reason to think that these processes, so successful in the simpler problems of inanimate nature, are broad enough or powerful enough—or are even of the right sort at all—for some social problems.

The social sciences should be given all possible help from the physical, biological, and medical sciences. In addition they must be given the support necessary to recruit and train more and better men—the funds for greatly amplified research, and an understanding which does not condemn them for their failure to advance more rapidly.

In planning the series of talks which gave rise to this volume, there was no regular provision made for the social sciences. Thus there is no idea of pretending that the present chapter covers the great expanding area which is common to both natural and social scientists. These four essays were written by men who are both natural and social scientists. They are merely samples—good samples, which, it is hoped, will stimulate further reading—of the way in which the natural sciences and the social sciences are drawing together, uniting for their mutual benefit.

W. W.

The New Geography

By Isaiah Bowman

Dr. Isaiah Bowman is president of Johns Hopkins University. He was chief territorial specialist to the American Commission to Negotiate Peace in 1918, and has similarly advised our government during the past few years.

CHANGING ideas about nature and changing instruments of power give geographical science a peculiarly human quality. To a high degree the earth is what we think it is. It is but a slight exaggeration to say that all geography is always new. When an explorer takes plants (maize, potato, wheat) from primitive centers of growth and carries them to new environments, he may succeed in growing highly resistant strains adapted to hard conditions where ordinary strains fail. Each plant-breeding success means the reappraisal of our climatic boundaries, soil types, and cultivation techniques. America has been rediscovered a score of times by new ideas, by plant experiment, by human enterprise.

The introduction of the maize plant and the potato altered the farm economy and stepped up the industrial power of half of Europe. The grasslands of the Canadian Prairie Provinces became an agricultural empire when new breeds of wheat were introduced that are adapted to light rainfall and a short growing season. When exploration is ended and the map of the world completed, the discovery will still go on—discovery of things we can do and grow and exchange and enjoy as science discloses new areas of opportunity.

Like plants, minerals both stimulate and limit man's occupation of the earth. When vanadium was found in the Peruvian Andes, and black diamonds in Brazil, they became magnets of opportunity. When English industrialists began large-scale mining and distributed coal far and wide across the seven seas to coalless towns and harborages, they changed the nothingness of many isolated island sites to vital stations in a network of world power—naval power, trading power, colonial power. The instruments of power were skillfully combined. Machines, combined with systems of credit and implemented by government, were among such instruments that altered the meaning and possibilities of the earth and gave geography as well as economics a new dynamic quality. Streams of power followed geographical exploration and colonization right down the years from John the Navigator to Peary, Scott, Nansen, Livingstone, Eyre, and the airborne moderns.

The surveying instrument is the first tool of the geographer. None knows better than a sailor raising a landfall that we must determine accurately where things are and make reliable maps. The adding machine is to human geography what the surveying instrument is to a map. We must count and measure and inventory people and their resources before we can begin to understand the significant relations of human societies, great and small. Every geographer must be trained to understand the structure of such human societies and how they work, for the social and economic system of a nation expresses the knowledge, idealism, standards, and dynamism of its people. It is in fact the chief national power plant. In theory the material power generated in the world is for human good. If a spiritual element is wanting in the power plant the result may be deplorable—what the critics call "scientific materialism." Only sustained loyalty to spiritual ideals makes either science or exploration desirable or beneficent in the long run.

Ptolemy's charts were used by sailors and it is incidental that sailors include warriors. He was not thinking of that modern devil's brew, the Nazi brand of geopolitics. He was curious, ingenious, and enterprising in the interest of navigation. Von Humboldt, also a geographical measurer and appraiser, said that the diversity of the earth was man's great opportunity: what all countries had, each could have, and be the better for it. South African fruit in London shops and Pacific copra for American soap is what he meant, put into homely modern terms. Lord Bryce once called the Panama Canal a piece of geographical surgery. Boulder Dam to add water and Florida canals to get rid of it are among similar triumphs that, lamentably, do not yet include control of destructive droughts and floods.

The earth is not a perfect home for man. Some of the drained swamps of Florida, now truck gardens, will not produce acceptably unless copper is added. Most soils are deficient in something, most climates call the tune on man's comfort and crop possibilities.

Using the tools of physics, chemistry and biology, geography puts together the parts of a region that have human meaning. All of the great geographers of history discovered human meanings, not merely coasts and mountain and river systems. They peopled new lands with imaginative human designs.

Popular cartographers have recently given a semblance of newness to the earth by inventing unconventional map projections. They have stimulated popular interest in maps, a good thing. Their novel projections are the equivalent of the candid camera. Just as we got tired of seeing men upside down or feet foremost, so map readers will tire of bizarre projections. Maps are conventions, not pictures. Also they spell out an international language for the wider comparisons of people and physiography. Every projection has a special meaning and purpose, and purposes are legion. For general scientific use and for international agreement we also need maps that are familiar in shape and size.

The greatest cooperative map enterprise, the millionth map (an inch on it represents a million inches in nature, or 15.8 miles) is designed to give each country a familiar national map in a world mosaic. Now completed, the millionth map of the world is almost as big as the façade of the Library of Congress. It took 7 men 25 years at the American Geographical Society of New York to do just the Hispanic-American part of it, or the equivalent of one man working about 175 years. It is not an enterprise in power rivalry, but in good neighborliness. Hispanic-American scholars and governments cooperated with mutual benefit, not war, in view. A number of boundary disputes have been settled in part because the map existed as an impersonal, scientific, and disinterested tool of conciliation at the moment it was needed.

Land settlement is becoming a science because critical geographical inventories of resources can now be made with scientific tools of investigation. No such failure as the Roanoke Colony need take place today. Yet displaced men and women, homeless because of war, search for the securities of life on an earth where the best places have already been taken. When we put science to work in a marginal region of potentially greater settlement, such as Western Australia or Alaska, we save human lives at the expense of brains and money.

An imaginative grasp of space and time is required of the modern scientific geographer. No other science puts humans and earth in their regional framework and tries to appraise the systems of resource-use that men have created. One important country took no census between 1876 and 1940. By 1900 no one knew, in many respects, what that country was! This means that its government administered territory which had not been accurately measured, and taxed or overlooked people it had not counted or classified. Among the earliest documents of Babylonia, Egypt, and Rome are census lists. Counting and administration are inseparable if good administration is the end in view—3000 years ago, and today more than ever.

The earth is in changing relation to man: this is the distinctive contribution of geographical science from Herodotus to Von Humboldt, Vidal de la Bache, and Mackinder. The new geography is new in materials and devices, and in knowledge of the laws of modern science. But its central principle has remained the same for countless generations. Whether men use the advantages of the earth for good or evil ends is a question in social and political morality. Science leaves the field at this point with a single challenging conclusion: the earth is big enough and rich enough for us all if we learn how to live in peace.

The Changing World Population

By Frank W. Notestein

Dr. Frank W. Notestein is the director of the Office of Population Research of the School of Public and International Affairs at Princeton University, and is also in charge of the Population Division of the United Nations.

In spite of the losses of two world wars, there are more than twice as many people on this planet as there were one hundred years ago. Over two billion people are now alive. In another hundred years, there may be more than four billion. Population growth is by no means a thing of the past. Though coming to an end in some parts of the world, it is gathering speed in others. The future population will not only be larger than it is today, but differently concentrated on the globe. These changes in the growth and distribution of the world's people must be studied carefully, critically, even if you will, cold bloodedly. The facts of population change are the facts of life on which any sensible planning for the world's peace and progress must be based.

The modern epoch of population growth is unique in the experience of the human species. If throughout the ages there had been similar growth, we would not now have standing room. For example, if Europe's population had grown as rapidly throughout the entire Christian era as it actually has grown in the past century, there would now be at least one person for every square yard of that continent's land area. The modern epoch of growth covers only the last three centuries. Why did it occur?

Populations are recruited by birth and depleted by death. Migration also brings changes, but, in general, the effects of migration are less important to growth than is the nature of the balance between birth and death.

Before the modern era, death rates were inevitably high. Mankind had neither the knowledge, nor the means to do an efficient job of keeping body and soul together. A new-born child probably had less than an even chance of living thirty-five years. In the past three centuries, the Western World has learned how to produce the means of subsistence in previously undreamed of abundance, and to control the ravages of disease as never before. It learned how to keep body and soul together through the active years of adult life, and put its knowledge to good use. Today, under the best peacetime conditions, a newborn child has an even chance of living, not thirty-five years, but more than seventy years.

It is true, to be sure, that at the same time that Western man was learning how to conserve health and prolong his life, he was also learning how to kill as never before, and was putting that knowledge to tragic use. However, it is also true, that with all its horrors modern war has been far less deadly than have poverty and disease, the silent killers of former times.

To survive, populations that are heavily drained by death must be rapidly replenished by birth. Of necessity, therefore, mankind entered the modern era with ways of life, customs and attitudes that favored large families. These attitudes and customs were deeply laid in long experience. They changed only gradually and under heavy pressure. Declines in the death rate came nearly as rapidly as external conditions permitted, but declines in the birth rate did not become common in Europe until the latter half of the nineteenth century. Then the size of families began to shrink in response to the heavy penalties put on large families by an age of city living that sets great store by the opportunities of the individual child for health, education, and advancement. Birth rates declined, gradually at first, then with gathering speed, until by the opening of World War II, they were again nearly in balance with death rates in much of the Western World.

Thus Europe's three-century period of growth came as a result of the transition from the wasteful balance of high birth rates and high death rates to the efficient balance of low birth rates and low death rates. The transition brought growth because death rates declined more rapidly than birth rates, pending the modification of age-old patterns of living that favored large families. In its period of modernization and transitional growth, the population of European extraction increased perhaps sevenfold throughout the world. Special factors, such as the availability of an empty New World, accounted for much of that increase. Modernization will bring different rates of growth to other peoples, but the fundamental ingredients of the process will be much the same. What then are the prospects for future change? First of all, we must realize that more than half of the world's population has scarcely begun its period of transitional growth. Most of these more than one billion people live in Asia, and among them birth rates and death rates remain much the same as in former centuries. In some regions famine and pestilence periodically check growth. In other regions, some semblance of modern transportation and the control of epidemics curtail such sweeping catastrophes. In these latter cases there is growth. For example, in India the population grew 50 million just in the last ten years. Its *increase* was larger than the *total population* of Great Britain. This growth came in spite of death rates that gave a new-born child less than an even chance of living thirty years. In such areas, birth rates have declined little. Nor can they be expected to decline while modernization touches only a few externals of existence and the whole fabric of life remains that of past centuries for the illiterate mass of the population. Such populations remain poised for spectacular growth whenever it becomes possible to reduce mortality. Their actual growth is impossible to predict. It depends largely on the prevalence of catastrophes. However, it would not be sensible to count on Asia's having less population a century from now than the whole world has today.

Northwestern and Central Europe are at the other extreme of the growth process. Their period of transitional growth is over. Even before the war, families were no longer large enough to maintain stationary populations, and the war has brought new checks to growth. Unless there is heavy immigration, such countries as England, France, and Germany cannot be expected to grow. Southern Europe, the British Dominions, and the United States are also nearing the end of the transition, but they probably have a generation of slowing growth ahead. On the other hand, Eastern Europe is still in the stage of rapid transition growth. Modernization of the area started late, and is much less advanced than in the West. We should expect Eastern Europe to grow rapidly in the next generation.

The Soviet Union is in an even earlier stage of development. Its position is a good deal like that of Western Europe two generations ago. Growth should be very rapid. It has been sharply checked by war losses, but even so, there should be more people within the old boundaries by 1950 than there were in 1940. All things considered, a population of about 250 million by 1970 seems likely in the Soviet Union.

This growth will have a profound political significance. By 1970, it is probable that the Soviet Union will have as many young men of military age as the seven next biggest countries of Europe put together. Just the *increase* in Russia's military manpower between 1940 and 1970 will probably exceed the pre-war size of Germany's total potential fighting force.

Taken by itself this growth is not critically important, for numbers alone do not spell either progress or power. However, Russia has large undeveloped resources. From these resources, the same processes of modernization that are bringing population growth should bring the material means with which manpower is made effective in rising standards of living and growing economic and political power. The fact is that there is every reason to expect the Soviet Union to occupy the dominant position on the Eurasian continent in the next generation. Like it or lump it, and I trust we shall like it, these are merely the facts of life on which sensible planning for the future must be based. Americans facing these facts should remember the sometimes awkward strength of their own country in its period of adolescent power. We have a special obliga· tion to cultivate a sympathetic understanding of this new giant in world affairs. In cultivating patience and understanding, each of us will be helping to build the peace.

Our Northern Neighbor, China

By George B. Cressey

Dr. George B. Cressey is the chairman of the Department of Geography at Syracuse University. He has done field work in all of the twenty-eight provinces of China, and has also traveled extensively in Mongolia, Tibet, Japan, Java, and Soviet Asia.

In the summer of 1944 I had the opportunity of flying across the Atlantic on my way back from another year in China. One afternoon at 4:30 I left Casablanca in North Africa and the following day I had lunch at La Guardia Field on Long Island.

Such speed is no longer surprising. But when I report that I came by way of Newfoundland, people at once tend to remark "why did you go up north in order to reach the United States?"

As we enter the air age, we need to relearn our geography. We must revamp our traditional ideas of the distance to certain lands, both because great circle routes do not show up realistically on flat maps, and because air travel over polar regions is now possible. Suppose I put it this way. If you want to fly from New York to Africa, you start out in the direction of Portland, Maine.

Some years ago Ann Lindbergh wrote an interesting account of her flight to China under the title of *North to the Orient,* for Alaska was on the short route from New York to Shanghai. When I flew the Atlantic I had been obliged to come the long way around and China was truly the Far East. But now that the war is over, the Pacific shores of Asia are no longer far, nor are they east to us.

We might possibly call this oriental world our Near West; but in fact China is actually our neighbor to the north. Hence the strategic importance of Alaska.

Until we were rudely awakened by the attack on Pearl Harbor, these United States had been an island in the midst of the Atlantic. We were aware of Europe but of little else. The world may have been round since the days of Magellan, but we had not lived as though it really were round. Columbus discovered America on October 12, 1492, but America did not discover Asia until December 7, 1941; it may be that history will record both dates as of equal importance. Of one prophecy I am sure. I am confident that we shall in the future not live on an island, nor in a hemisphere, but in a world which is truly round. In such a round world, world citizenship is inescapable, and for such citizenship an awareness of global interdependence is a first requirement.

We Americans have never before had to visualize such a round world. Never before have we had to plan the logistics of a war as far away as China, or across an ocean as huge as the Pacific.

Do you realize what a whale of an ocean the Pacific really is? From Panama to Singapore is 10,000 miles and from Bering Strait to Antarctica is another 10,000. Will this Pacific become a community?

Only as we understand China can we act intelligently for America. Good will is essential, but it must be intelligent. As I have traveled across Asia I have been impressed with the tremendous body of good will which exists in these lands toward the United States. And it is equally true that we have a sentimental attachment toward Asia. This is not enough. We must have both respect and realism.

I need not tell you that these are difficult days for China, perhaps the most critical for a century. China has had a great past and undoubtedly has an important future. The question today is not whether China is good or bad, but whether she is important to us, and what weight she can carry among the United Nations.

Let me report to you one or two of the bright spots which I saw in wartime China. One of the most encouraging developments was the achievements of the Chinese engineers. What they did in building blast furnaces, steel mills, and machine shops far in the interior, and with little more than a screw driver and a pair of pliers to start with, is very creditable. China needs more engineers and they need more experience, but there is no question but that they have the know-how.

Within a decade after the return of peace I am confident that we shall see something of the same industrialization in China which characterized the Soviet Union during its five-year plans. China will remain an agricultural nation, for her mineral resources are modest except for coal, but in a few places there will nevertheless be spectacular large-scale industry. What are the resources for such development? China does have coal but only modest amounts of oil, iron, copper and the principal metals. These may be enough for many of her own needs for some decades, but there is no likelihood that China will ever become a major industrial power.

I should like to stress the moderate amount of China's mineral wealth as there seems to be such widespread misconception as to her buried treasures. Ever since the days when Marco Polo returned to his native Venice from his wanderings in far Cathay, a certain mystic halo has surrounded the Orient. Marco Polo reported that in China the people burned black stones, meaning coal; and that their knowledge of metallurgy exceeded that of medieval Europe.

Later travelers brought back similar reports, and this glamorizing of the Orient was emphasized by the character of the trade in silks and porcelains which crossed Central Asia. When the first European geologists saw China they too were impressed with China's wealth, and wrote to their friends that "China had enough coal to supply the entire world for a thousand years." By inaccurate implication this judgment came to include iron ore as well as coal.

The geology of China is now reasonably well known, and the actual situation is this. China does have a wide variety of minerals and they are widely distributed, but it is incorrect to interpret widespread occurrence to mean abundance.

Except for coal, most deposits are small and ill-suited to modern exploitation. The metal may be present in limited amounts which could be worked by primitive methods, but the reserves are inadequate for modern industry.

There are three minerals which China does have in abundance; tin, antimony and tungsten. These are valuable indeed; but they are no substitutes for iron, copper, lead or oil. Newly discovered deposits of aluminum ore may prove of value. The great resource is coal, and here China stands in fourth place among the nations. Much of it, too, is high grade. China's economic future rests not upon her minerals, but on her soil, her location, and her man power. And the last, man power, is also her major problem. Five hundred million people are too many for the good earth of China to support in comfort.

Certainly China need not be either a military or economic threat to the United States, but she can be a good customer and a good ally. It is to our interest to see China modernize, and as rapidly as possible. I know of no cheaper way to help maintain peace in the Orient than for us to assist in the construction of a strong, democratic China.

In proportion as we are of help to China now, we shall reap a rich dividend later.

When Mr. Churchill was last in America, he remarked that "The price of greatness is responsibility." We have responsibilities in Asia, and we have friends in China. It is of no service to China nor to ourselves to idealize the Chinese, or to misunderstand their problems.

Fortunately China does have coal, and that is the key to power and to chemical engineering. With proper assistance China has an important future. No longer will she be "far" or "east" to us; China lies to our north, just beyond Alaska. The shortest route from New York City to Chungking runs directly over the North Pole. As China becomes our near neighbor, we will find in her a friend and a major ally.

Energy and the Development of Civilization

By Leslie A. White

Dr. Leslie A. White, professor of anthropology at the University of Michigan, is a specialist in the study of the civilizations of mankind.

HUMAN civilization is about one million years old. During this long course of time, civilization has grown from the level of our prehuman ancestors to the status in which we find it today. We know a great deal about the process of development of this civilization. Our knowledge of this development has come mainly from three sources: First, from archeological exploration of extinct civilizations —or of extinct cultures, to use the term preferred by anthropologists; second, from the study of primitive peoples still living in the modern world; and, third, from investigations into the nature of man himself. On the basis of this total knowledge we are able to formulate a theory that will explain the growth of civilization thus far, will make clear to us the status of civilization as it exists today, and will, we hope, give us some indication of its probable course in the future.

Man, like all other animals, is engaged in a struggle for existence. This struggle takes place not only between man and his natural habitat, but within the human species itself—between tribes and nations. Civilization, or culture, is the means employed by man to carry on his struggle for survival.

Culture is made up of many things. It includes tools and weapons, customs and institutions, ceremonies and rituals, art, science, philosophy, religion, and so on. An essential feature of culture is its continuity; for a large part of the culture of one generation or age is passed on to the next. Culture is thus a continuous process which grows and develops in accordance with principles of its own. We are able to formulate the laws of this development. And the basic law relates to energy.

All living organisms require energy. In order to maintain their existence, organisms must be able to control and to utilize energy in one form or another. In the human species, culture is the characteristic means of harnessing energy and of putting it to the service of man's needs. By means of tools and weapons, social organization and knowledge, man is able to harness the forces of nature and to put them to work for him. It follows, therefore, that as more and more energy is harnessed, the more highly developed does the culture become. When only a small amount of energy is controlled per capita, the culture will be low; man will be a savage or a barbarian. If, however, the amount of energy harnessed and put to work be great, the culture will be high.

We see therefore that civilization has developed because ways and means have been found from time to time to increase the amount of energy per capita under man's control and at his disposal for culture building. This is the fundamental law of the growth of civilization.

The first source of energy to be utilized in culture building was the human body. The amount of energy that can be obtained from human bodies is, of course, small. It is equivalent to only about one-tenth horsepower per adult male. When all its members were considered, including infants, the weak, and the aged, the earliest human society had no more than about one-twentieth of one horsepower per capita. Naturally the culture, or civilization, built with these meager resources, was exceedingly low and crude. And mankind would have continued to live in this primitive condition indefinitely, had not a way been found to increase his energy resources—to harness and control more energy per capita.

The first really great step in cultural advance was taken when man learned to domesticate animals and to cultivate plants. This happened some twelve to twenty thousand years ago. Plants and animals are, of course, forms of energy—solar energy stored up in cellular form.

And when man harnessed these natural forces through animal husbandry and agriculture—especially agriculture—he greatly increased the energy resources at his disposal for culture building. As a consequence, there was a great increase in population; villages grew into cities, and tribes into nations and empires. More and more people were freed from the labor of food production as agriculture became more efficient and their time and talents were devoted to the arts, crafts, and professions. Architecture, metallurgy, writing, mathematics, astronomy, the fine arts, and philosophy advanced rapidly in the hands of specialists. It is significant to note that after hundreds of thousands of years of slow progress in the Old Stone Ages, civilization leaped forward and progressed rapidly following the introduction of the agricultural arts—in ancient Egypt, Mesopotamia, India, China, and, in the New World, in Mexico, Middle America, and Peru.

The second great step in cultural advance was taken only a century or two ago when solar energy was again harnessed, this time in the form of coal and oil by means of steam and internal combustion engines.

And today we are on the threshold of a third stage of cultural advance: that of harnessing the energy of the nucleus of the atom.

The social systems of mankind are closely related to their underlying technological systems—to the ways in which energy is harnessed and put to work. Thus, a people, who derive their subsistence wholly from hunting and gathering wild plant food, will have one type of social system. A pastoral or an agricultural people will each have another type, and an industrialized people still another type of social system. Social systems are always determined by the amount of energy harnessed per capita, and by the ways in which this energy is expended in gaining a living from nature and in waging offensive and defensive competition with neighboring systems.

The introduction of agriculture brought about a social revolution as well as a technological revolution. It destroyed the clan and tribal system of primitive peoples and instituted civil society with the political state. The recent technological revolution powered by coal and oil has likewise inaugurated a series of great social changes that has not yet run its course. But today we are confronted with this entirely new development: atomic energy. The age-old struggle to conquer and subdue the forces of nature has at last harnessed a power so great as to become a threat to man's existence, at least as a civilized being.

At the same time, atomic energy offers a promise of peace and abundance in the ages to follow.

The crucial question today is: how will the vast powers of atomic energy be used? This brings us again to the two sides of man's struggle for existence. On the one hand he is struggling with the forces of nature, trying to subdue them and to bend them to his use. On the other hand, he is struggling with his fellow men for the possession of the resources of nature.

It is on this stage that the drama of atomic energy will be enacted. We are told by physicists that within a decade or so it will lie within the power of warring nations to destroy much, if not most, of the civilized world. If this should take place, civilization will unquestionably regress to earlier and lower levels of development.

But social evolution has moved forward with technological advance in the past and it may do so again.

It is possible that the military use of atomic energy may break down, once and for all, the political barriers that now divide the human race and set man against man—and it is possible that this may be done without crippling civilization. If this should be the outcome, mankind can at last become united in a common purpose and in common endeavor: the Good Life for all.

CHAPTER 14

SCIENCE AND THE WAR

THE SCIENTISTS, we have been told, were essential in winning the war. Radar, the proximity fuse, improved gear for aiming guns, the various instruments and weapons used to hunt and destroy submarines, the atom bomb—these are examples of the victorious new devices which the scientist produced. The scientists, working both in the laboratory and at the actual fighting front, produced not only new devices, but also new tactics and strategy for their most efficient use.

Since scientists were so active during World War II, and since they were by all accounts so successful, it was natural for the public to conclude that the war stimulated science.

With minor exceptions this conclusion is entirely false. Several of the leaders of our war-time science have told the public that this conclusion is false; but it is so vital that all the citizens understand the matter accurately, that it must be stated again and again.

In the first place practically all of the "new" discoveries were not really war-time products at all, in the broader sense of the term; for the knowledge which made them possible came from scientific research carried out long previously, in peacetime. The atomic bomb development, for example, depended on a series of basic discoveries in theoretical and experimental physics essentially all of which had occurred before the war and some long before.

Thus the scientist during war turns to his stock-pile of fundamental knowledge, to the facts he has won during patient and peaceful years of research. With feverish haste and at wasteful expense he applies this basic knowledge to the development of new devices. War-time science makes some terrifyingly clever gadgets, but it does not have time to keep working on the principles which made them possible.

In other words, scientific activity during war is, for the most part, of an *applied* sort that is concerned with developing certain definite machines. Since these are, again for the most part, machines for destruction, war-time scientific activity cannot be judged very productive. It is vitally necessary, to be sure; but in general it impedes progress in pure science, interrupts training of scientific personnel, and reduces to a dangerously low level the stock of knowledge with which to meet a possible further emergency.

There are certain important exceptions to the general statement that war does not aid science. Advances are sometimes made possible in the medical sciences by the horrible experiment which we call war. Progress in some sorts of surgery, in the use of blood plasma and other blood derivatives, in the development of new drugs, in the control of certain epidemic diseases—these may well be accelerated by the urgency of war and by the ugly fact that battle produces in one place at one time hundreds of opportunities for desperate but necessary experiment. The energy and devotion with which men work under war conditions also speeds the progress of medicine; and so, in some cases, does a level of financial support which may be lacking in peacetime.

Even in the physical sciences, there are exceptions too. Radar, and long-range radio navigation, will certainly make aviation safer. The tiny radio tubes developed for certain military devices make possible smaller and lighter and better hearing aids and portable radios. The giant electronic calculating engines which grew out of war developments will prove valuable in all fields of science. The high energy beams and the radioactive substances associated with the atom-bomb development will surely be of great use in biological and medical research.

Yet for all these gains we pay too high a price in blood and horror. Perhaps the most important benefit science might reap from war would be the realization, on the part of all the citizens, that science can accomplish great things, that it is an essential part of national life and strength, and that it deserves in peacetime the support which we are scared into giving during war.

W. W.

Science at the Front

By Karl Taylor Compton

Dr. Karl Taylor Compton, who was one of those responsible for the mobilization of science during World War II, is president of the Massachusetts Institute of Technology.

A FEW DAYS before the Japanese surrender in August, 1945, I was talking with General Krueger in Manila. The reader will remember him as the wily strategist under General MacArthur. It was General Krueger's Sixth Army, with the close cooperation of Admiral Barbey's Seventh Fleet, that made the decisive series of amphibious landings along the New Guinea coast and on to the Philippines. They leapfrogged around superior Japanese forces, established air fields from which General Kenney's air force could immobilize and starve out the enemy, and all the time were pushing our advanced bases ever closer to Japan.

I asked General Krueger what, in his judgment, had been the most useful technical device employed in his operation. He replied: "Our principal technical devices were the bulldozer, the C-47 cargo plane, radar, and the amphibious landing craft."

Later, in Tokyo, I had opportunity to witness the destruction wrought in that city by the then newly developed oil-incendiary bombs. In just two B-29 air raids with these bombs, 85 square miles of crowded Tokyo were completely burned to the ground; and in the city's remaining 125 square miles about half the buildings were destroyed. The people driven out of Tokyo by these bombings were equal in number to twice the population of Chicago.

Finally came the atomic bombs—the first on August sixth, and second on August ninth. On August tenth the Japanese negotiated for surrender.

These are dramatic illustrations of the applications of science at the battle front in the final stages of the war.

General Krueger listed radar among the most useful of the new weapons. It will be recalled that in the early naval encounters in the Pacific, our fleet won a series of decisive engagements against superior odds. The battles of Midway and the Coral Sea are examples. These engagements were all fought at night, and it was radar which enabled our gunners to see the enemy when he could not see us.

Turn now to the war in Europe. It was radar which enabled the British to win the crucial battle of Britain. It was radar and magnetic detectors, mounted in airplanes armed with bombs and depth charges, which enabled American forces to drive the German submarines off our own shores. It was radar, in combination with clever new navigation devices and ingenious bomb sights, which enabled our air forces to cripple German war industries and communications. It was the combination of radar, a new computing machine for controlling anti-aircraft guns, and the new proximity fuse—these three devices in collaboration—which intercepted German buzz bombs and averted great destruction in London.

It is not generally realized that it took scientists at the front, as well as scientific devices at the front, to make science at the front effective. These "combat scientists," as they have been called, are an important new element of modern warfare.

All technological developments have their origin, of course, in the minds of inventors and in the research laboratories of scientists. Following the researchers and inventors, the engineers adapt the result to factory production, with military supervision to insure that the design is practicable for military use. Then the device is manufactured and issued.

But this is not the whole story. If it were, the new device would usually be doomed to failure. In the first place, the troops would not know how to use it or to maintain it in operating condition. The officers would not know its powers or its limitations, and therefore could not order their strategy to best advantage. Moreover, the device itself might have serious defects not foreseen by the scientists in the laboratory, and disclosed only by its performance under front-line conditions. For these reasons, it was found necessary for scientists to accompany their new devices to the military training centers, and ultimately right into the active theaters where the new weapons were used against the enemy.

These combat scientists not only helped the troops to maintain and to operate the new devices at the front, but they frequently improvised new gadgets on the spot to meet emergencies. One group called "operations analysts" became skillful at evaluating the military effectiveness of various weapons and the different strategies for using them. And all the time that these combat scientists were serving at the front, they were sending back to the laboratories at home suggestions for improving the equipment or requests for new devices to meet newly discovered needs.

When the war began there was little realization that scientists would be thus called upon to operate so far from their home laboratories. Scientists were first mobilized in these home laboratories to work on problems suggested to them by the War and Navy Departments. Soon the scientists began also to develop original ideas of their own regarding new weapons and tactics. In the latter stages of the war there were scientists at every Army headquarters, on naval vessels, at advanced air fields, in the New Guinea jungles, behind the Japanese lines in China, with the first troops entering Germany. In all these activities there was splendid cooperation between the military and the scientists.

The United States agency known as OSRD—the Office of Scientific Research and Development—maintained a London headquarters for the civilian scientists assigned to the European theatre. Branch laboratories for radar and for radio countermeasures were established in England. Four or five hundred American scientists and their assistants were thus operating in Europe under OSRD auspices, with twenty or thirty per week going back and forth across the ocean to maintain intimate liaison with the supporting scientific groups in America. Such activities led the Director of OSRD in 1943 to establish the Office of Field Service.

As members of this field service, some civilian scientists were sent from the Secretary of War's Office to serve as scientific advisors to commanding officers. Also under the Navy and the Army Air Forces were the civilian teams of operations analysts.

In the Pacific there were scientific groups from OSRD based in Honolulu and successively in Brisbane, Hollandia, Manila, and Tokyo. From these advanced bases, individual scientists or teams ranged far and wide as needed.

The organization of civilian scientific cooperation with the military reached its peak in the last months of the war with the creation, by General MacArthur, of a special staff section known as the "scientific and technical advisory section." General MacArthur also incorporated the Pacific Branch of OSRD as a regular operating unit in parallel status with his Army, Navy, and Air Forces. These organizations were headed by civilian scientists with assimilated rank of major generals. They operated under military regulations but with the freedom necessary for fast action on technical matters.

This war-time experience has shown that science and scientists can be used with great effectiveness as an element in our national security. We must see to it that there is still further progress of science, increased training of scientists, and continued cooperation with our armed forces in order to maintain an appropriate degree of peace-time strength and preparedness.

Then, there is a second lesson. Just as science was effective at the front in war, so has it been effective in peace on the industrial front, the agricultural front, and the medical front.

The mobilization of science for war gave an extraordinary demonstration of what it can accomplish with unity of purpose, cooperation, and public support. Let us see to it that science is mobilized with similar purpose, cooperation, and support to serve still more effectively on the active fronts of peace.

Aviation Medicine

By Detlev W. Bronk

Dr. Detlev W. Bronk, professor of biophysics and director of the Johnson Research Foundation at the University of Pennsylvania, is at present also serving as chairman of the National Research Council.

One of the unforgettable experiences of World War II was to stand at evening outside Isaac Newton's rooms in the Great Court of Trinity College, Cambridge, and watch the Flying Fortresses return by hundreds from across the Channel. The stately formation of their silhouettes stirred one with admiration for man's mechanical genius, which had driven his machines into the skies, against the force of gravity.

A little later, in the gathering dusk, the Fortresses would glide down to the runways of their scattered fields, and the machines were revealed as merely the instruments of human crews. Waist-gunners sat casually at their posts, waving as they passed; bombardiers were in their transparent cages; pilots taxied their ships to rest. These were the crews who made the majestic armadas of the air a symbol of man's liberation from his natural limitations, gained by courage and by science.

The history of aviation is a long record of man's efforts to increase his powers. But the usefulness of each new accomplishment of the physicist and engineer has been restricted by human limitations, and further progress has had to wait upon new discoveries concerning man.

Finally, in 1862, an English scientist reached 29,000 feet, at which height he became unconscious. On returning to the earth and consciousness, he voiced his faith in the power of science to break the bonds of human limitations: "I shall not take it upon myself," said he, "to set the limits of human activity and indicate the point, if it exists, where nature tells the aeronaut you shall go no farther." His faith is justified by the fact that airmen now fly six or seven miles above the earth.

Why life could not be maintained in those rare atmospheres was first shown by a French scientist, Paul Bert. Stimulated by the invention of the balloon, he studied the behavior of animals and men under those conditions which are found at high altitudes, and he proved that the mental failure of the aeronauts was due to insufficient oxygen in the air they breathed.

From then till now biologists have studied the role of that essential gas in the maintenance of life. This research has shown that the delicate nerve cells of the brain require a continual supply of this element. If they are denied oxygen for a few minutes, they lose their power of action, and death ensues.

To protect our airmen against these dangers, flight surgeons, in the recent war, used the physiologists' discoveries for the design of equipment which supplied each man with enough oxygen to meet his needs at any altitude. This was done by regulating, through a valve, the flow of gas from storage tanks to a mask which covered nose and mouth. The valve opened with each inspiration, admitting oxygen to the mask according to the depth of breathing. The body of the flyer thus controlled automatically his own supply to meet its needs. With these aids, military aircraft were flown to 40,000 feet.

At these great heights new hazards appear. For physiologists have shown that the pressure of the atmosphere at those altitudes cannot force enough oxygen into the blood as it passes through the lungs. To meet these needs some aircraft now have sealed cabins in which mechanical devices maintain an atmosphere adequate in pressure, oxygen and warmth. In these cabins scientists have at last restored to flyers their natural environment.

The powerful motors which took our airmen to those heights also make possible swift and sudden motion. This was especially true in fighters and dive bombers, where speed and maneuverability were essential. The strength of a plane necessary to withstand disintegration under the centrifugal force of a high-speed turn is a triumph of engineering and metallurgy. But the full benefits of that accomplishment could not at first be utilized, due to failure of the pilot's body.

For flight surgeons and physiologists discovered that the heart is incapable of pumping blood against the forces which occur in sharp turns, or in the pull-out from a power dive. The brain is thus deprived of oxygen, and vision or consciousness may be lost during aerial combat. To help the human body withstand these forces, physiologists developed suits for airmen which aid the heart. As a turn begins, the suit is automatically inflated and by its pressure prevents the flow of too much blood into the lower parts of the body. This sustains the flow of blood to the brain and maintains consciousness. Fighter planes which would have been relatively useless were thus made available for the swift movements of modern combat.

Man is naturally a land-borne creature, and all his movements are directed by sensory contacts with the earth. Vision plays a part, and gravity acts on hidden nerve cells which report to the brain our movements and our posture. But when we take to the air, we do so with motor power that exceeds the pull of gravity. The resultant forces may then contradict the gravitational sensations, and confusion follows. Under the influence of the centrifugal force in a steeply-banked turn, the earth seems inclined to its true position, or in the execution of a loop seems to change position with the sky. Vision helps correct these misconceptions and preserves a truer sense of orientation. But, when clouds or darkness interfere, the pilot is no longer aware of his position in space, and directed fight becomes impossible. These were problems twenty years ago. Since then the study of human reactions to the forces of aerial flight has explained the causes of man's inaptitude for flying blind. That, in turn, has stimulated the development of instrumental aids to the human senses. Thus men have been enabled to use more fully, and with safety, the power of machine flight.

These three examples show the pattern of progress in military aviation. Research in the physical sciences has made possible new inventions, and these have given men new powers and new freedoms. But with these powers have come new conditions of life.

And not until biologists had understood the body in flight could men use their aerial machines for their difficult and desperate jobs.

The mission of medical science to our air forces did not, however, end in the laboratory or the factory. On the training fields of America, with the bombers based among the hedgerows of England, at landing strips on Pacific Islands, and in the mud and snow of the fighter fields in France, physiologists and physicians used modern science to aid our flyers. Selection was first made of those best able to withstand the stresses of aerial war. Each man was trained to know the powers and limitations of his body. Equipment was provided which protected the air crews against the hazards of flight and enemy action. And finally, the flight surgeons converted the aerial instruments of destruction into wings for the wounded.

As science shapes the world of the future, it will become ever more important to keep before us the human purpose of machines and technology. The partnership of physicists, engineers, biologists, and physicians, that gave our airmen their powers of flight, can give to all men the means for a better life, free from the domination of man and nature.

Microwaves

BY LEE ALVIN DUBRIDGE

Dr. Lee Alvin DuBridge, who was head of the Radiation Laboratory (microwave radar) at the Massachusetts Institute of Technology during World War II, is now president of the California Institute of Technology.

MICROWAVES are radio waves, similar to those used in ordinary broadcasting, only of much shorter wave length and of higher frequency. There is a direct relationship, it will be remembered, between wave length and frequency. As the wave length is shortened, the frequency of the vibrations becomes correspondingly higher.

The length of the radio waves which brings broadcast programs into your homes is probably between 200 and 600 meters. That is, these broadcasting waves are from one-tenth to one-third of a mile long. And their frequency ranges from about one-half million cycles or vibrations per second for the third-of-a-mile waves to about one and one-half million cycles for the tenth-of-a-mile waves. If your radio set can be tuned to the short-wave band, such as is used for communication with Europe, you may receive wave lengths as short as twenty-five meters, about seventy-five feet. Before the war the shortest waves in practical use measured about one and a half meters, or five feet. This one-and-a-half meter wave has a frequency of two hundred million cycles, or 200 megacycles. Radio waves of higher frequency were, in those days, only laboratory curiosities.

Today the situation is very different. As a result of years of intensive war research, radio waves of only ten centimeters, or four inches long, have become common. Waves as short as one centimeter, or less than half an inch, are now a practical possibility. The frequency of these one-centimeter waves is thirty thousand million vibrations per second.

It is these very short radio waves that are called microwaves—specifically, those of wave lengths shorter than about 20 centimeters. During the war these high-frequency radiations were not

315

only brought out of the laboratory, but nearly two billion dollars worth of radar equipment using microwaves had been produced or was on order at the end of the war. For five years this huge development and manufacturing effort was carried on behind closed doors, guarded by military security.

Microwaves in themselves are not particularly new or revolutionary. Physicists and engineers had been experimenting with them in the laboratory for many years. What happened under the spur of war is that microwaves have been made available for practical use.

Two things made this possible. One was a small metal vacuum tube developed by the British physicists Oliphant and Randall at the University of Birmingham in 1940. The second influence was something quite different—the organization of a huge international scientific and manufacturing enterprise which concentrated on the problem for five years.

Let us look first at the little vacuum tube. It was brought to this country by the British more than a year before we entered the war. It is known as a resonant cavity magnetron. Magnetron is the general name for a vacuum tube that operates in a magnetic field. Many magnetrons of different kinds had been developed and used long before the war. The resonant cavity magnetron is one in which the oscillating circuits are in the form of cavities or holes drilled within the body of the tube. The British physicists had invented an arrangement of these cavities and other features which enabled the tube to produce very high power at very high efficiency at extremely short wave lengths.

Previous microwave tubes generated such small outputs of power that ultrasensitive instruments were necessary to detect it. This new tube generated so much power that a piece of steel wool held near the tube burst into flame. It is difficult to describe the amazement of physicists and engineers when they first witnessed this tube in operation. Such a power at a frequency of three thousand million cycles had never been thought possible. But now, five years later, we look back on that tube and realize that, miraculous as it was, it was only a crude beginning. Present-day magnetrons are 100 times more powerful. They can produce pulses of high-frequency power up to 1,000 kilowatts.

But one vacuum tube does not make a radar set. A large scientific, engineering, and manufacturing effort was called for to produce the microwave radar that was so urgently needed in the war.

In the summer of 1940 the National Defense Research Committee, later to become part of the Office of Scientific Research and Development, undertook to organize this scientific effort. Being assured of cooperation from the British authorities, the United States Army, Navy, and American industry, the National Defense Research Committee established a microwave laboratory at the Massachusetts Institute of Technology. This Radiation Laboratory eventually grew to nearly 4,000 employees and served as a focus for the large international cooperative research program. As a result of this effort, microwave radar was made available for use on every battle front.

Microwaves are fascinating to work with. They are just like ordinary radio waves except for wave length. But the short wave length causes them to exhibit many properties normally associated with light. A microwave antenna, for example, often resembles a searchlight. By combining the techniques of dipoles, horns, and parabolic reflectors, one can produce and project into space a microwave beam of almost any desired shape and sharpness. Turned around, as a receiver, the antenna will receive energy only from certain areas, ignoring others.

The energy within a beam of microwaves can be sharply concentrated. It may well turn out to be more economical to carry radio and television programs or even telephone conversations from point to point across the country on such beams rather than through telephone cables. However, microwave beams travel through space in straight lines only and are not bounced back from the ionosphere. Hence, in a transmission across the country, the beam would have to be projected from tower to tower, 30 to 50 miles apart.

For transmission over short distances—a few yards or so—microwave beams can be still further concentrated by passing them through hollow metal pipes called wave guides. This remarkable behavior of the waves was discovered before the war and extensively studied at the Bell Telephone Laboratories, at the Massachusetts Institute of Technology, and other places. The pipe may be circular or rectangular, but its dimensions must be properly related to the wave length. The longer the wave length, the larger must be the pipe.

The pipe may have bends and twists, and, if properly designed, the waves follow them without loss. Even flexible metal pipes have been developed and are used like a water hose. The microwaves, like the water, do not care whether the hose is bent or straight. One can even provide a sort of nozzle at the exit end of the pipe and direct the waves into a narrow stream or a wide spray. In this particular, however, the waves behave just the way water would not. If the nozzle is a wide-mouthed horn, the microwaves will contract into a slender stream. If the nozzle is narrowed, the stream will flare into a wider cone.

It was the attainment of narrow microwave beams that gave radar the sharpness of vision which proved so important for many military applications, such as the control of bombing and of gunfire.

The next great field for microwaves may be in communications. At these superhigh-frequencies, atmospheric static does not exist. Directional radio communication from point to point, from ship to ship, or from ground to aircraft, is a practicable possibility. With a sharp beam one may have almost the advantage of a private wire telephone. In the microwave region there are thousands of radio channels available, so it would even be possible to assign to each airplane its own private frequency channel.

There are other possible applications—to induction heating, to industrial control, and in physical research. It is an interesting fact that these microwaves, indeed all radio waves, are vibrations of the same nature as light rays, infrared, ultraviolet, and X rays, differing only in wave lengths and frequencies. They are all electro-magnetic radiations. And when a new part of the electromagnetic spectrum becomes available for practical use—as here—no one can predict its future. We only know that a new area of applied science has been opened. Experience tells us that whenever this happens, the new area yields dividends in all sorts of unexpected ways for years to come.

Direct Lift Aircraft

By Igor Sikorsky

Mr. Igor Sikorsky, a citizen of the United States since 1928, has a long record in Europe and this country as a designer of successful aircraft. He is engineering manager of the Sikorsky Aircraft Division of United Aircraft Corporation.

The last decade witnessed a brilliant and spectacular advancement in all branches of aviation. Meteoric jet-driven aircraft traveling at speeds that exceed the velocity of the cannon shells used in the Civil War, huge air transports and stratoliners crossing continents and oceans with great speeds and with considerable loads and regularity, and the many other remarkable types of aircraft, have assured aviation a position as one of the most important factors in war and peace.

The airplane, in spite of its tremendous development, has succeeded in materializing only one of the two fundamental ideas associated with flying for thousands of years—the ability to fly freely along any desired course. However, the airplane with respect to take-off or landing is definitely limited to areas usually located miles away from residential or business sections. An automobile can carry a traveler from home to destination; the airplane can only travel from one airport to another. The creation of an aircraft that would be completely free from this limitation, that could, like a humming bird, rise in the air or land on any small clearing even though it be surrounded by obstacles, formed the second vital problem which for a long time challenged the resourcefulness of aeronautical engineering.

It is significant that one of the earliest crystalized dreams about human flight—the legend of Icarus—stresses this second problem, namely, the ability to get into the air from small, inaccessible places. The answer to the problem—the helicopter—remained unsolved until the fifth decade of the twentieth century.

The fundamental principle of the helicopter is that all lift is obtained from one or more lifting motors driven directly by the engine which pull the craft straight up into the air. The idea was

319

extremely simple but its conversion into practice necessitated the correct solution of a number of problems so difficult that, for a long while, doubts were expressed that a successful helicopter would ever become a reality.

Nevertheless, the extensive research and engineering development that has been carried on for a long time, and particularly during the last five years, has eliminated all such doubts and the helicopter is now an assured aircraft. It is capable of taking off directly with no run whatsoever, hovering in the air over one spot, flying forward, backward, or sideways, at any desired speed between motionless hovering and the maximum speed of the craft. It is possible for the helicopter in flight to approach a man and hover in the air while a suitcase is placed on board, or permit a mechanic to unscrew a nut and remove a wheel from the craft, and replace them while the aircraft is still hovering near by. Many times a helicopter has taken off and landed on the roof of a small shed, landed in small backyards surrounded by trees and buildings, and in many areas and spots that would be completely inaccessible to other types of aircraft.

The possibilities of the helicopter can best be judged by a few examples of actual service performed. Early in January, 1944, an explosion on board a ship in New York Harbor resulted in a substantial number of casualties. Blood plasma was urgently needed to save lives. Accordingly, a helicopter was dispatched and under the capable piloting of Comdr. Erickson of the U. S. Coast Guard, it landed in Battery Park in New York, took on board two cases of the precious blood plasma and in spite of bad weather, wind and snow, delivered them 14 minutes later to the hospital in Staten Island where it was badly needed and immediately applied.

On other occasions this aircraft demonstrated its ability to travel a substantial distance as was the case when Col. H. F. Gregory of the U. S. Army flew one of the helicopters non-stop from Washington to Dayton, Ohio, covering a distance of almost 400 miles against a head wind in little less than 5 hours.

The outstanding characteristics of the helicopter offer vast possibilities of its use for saving lives. It is a source of great satisfaction to state that there have already been several cases when our helicopters have penetrated into inaccessible places in order to pick up and carry to safety men who were in danger, or who were injured. In some cases reasonably long flights over wild jungle and over mountains several thousand feet high were needed to accomplish these dramatic rescue missions.

In line with these achievements, it is interesting to note that less than four years ago the longest distance flown by a helicopter in the U. S. was less than a mile, while the highest altitude reached in flight was about seventy-five feet. And there was in the whole western hemisphere only one craft capable of even these modest performances.

I was the test pilot of this aircraft on a number of occasions, including its very first flight in October, 1939. It was a most interesting pioneering work. We had to design and build aircraft when very little theoretical and no practical information was available. And when the craft was ready, I had to climb into the cockpit and attempt to get it in the air without knowing how to pilot it. All that I knew was that the action of the controls was completely different from an airplane and in fact from any vehicle ever produced by man. It was a period of intensely interesting but also very hard work. Bright hopes were frequently superseded by disappointments. To obtain sufficient lift to get the craft into the air proved to be easy. In fact, it was done many times before. But a number of other problems, and particularly the stability and control, proved so difficult that at times it appeared that a successful helicopter was still very far away.

However, the hard work of a resourceful and competent engineering group succeeded in overcoming the obstacles and finally a truly successful helicopter with adequate and very precise control characteristics ceased to be a dream and became a reality. Recognizing the immense potential value of the direct lift aircraft, the U. S. Army placed orders permitting the expansion and acceleration of its development. This gratifying support has in fact made possible a large amount of scientific study and vast experimental work which has resulted in the creation of more refined and powerful helicopters capable of carrying several passengers.

One of the most interesting features of a helicopter is the possibility of using inflated rubber bags as a landing device. With this gear, it can be safely operated from ground, from water, from a swamp, from deep snow and even from thin ice because if that should break, the machine would still remain afloat. In this form the helicopter can be considered the most universal vehicle ever used or devised by man. For instance, a treacherous swamp or thin ice may form an obstacle or danger not only for any ordinary vehicle but even for a pack mule or a pedestrian. But a helicopter on rubber floats could still land and take off with perfect ease and safety.

Flying a helicopter is very interesting and pleasant. It is a strange and unique sensation when the craft, in obedience to a slight movement of the pitch lever, lifts one straight up into the air and then poses motionless some ten or fifteen feet above the ground, as if waiting for further orders. And it is like a dream to feel that a slight movement of the other control lever will immediately send the craft floating in the direction in which the stick has been moved —whether forward, backward or sideways.

It must be noted, however, that flying a helicopter requires as much or even slightly more skill than piloting a small airplane. The helicopters of the present and of the immediate future must be flown by good professional pilots and maintained by experienced mechanics. Several years of extensive engineering work are still necessary in order to perfect the helicopter and to simplify its controls to the extent of permitting its safe and economical use by average individuals. However, medium sized craft and light helicopter buses operated by professional crews will probably appear in service much earlier. They will carry mail, express, and passengers from small landing spaces or roof top platforms situated close to business or industrial centers or residential sections. In particular, they will render excellent service by carrying mail and passengers between these centers and the airports. Next will come the helicopter taxi cabs which will conveniently and quickly carry passengers straight to their destination independently of traffic congestions or detours. Still later will arrive a simple, small helicopter for private use.

In conclusion, I would like to express my firm belief that within the next decade the helicopter will prove a faithful and useful servant which will support a great new industry and a vast number of auxiliary enterprises. It will permit us to reside in beautiful, less expensive country places and still spend very little time for commuting. It will open undreamt of possibilities for recreation, exploring, prospecting, scientific study, and countless numbers of other uses. Equipped as an ambulance or fire fighter, it will prove by far the quickest friend in emergency. It will enlarge the area of this great country of ours by opening for residence, recreation development, mining, fishing, and so forth, wide new lands which cannot now be used due to lack of convenient transportation. There is a vast and bright future for this modest newcomer in the field of aircraft. I am confident that within a few years the helicopter will become a familiar sight to all and a most convenient method of travel for many, rendering a vast number of services which no other vehicle can perform.

Medical Research During the War

By Alfred Newton Richards

Dr. Alfred Newton Richards, for thirty-six years professor of pharmacology at the University of Pennsylvania, is now its vice-president in charge of Medical Affairs. He has recently been elected president of the National Academy of Sciences. During World War II he served as chairman of the Committee on Medical Research of the Office of Scientific Research and Development.

Among those, who in 1939 foresaw that our country would be drawn into the war, were some who envisaged the part that science would play in the winning of it. From their foresight Government organizations resulted through which civilian scientific resources were made to supplement those of our military forces. The National Defense Research Committee was created in 1940 and under it were mobilized the country's chemists, physicists, and engineers. Their efforts, now recognized as having been decisively responsible for such developments as radar, proximity fuses, amphibious vehicles and the atomic bomb, were at once so impressive that President Roosevelt in 1941 ordered the formation of the Committee on Medical Research with similar responsibilities in the field of medical science. By the same order he created the Office of Scientific Research and Development within which the two committees were to operate under its director, Dr. Bush.

In the beginning the tasks of the Committee on Medical Research were greatly facilitated by an alliance arranged with the Division of Medical Sciences of the National Research Council. For many months previously the Surgeons General of Army and Navy and their staffs had been in frequent consultation on problems of military medicine with committees of experts brought together by the Chairman of that Division. The personnel of these committees, numbering hundreds, consented to become advisers to the Committee on Medical Research and hence, utilizing their familiarity with the pressing problems of the medical services, the Committee on Medical Research was enabled without delay to inaugurate a well-conceived investigative program.

What were the problems then and subsequently presented to the Committee, concerning which new or additional knowledge was desired? To list the titles alone would take more than my entire allotted space. One purpose was common to all, namely, to increase the applicability of what was already known to the better protection of fighting men against injuries, disease, exposure and fatigue —whether in camps, in transports, in naval vessels or in the field— in the North African desert, in tropical jungles or in the Arctic.

The nature of the tasks can be illustrated by a few broad, categorically stated demands.

Find practical ways to restore blood volume in wounded men, thus to avoid or combat shock—ways adaptable to field as well as hospital use.

Show us how best to use sulfa drugs or other antibacterial agents to control infections of wounds and burns: how to accelerate wound healing and convalescence.

Give us improved protection against those infections which caused highest mortality during the last war—influenza, pneumonia, gas gangrene.

Give us equipment with which our aviators may better endure the lack of oxygen, the cold, the strain, and fatigue of combat at hitherto unreached altitudes.

Since the war had deprived us of quinine, tell us whether atabrine, a drug of German origin, can take its place as an antimalarial. Is it safe? Is it effective? In what regime of dosage shall it be used? Find, if you can, an antimalarial drug better than either quinine or atabrine.

If the enemy shall employ poison gases, what will they be and how will they be used? Design protection against them.

Find or invent insecticides and repellents by which to make a soldier's life in tropical jungles endurable as well as safe against his insect enemies.

The investigations designed to answer such demands as these were carried on in many institutions—universities, medical schools and hospitals, research institutes, and industrial organizations. Our aim, imperfectly realized we admit, was to enlist every available man whose knowledge and experience gave promise that he could contribute to the solution of the questions before us. On the Committee's recommendation, the Office of Scientific Research and Development entered into some 600 contracts in the field of medicine with nearly 150 institutions distributed throughout the country. Investigators numbering about 5,500 were involved; the cost to Government for 4½ years' work was approximately twenty-four million dollars.

While some of these investigations failed to yield results directly applicable in military medicine, it is safe to say that every one has given information which may find a place in the advance of medical knowledge; some, however, have been so brilliantly successful as to make the entire effort exceedingly profitable in lives saved, disabilities lessened, and combat effectiveness increased.

When one reviews the more conspicuously successful of these projects, he is struck by the fact that the fundamental groundwork had been laid long before the war.

Let me cite examples: (1) the safety of routine dosage with atabrine as a suppressive of malaria was decisively assured by our chemists and pharmacologists through experimental studies of its effects in animals and man; from their knowledge of its behavior in the body they showed how often and in what amounts it must be given; and on the basis of this information was built the atabrine discipline of our troops which reduced malaria from its position as a menace far more dangerous than enemy bullets, to one of relative inconsequence.

(2) A small fraction of the blood plasma which was collected through the agency of the Red Cross Blood Donor program was given to a group of chemists whose peace-time studies had been concerned with the characteristics of protein molecules. The combination of that priceless material with their knowledge and skill yielded important dividends in death prevention. From that plasma they were able to prepare pure albumin in concentrated solutions of small bulk as effective against shock as the original plasma. They extracted the clotting elements of blood and gave them to the surgeons in the form of pledgets, marvelously effective in stopping obstinate hemorrhage. They separated in the form of a dry powder the proteins of the blood which give us immunity against infections and found that it was an effective agent against two virus diseases with which numbers of our troops were being disabled, namely, measles and infectious jaundice.

(3) The compound known as DDT was made some 70 years ago by a German chemist with no other motive than to contribute to the body of knowledge of organic chemistry. Swiss agriculturists discovered its power to kill potato bugs and certain flies. From this scanty information which came to us along with samples of the substance in 1942, American science and industry developed the means by which the epidemic of typhus in Naples was aborted and by which future epidemics of that disease will be controlled— by which, too, the efficacy of sanitation against mosquito and other insect-borne diseases has been and will continue to be vastly increased.

(4) Penicillin: Alexander Fleming discovered its existence and predicted its usefulness in 1929. Florey succeeded in purifying a little of it and confirmed its therapeutic promise. Stimulated by Florey, American scientists learned how to increase its production and how further to purify it. American physicians proved its power and its limitations; and against enormous difficulties American manufacturers succeeded in transforming a difficult laboratory operation into a great industry. In less than three years they gave to our forces and to those of our British Allies huge supplies of this most remarkable weapon against infections yet discovered. Already the saving in lives and prevention of crippling has been incalculable; and a permanent asset to the health and welfare of the

human race has been created; all from the understanding which a modest scientist brought to bear upon a chance observation 16 years ago.

These accomplishments illustrate the usefulness which can be made to emerge from pre-existing basic knowledge, developed to practical ends under the stimulus of a national emergency—an emergency which brought together in unselfish cooperation Government agencies, academic and private research institutions and industrial scientists and technologists. The roots from which these and many other fruits have grown were long ago put forth in the soil of our academic institutions where knowledge is pursued for its own sake.

Progress in Aviation

By Jerome C. Hunsaker

Dr. Jerome C. Hunsaker is head or the Department of Aeronautical Engineering at the Massachusetts Institute of Technology, and chairman of the National Advisory Committee for Aeronautics.

The basic inventions of the automobile and the airplane marked the beginning of our century. The automobile has already changed life in America, and the airplane promises to do so in the immediate future.

Flight came at a time most favorable for the application of science to its development. Probably at no previous time in the history of the world could the airplane have been perfected. It entered a technical world ready with gasoline, metals, electricity, and tools.

The airplane also entered a scientific world ready with the fruits of nineteenth century science, including the most powerful tool of all, scientific research. The airplane was certainly fortunate in the date of its birth.

Like other newborn things, the first airplanes were without utility. However, the infant industry founded on the invention of the Wright Brothers became at once the darling of the public, which always longed to fly through the air. It also became the concern and ward of governments. The social gains expected from

technological progress displaced economic considerations. The airplane industry, consequently, was not required to go through the
usual long and painful stages of growth, before it could afford
scientific research.

July 25, 1909, a Sunday, Bleriot's little French monoplane flew
across the English Channel. On that day Britain ceased to be an
island protected from intrusion by surrounding seas.

The significance of Bleriot's crossing of the Channel was not lost.
The great physicist Lord Rayleigh was asked by the British Prime
Minister in 1909 to head an Advisory Committee for Aeronautics,
composed of the leading scientists and engineers of the Kingdom.

In Germany, the Government called on science to become air-
minded. "The Kaiser Wilhelm Fund" subsidized an aeronautical
research laboratory at Göttingen University under Professor Prandtl.
This laboratory made outstanding contributions to our knowledge
of aerodynamics.

In America, organized aeronautical research began in 1915 when
President Wilson asked Congress to establish the National Advisory Committee for Aeronautics to undertake the scientific study
of the problems of flight. For some 30 years the NACA has supplied designers with research results.

As I have indicated, scientific research, conducted at public expense, has aided the airplane from the beginning and, as a result,
aviation has come fast and far within our lifetime. Recall that the
Wright airplane of 1908 flew at 40 miles per hour. During the
First World War, a speed of 150 miles per hour was considered
fast for a fighter. In the recent war, the speed of fighter planes
in use exceeded 400 miles, and jet-propelled fighters showed bursts
of speed well beyond 500 miles per hour.

I chose speed as a simple index of technical progress. I might
just as well have chosen range or payload. Compare the thirty
mile cross-channel flight of Louis Bleriot, flying alone, with the
hourly departures of great transports from America to Europe and
the Far East! Surely, this is progress of a practical nature.

Let me illustrate how research leads to practical advances by
giving an example.

The Wrights had experimented with small model wings of bent
sheet metal held in a wind stream to determine the best curvature.

Their experiments correctly predicted the lift per square foot of such thin wings. In order to support the weight of their airplane in flight it was necessary not only to have large wings but to keep the wings themselves light. This forced the Wrights to use the biplane construction developed by Chanute, the glider pioneer.

Biplane construction requires bracing by struts and wires, exposed to the wind and holding down speed. An obvious improvement would be to put all the wing area into a single wing, a monoplane, and to eliminate the external bracing as in a biplane.

At this point the basic science of fluid mechanics entered the problem to show that lift comes from the difference in pressure on the top and bottom of the wing, and that this pressure difference is created by speeding up the air above the wing and slowing it down below.

The theory showed how to create the necessary velocity difference by the use of a thick wing having the top surface strongly curved and the lower surface less so.

Thick wing shapes based on this theory were found to give not only as good a lift as the thin wings, but also to disturb the air less and so to offer less resistance to forward motion. And thick monoplane wings could thus be made stiff enough to do without external bracing. Thus shortly after the First World War, the biplane became obsolete because of the superior efficiency of the monoplane.

But the effects of improvements are cumulative. As soon as thick monoplane wings were proved useful, structural research suggested that the wings would be stronger if built like a canoe, with a stiff skin replacing the fabric covering. Such wings were first made with plywood skin, but plywood in the nineteen-twenties did not weather well and became unsafe.

Metallurgical science then offered a strong, light metal, duralumin, an alloy of aluminum with copper. Thick, unbraced monoplane wings of metal were eventually perfected and have now become standard. All-metal airplanes, therefore, became possible from new knowledge of aerodynamics, structural theory, and metallurgy derived from scientific research.

Another important improvement was made possible by the thick wing. Most birds tuck away their feet and legs in flight. Why not have a retracting landing gear? The question was easy to ask, but there was no place to house the landing gear in thin-winged biplanes.

As soon as thick-winged metal monoplanes were available, however, designers devised mechanisms to fold the landing gear into the interior of the wing in flight. The resulting improvement in speed was notable.

Research lies behind nearly every detail of the modern airplane and its engine, propeller, radio guns, and bombs.

Military security still makes it impossible for me to describe the latest research results now being applied to our military and naval airplanes. But I can say that new knowledge is rapidly coming to hand. Certain research results reduced to practice as part of the military program are also becoming available for commercial use.

There are some signposts already visible which may indicate something of what we may expect. Recall that the gasoline engine made the airplane possible and that the engine is still the heart of the airplane. The power available from a single engine has grown from the scant 40 horsepower of the Wright 1908 biplane to more than 3000 horsepower for each of the engines of the new bombers and transports. Recent increases in engine output have, however, been increasingly difficult to secure, and there is reason to believe we are approaching the economical limit for the reciprocating engine.

On the other hand, the combustion gas turbine gives every promise of being most efficient in large units. Its practical use depends on new alloys to withstand high temperatures. The turbine blades must run red hot. All of our bombers successfully used small exhaust gas turbines, driving superchargers. The modern jet-propelled fighter planes have a gas turbine to run the compressor that supplies combustion air for the jet.

Very high speeds are now possible. Whether extreme speeds, approaching the velocity of sound, about 750 miles per hour, are commercially feasible is very doubtful, but for military purposes maximum speeds are always wanted.

Many aspects of research affect safety. Research on the physics of ice formation suggests effective means to keep ice from forming on the surfaces of an airplane by utilizing exhaust heat.

Research on the nature of atmospheric electricity suggests precautions to be taken against lightning.

Research in high-frequency radio provides radio apparatus to increase the precision of navigation, to avoid collision, and to promote safe landings when visibility is impaired or absent. Scheduled air transport should eventually be free from interruptions due to weather.

Public use of the airplane will grow with improvements in its performance, economy, and safety. Continuous progress can be expected from an advancing technology derived from scientific research.

CHAPTER 15

THE LONG-TERM VALUES

IN THE previous chapters the reader has had authentic and illuminating glimpses of many problems and fields of science. Perhaps, as he draws near the end of the book, he is curious to return to some of the questions raised at the beginning. How does scientific research accomplish its purposes? What does science mean to us? What relation does it have to the rest of life?

Science is, of course, simply the sum total of the activity of scientists. That is why a book such as this, which gives the reader direct contact with a considerable number of top-notch scientists, is a really dependable indication of what science is.

No one should think that science is something strange, something alien to the rest of life. Every person, every day, is affected by science. It protects him, serves him, makes him comfortable, keeps him healthy, cures him when he is sick. It is interwoven into the fabric of our lives, and is an essential part of it.

Science is not foreign to any one of us, or at least should not be. For science is simple organized common sense, highly perfected to deal with certain sorts of problems. If a window sticks when you try to open it, and you respond by giving it a terrific bang or pull, then you are not being scientific. If you stop to look at it, see where and why it sticks, see if by chance it is tilted in the frame or perhaps actually locked, then you are being a scientist.

Even the most primitive peoples achieve scientific results, but do so unconsciously and inefficiently, at great waste of time and energy. Some African natives, when they move their primitive dwellings to a new location, take a few handfuls from the dirt floor of each old hut, and put them on the floor of the new. They say that by continuing to live on the same bit of earth they are avoiding incurring the anger of the gods who might object to their moving.

Actually, in this handful of dirt, they are transferring to the soil of their new homes certain microorganisms which will help to protect them from disease. If they transfer this protection to the new huts, they are less likely to have an epidemic of disease after moving—less likely, as they would say, to incur the anger of the gods. Their understanding is faulty, and their technique inefficient. But it is important to recognize that in this instance, as in the case of many other superstitions and habits of simple people, the slow and clumsy distillation of human experience arrives at the same sort of results which scientific methods would reach much more quickly and accurately.

Thus science has really done nothing more than sharpen up to a very keen edge, mental tools which we all possess. We are all scientists, to some degree or other.

So science should be an important part of the life and thought of each one of us. And being a natural and universal part of life, it should not be considered antagonistic to other parts of life. Recurring to the metaphor of mental tools, science is a fine-grained oilstone which puts an exquisitely keen edge on scalpels for certain mental operations. But every tool has its proper use. The delicate precision of the scalpel should not in any sense prejudice us against the sculptor's chisel or the bread knife we use every day in the kitchen, the jackknife with which we whittle just for fun, or the paper cutter with which we open a book of poems.

W. W.

Science and Our Nation's Future

By Arthur H. Compton

Dr. Arthur H. Compton, Nobel Prize winner in physics, is chancellor
of Washington University, St. Louis.

DURING World War II the nation was calling for all of its scientific strength. On the battlefields of Europe and the Orient and on the Seven Seas new weapons were turning the tide of battle. On both sides of the conflict determined men fought with courage and skill. If we were to win a decisive victory we had to have weapons not only greater in quantity but superior in quality. Superior quality required skilled labor, and great industries with knowledge of the best techniques. It required ingenious inventors with fertile imaginations. But basic to all was required the science that makes possible the new inventions.

Now that the war is won, the task of maintaining a strong leadership in science is still with us. After the hates and injustices that the war has brought, the safety of the United States in a post-war world demands eternal vigilance. But not even vigilance is enough. If we are in earnest in striving for a peace with freedom to work for the best we know, there is only one course for us to follow. This course is to maintain with the nations friendly to us such strength that we shall not be challenged while we seek to build a world in which war will be considered as a disaster rather than as the only hope for the improvement of a people's lot.

How shall we maintain order while this peace-loving world is being built? Only by keeping ourselves strong and working for friendly relations with our neighbors.

It will require a long time thus to make the world forget war. If we are to retain our leadership it will be only through superiority in those things that make a modern nation great. Foremost among those things is science.

Have you ever paused to consider why the Occident has, during the past two or three centuries, come to dominate the world? You may remember that at the time of Marco Polo under the great

Khan of China there flourished a civilization more powerful and more refined than Europe could boast. Somehow there arose in the West the ardent desire to know. Henry of Portugal, and Columbus of Genoa, following Polo's example, went out to explore the world. Leonardo and Francis Bacon and Galileo sought to learn the hidden nature of things that they might enlarge the bounds of human empire. Newton and Lavoisier, Franklin and Faraday, Henry and Helmholtz—these great men of science opened up a vast new world. They gave to Europe and America the steam power and the firearms that meant military might. They made possible the machines of industry which supplied the means of living to greatly increased populations.

It is only very recently that the United States has taken a leading place in searching out nature's secrets. We were busy carving a nation out of the wilderness.

While Europe was refining her science, we were applying our knowledge to the everyday jobs of making agricultural machinery, electric lights and transcontinental railroads. We found these things worth while because they enabled more people to live better. During the First World War we learned, however, that in spite of our great industrial strength, our European allies and enemies were ahead of us in devising new weapons. We found them leading us in almost all branches of fundamental science. When that war was over, our soldiers returned with a determination to learn the science that had shown itself of such value. The great educational foundations established fellowships to encourage scientific study and research. The universities rapidly built up their departments of science. By the time the Second great World War came, we had become respected the world over for our work in science. In medicine and chemistry and physics and astronomy we trained thousands of capable young men and developed many recognized leaders. We are proud of what our men of science did in the last war. We took our full part beside our great allies in the scientific as well as the industrial aspects of the great struggle. Our enemies had years of head start on us in developing machines of war. Some of these developments, such as the long range bombs, began to be effective only near the end. Yet with our control of the submarine menace, our precise techniques of ladio location and our airplane developments, the score turned in our favor.

The international competition for leadership in science, though on a friendly basis, is nevertheless intense. I recall in 1927 commenting to the Director of Germany's great National Institute of Physics and Chemistry with regard to the high quality of his scientific instruments. Though Germany was complaining then of her poverty, in our country no universities or Government laboratories could afford such equipment. The reason, said Dr. Paschen, was not far to seek. The Reichstag was determined to give all possible support to German science. They no longer had any Kaiser, nor any army. In what could they take pride? "Our men of science," they said. "Let's make of them the best in the world."

This was the spirit that enabled our enemy to match step by step the combined technical developments of ourselves and our allies. It is true that when the Nazis came into power, the study of fundamental science was greatly curtailed and even the technical schools fell to roughly 25 per cent of their full enrollment as they were building up their armies just before 1939. Yet this did not go as far toward destroying their scientific strength as we went in weakening our own science in the late war. Just as the war began, the Germans came to realize the danger to their future because of their failure to train enough scientific and technical men. They set aside an increased group of young men best qualified for science and barred them from entering the armed forces.

At least until near the end of the war these students continued their training for careers in science and technology. The result is that the German war industries and research organizations had a continuing supply of fully trained men.

Our national policy with regard to the training of scientific men was precisely the reverse. We gambled on a short war. Science professors and students alike left the universities. All of their effort was concentrated on devising and developing new and improved weapons. Because we were caught unprepared for a war in which scientific developments have become so vital, this has seemed to be the only possible procedure. Yet during the war practically no students over 18, except a few 4-F's, studied science.

If the war could have been completed within a year or two this policy would have been a good one. The idea was that everyone would put all that he had into the fight, and get it over with, and then return as promptly as conditions permitted, to resume normal tasks. But if the war had continued for a few years longer than it did, our policy of no advanced scientific and technical training would have spelled national disaster.

It takes at least six years for a capable eighteen-year-old to train himself for effective scientific research. Even when a nation starts to resume such training, it is at least six years before a normal supply of young professionals is again available. Can any nation ever afford to interrupt basic scientific training?

This is a situation of national concern which needs to be carefully watched in any time of crisis lest we find that we have gained a Pyrrhic victory, having lost so much of our technical strength that we are then unable to carry on the great task of world leadership before us.

Other authors in this book have explained how the growth of science brings to us life of greater human value. Increased cooperation and concern for each other's welfare, greater attention to education for everybody, fresh consideration of the goals of living worthy of our great new powers, such human developments are sure consequences of the emphasis that science places on specialized skills and on coordinated effort in learning and using knowledge.

What I want especially to stress is the fact that greatly increased emphasis on science is a "must" for our nation's safety and future welfare. If a wise course is followed with regard to recruitment, training, and in other support of science, our nation is in a favorable position to lead the world in the scientific age that lies ahead.

Unforeseeable Results of Research

By Irving Langmuir

Dr. Irving Langmuir, Nobel Prize winner in chemistry, has for many years been the associate director of the research laboratories of the General Electric Company.

MUCH of the work of an industrial research laboratory is directed toward the solution of specific problems that are known to exist within the industry—problems that can presumably be solved by the application of scientific knowledge already available.

There is another type of research, which I like to call fundamental research, that aims to extend the frontiers of knowledge. The results of such new knowledge cannot be foreseen; and through fundamental research, problems are sometimes solved which were not even known to exist.

Let me illustrate these points by describing the history of some developments in incandescent lamps—which many of my readers doubtless call electric light bulbs.

Up to about 1905 all incandescent electric lamps were of the type that Edison invented in 1880. They had a threadlike filament of carbon sealed into a glass bulb from which the air was pumped out. By passing electric current through the filament it could be heated to such a high temperature that it gave off a bright light. It was necessary to produce within the bulb a vacuum so good that only about one part in a hundred thousand of air remained.

In 1908 the tungsten filament type of lamp became available. Tungsten, a metal which has an extremely high melting point, gave filaments which could be heated much hotter than Edison's carbon filaments and thus the light output was increased about three times for the same power consumption and the same cost of operation.

Dr. W. D. Coolidge in our laboratory discovered how to make tungsten filaments that were tough and strong, but at the time that I came to the laboratory in 1909 a difficulty was being experienced that the filaments became brittle if the lamps were operated on alternating current.

Instead of being assigned to a specific problem, I was encouraged

338

to become familiar with all the work going on in the laboratory and to select a problem which would be of the greatest interest to me.

I proposed determining whether the brittleness which developed with alternating current was in any way associated with gas in the filaments, so I heated these tungsten wires in bulbs having good vacuum and measured the quantity of gas given off. This, however, was not found to have anything to do with the brittleness. Incidentally, however, I had found some queer effects which greatly interested me. Traces of gas within the bulb usually disappeared when the filament was heated. Purely out of scientific curiosity and without any thought of applying the results to an improvement of the lamp I started to put various kinds of gas into the lamp—gases such as oxygen, nitrogen, etc., just to see what happened. I discovered that the molecules of hydrogen gas in contact with the hot filament were broken down into their constituent atoms. This atomic hydrogen had tremendous chemical activity.

Some comparative experiments with nitrogen showed that nitrogen atoms could not be produced in this way. I noticed, however, that filaments could be heated in nitrogen almost to 6000° for a much longer time than would have been possible with a filament in vacuum. In order better to understand the way that heat was carried from the filament by gases I tried filaments of various sizes and got the rather unexpected result that although one filament, twice the size of another, would give twice as much light, the larger filament needed only very little more power.

In the course of this work it developed that no gas, with the exception of water vapor, ever produced any blackening of the bulb, although the general opinion among lamp engineers had been that all gases in lamps caused increased blackening and shortened the life of the lamp.

I suddenly realized that by using such a gas as nitrogen at atmospheric pressure, and by taking exceptional precautions to avoid all traces of moisture in the gas or on the surface of the bulb, it might be possible to increase the life of the lamp and even improve the efficiency.

After months of experimenting we found that we could, in fact, make durable lamps which, as compared with the previous vacuum lamps, gave twice as much light for the same electric power. Later it occurred to me that the advantageous effect of the large diameter filament could be realized by using a small filament in the form of a closely wound coil.

Although all of my readers are doubtless very familiar with the appearance of an electric light bulb, I may have used some terms in describing its development, which are strange to you. But I hope I have explained clearly why you now have the advantage of an electric lamp which is vastly superior to that which existed some forty years ago. It was only by combining several types of new knowledge that the improved lamp became possible. It is highly improbable that this necessary new knowledge would have resulted from any planned research program aimed directly at improving the efficiency of tungsten lamps. The new knowledge did in fact result from fundamental research whose direct aim was only to extend the frontiers of knowledge.

During the ensuing years, there has been almost continuous further improvement in the efficiency of lamps. By replacing the nitrogen by the previously useless gas argon and by developing better types of tungsten wire it has been possible to make efficient gas-filled lamps consuming as little as 40 watts.

Because of the large number of lamps used, a one per cent improvement in efficiency saves the consumers in the United States alone over $10,000,000 per year. In the last twenty-five years the efficiency has increased one hundred per cent and the resulting savings reach many hundreds of millions of dollars yearly.

The fundamental scientific knowledge which has been the basis of the technical developments that have so greatly increased our standard of living and our power to survive in war, have come from the freedom of the scientist to explore unknown fields. Outside support for research, and particularly for fundamental research aimed at acquiring new knowledge, will have a stimulating effect insofar as it makes facilities available to scientists and helps to attract young students into this field; but great harm might come from any attempt at regimentation based upon a belief that fundamental research can be wholly directed from the top down.

It is not reasonable to expect that the directors of laboratories, or boards set up to direct scientific work, are supermen who can foresee new knowledge before it exists. Only a small part of scientific progress has resulted from a planned search for specific objectives. A much more important part has been made possible by the freedom of the scientist to follow his own curiosity in search for truth.

The Role of Chemical Research

BY ROGER ADAMS

Dr. Roger Adams has been, for many years, the head of the Department of Chemistry at the University of Illinois; and in that laboratory and in many other national connections has been active in research in organic chemistry.

MOST Americans know that scientific research helped our nation win the war. And they know that this same research in peacetime creates new industries and products, and makes possible a continually higher standard of living.

Indeed, our investment of trained men, equipment, and money in scientific research is one of our principal foundations for postwar development. If scientific research is wisely and effectively utilized, it may lead to a peace-time economy and to standards of living that may do much to help preserve the peace.

I want to describe briefly part of the story behind this research. The layman often is inclined to regard the results of this scientific quest as miracles. Well, research has produced a host of brilliant discoveries. But they were not miracles. Instead, they were the product of years of patient, painstaking work by highly trained scientists, usually working in teams and utilizing the skills of numerous specialists.

I could mention dozens of scientific accomplishments which appear to be miracles, but each of which was actually the culmination of long-continued cooperative effort of experts. Let me be content to mention only a few outstanding examples, such as high-octane gas, which powered our fighting aircraft; synthetic rubber, without which the wheels of war could not have moved; atabrin, which protected our soldiers and sailors from malaria; the sulfa drugs; penicillin; DDT; the beautiful transparent plastics which during the war were used for windows in the turrets and noses of our bombers; powerful new explosives; marvelous new alloys.

How are such discoveries made? How are these attractive, useful and essential materials created? Not a single discovery is the result of a miracle or of crystal gazing. When it is announced that some important product has been developed from the basic chemicals found in coal, air, and water, you are usually not told that a vast chemical industry utilizing these basic chemicals has been in operation long before research on the new discovery had even been started. Without these industries the new discovery could not have been brought to fruition. These spectacular discoveries spring from the cooperative effort of groups of chemists and chemical engineers. The initial discoveries are usually made in the laboratory by chemists. The devising of methods for producing the new products in huge amounts and the building of plants is the responsibility of the chemical engineer. The contributions to science of academic research supply the food for the applied scientist, who is seeking to develop useful, effective commercial products.

These chemists and chemical engineers are the professional men and women behind our chemical discoveries. They have been trained for years in the basic principles of chemistry, physics, and engineering. The research chemist requires an education equivalent in years to that of the physician. And, just as the physician must serve an internship before he starts to practice, so the research chemist must have additional experience before he becomes an effective, independent investigator. To be completely trained, the scientist must be adept in foreign languages and he must read regularly the many series of scientific journals and publications describing the results of research in university and industrial research laboratories throughout the world. His work is fascinating and rewarding; but nevertheless it is real work, not play or magic.

The research chemist must know, of course, the basic laws of chemistry. These laws have been evolved through long-continued study of products found in nature. The chemist isolated pure chemicals from nature's complex mixtures such as in coal, petroleum, minerals, and animal and vegetable life. From nature's mixtures the chemist isolated and purified such things as starch, vegetable oils, perfumes from flowers, medicinals and dyes from plants, and metals or metal-containing compounds from ores and minerals. Then, studying these pure products, the scientists formulated laws governing the breakdown of complex substances into simpler ones. More importantly, they gradually learned how to rebuild simple substances into complex ones according to almost any pattern desired.

Sometimes the chemist merely duplicates a product that nature already furnishes, as in the case of indigo. This important blue dye was originally obtained from certain shrubs; but can now be produced more cheaply by chemistry in the laboratory.

Sometimes the chemist improves on nature. For example, the local anesthetic, cocaine, was first isolated from coca leaf and purified. Chemists found only part of this complicated molecule was needed for its anesthetic action, and they went on to make, synthetically, simple compounds patterned on this essential portion of the cocaine. In this way, numerous local anesthetics such as procaine were discovered which have proved far more valuable to the doctor and dentist than cocaine. But all this took the concentrated effort of many research chemists for a period of over 10 years.

Sometimes the chemist does not succeed in duplicating nature; but in the process of studying nature and imitating her, many useful results occur. For example, nature is particularly efficient in producing very useful complex substances, such as wool, silk, cotton, and rubber, which are so complicated that chemists have not yet succeeded in clarifying their character completely, or in synthesizing them. They have learned that they are made up of a very large number of the same or different simple substances which nature has combined together chemically.

The formation of these large molecules, usually chain-like in structure, can be compared to the mechanical tying together, end to end, of a large number of short pieces of twine until a very long single string results.

Bakelite, the first of these synthetic complex substances to be produced commercially a few decades ago, was developed on a cut and try basis by combining many molecules of carbolic acid and formaldehyde together. Until recent years, no careful scientific study was made to provide general laws by which the synthesis of these giant substances would be formed.

It was primarily through the carefully planned and ingenious research program of the late Dr. W. H. Carothers and his staff that a systematic knowledge of synthetic procedures for this type of complex molecule was acquired. The first experiments explored the conditions by which the small molecules could be made to combine with each other until very large ones resulted, without having the process stop at some intermediate stage and yield products which did not have inert properties.

When success in this was achieved, the huge molecules thus formed were something like warm molasses candy which can be pulled. A large variety of simple substances and combinations of more than one kind then were converted to their giant counterparts. When the right selection of simple molecules had been made, the large molecules had fibre-like properties and one of these was nylon. Ten years were spent on the fundamental studies and the large-scale development by dozens of chemists and chemical engineers before the product was manufactured into a commercial article.

Achievements such as these can be accomplished only by close cooperation between academic and industrial research laboratories. The war all but stopped this basic, academic research which finds new truths, and supplies new material upon which much of the industrial progress of the future depends. Years will be required before basic research activity again reaches its prewar level. The war also stopped the training of new research chemists. Thousands of academic and industrial chemists were drafted into the armed services, with only a few of them in positions where they could use their technical knowledge. Furthermore, the research organizations associated with industry, which find new products and upon which industry relies for expansion and for creation of new jobs, were at a low ebb. There is no possibility that they can recover quickly in the near future. This is a matter of great concern to the scientists and should be to the public, for only by years of patient research by trained and competent investigators can we maintain the high level of achievement in the field of science, on which is based our position of eminence among nations.

Science and History

By Henry E. Sigerist

Dr. Henry Ernest Sigerist recently retired from his position as professor
and director of the Institute of the History of Medicine, Johns Hopkins
University.

We all know that science has a future and probably a very great
future. The progress achieved in our lifetime has been stupendous.
I graduated from medical school in 1917 and find it hard to realize
how greatly medical science has changed during the 30 years since
I was a student,—how many basic discoveries have been made. We
all agree that science has a future, but few stop to think that it
has a past also. Oh, we remember the quaint automobiles at the
beginning of our century that looked like horseless carriages, and
we have seen in the movies the locomotives of a hundred years ago
that looked like toys. Funny as they seem today, they represented
a great progress at their time and were the result of real scientific
research. We remember, too, that the navigators who in the fifteenth
and sixteenth centuries discovered new continents could not have
sailed unless they had been supplied with instruments invented for
them by scientists.

But these are matters of the past, and one is perfectly justified to
ask why anybody should spend his time studying the history of
science. Is it more than a history of errors, or at best of curiosities?
To raise this question is to raise another one: why do we study
history at all?

Many people consider the study of history a kind of luxury. Oh,
they will gladly admit that it is interesting to know what happened
in the past, and how people lived in the early days. They will con-
cede that one should have some knowledge of history; but after all,
we are living in today's world with its hard realities, in ever-changing situations and, they usually add, nobody has ever learned from
history.

This is a very wrong view. History, the knowledge we have of
our past, the picture of our past that we carry in us—these are
powerful driving forces which often determine our actions. Every

situation in which we find ourselves, every event that takes place, is the result of certain historical developments and trends. All of a sudden we found ourselves in the midst of a bloody war. Why? What had happened? Could the war have been prevented? Today we find ourselves confronted with the gigantic task of organizing the peace. Why is it so difficult? We cannot understand the world in which we live, and in which we are expected to play an intelligent part, unless we are thoroughly familiar with the historical developments that have shaped this world and created its problems.

And now I can speak again about science, because what is true for history at large applies also to the history of science.

Science has played such a tremendous part in shaping our world, and is bound to play so increasingly important a part in the world of tomorrow, that it is impossible to understand historical developments without considering science. Science has revolutionized our economic and social life. It has also profoundly influenced our religion, philosophy, literature, and art.

In studying the history of science, we have two purposes. The first is to obtain a more complete and more correct picture of the history of civilization. We must ascertain accurately what the impact of science and technology has been on the people's life, what part it has played in shaping events in the past and what part it is playing today. In the pursuit of these studies we address ourselves not to the specialist but to the citizen at large who is groping for an understanding of the world and feels bewildered by many recent scientific developments.

But scientists study the history of science also for their own benefit. Every profession needs heroes, men whose example we can follow. Whoever has engaged in scientific research has experienced moments of profound despair, when every experiment went wrong, or the results could not be understood.

In such moments we remembered men like Copernicus who struggled to create a new astronomy, or Galileo who founded a new physics despite persecution, or Lavoisier, the father of modern chemistry who was beheaded at the time of the French Revolution, or Edward Jenner whose vaccine saved hundreds of thousands of human lives. Remembering such men, our faith and courage are renewed.

We also study the history of science and teach it in our colleges because today, more than ever, we need a broad scientist who is not a mere technician but is prepared to take an active part in the general life of the community. We must be aware that science alone is useless as long as it is not integrated into the pattern of our social and economic life. For example, we have today a highly developed science of nutrition. We know what people should eat in order to be healthy and in full possession of their physical and mental faculties. We also know how to produce food, because we have a highly developed agricultural science. We can increase the fertility of the soil and improve the quality of the crops. And yet with all this scientific knowledge we have not been able to prevent a world famine. Even under normal conditions, without world war, it is no exaggeration to say that one-half of the population of the world, over one billion people, permanently suffer from malnutrition.

Similarly, we have the scientific and technical knowledge that permits us to produce commodities in almost unlimited quantities. And yet, with all this technical knowledge, poverty is still the curse of mankind. Untold millions of people live on the lowest conceivable standard. We have new means of transportation. They have truly reduced the size of the globe and have made this planet one world. But although we find it very easy to fly from one country to another, yet we all know how difficult it is for the people of the world to understand one another and to cooperate.

In my own field of medicine, scientific progress has been very spectacular. A great many diseases that were deadly only yesterday have been overcome. Health conditions have greatly improved, at least in the economically advanced countries, but they are by no means good enough. We still lose thousands of children every year that could be saved. We still lose mothers needlessly. We still have diseases that could be wiped out entirely with the scientific knowledge we possess. We estimate that even in the United States one-third of all deaths are premature. In other words, one-third of the people who die at a certain age could have lived and could have been productive much longer, if they had had all the benefits of modern medical science. Why these shortcomings?

If we analyze the situation historically, we find that medicine and the society in which we live have changed tremendously during the last hundred years. By applying scientific principles, medicine itself became very technical, very highly specialized, very effective, and very expensive. The cost of production of the service increased more rapidly than the purchasing power of the population. While these developments took place in medicine, the structure of our society was transformed radically by industrialization. After two great industrial revolutions, we live in a society that is itself highly specialized, highly technical,—but insecure because it is primarily a society of wage earners which depends on a labor market that, in spite of our efforts, is subject to wide fluctuations. History, in other words, indicates that our new medical science must face a variety of new social problems.

In every field of human endeavor the new science that developed from the Renaissance on, slowly first, then with increasing rapidity, has created new conditions, raising new problems. These problems are not scientific in themselves but social, economic, political. Their solution requires the cooperation of men trained in many fields, and indispensable among these cooperators is the scientist.

But the scientist must be aware of more than his science—he must also be aware of the social implications of his science and sensitive to its human responsibilities and obligations. From this it follows that history and science are essentially co-partners and co-laborers in the work of the world. We must study both, and apply to our common problems the joint lessons of both science and history.

A Layman Looks at Science

By Raymond B. Fosdick

Mr. Raymond B. Fosdick, the president of The Rockefeller Foundation, is a lawyer by profession. In addition to service for the government during two wars, and a period as Under Secretary General of the League of Nations, he has been for over thirty years associated with the various Rockefeller educational, philanthropic, and scientific Boards.

AUGUST 6, 1945—the day the atomic bomb was dropped on Hiroshima—brought home to all of us in dramatic fashion the significance of science in human life. The impact of that bomb has left us stunned and confused. Certainly we laymen are frightened by science as we never were before. And certainly, too, we are bewildered by the power which science has suddenly placed in our laps —bewildered and humbled by our realization of how unequipped we are, in terms of ethics, law, and government, to know how to use it.

That, I think, is the first reaction of a layman to the stupendous repercussion of that bomb on Hiroshima. And the first question that comes to his mind is this: What use are radios and automobiles and penicillin and all the other gifts of science if at the same time this same science hands us the means by which we can blow ourselves and our civilization into drifting dust? We have always been inclined to think of research and technology as being consciously related to human welfare. Now, frankly, we are not so sure, and we are troubled, deeply troubled, by the realization that man's brain can create things which his will may not be able to control.

To the layman it seems as if science were facing a vast dilemma. Science is the search for truth, and it is based on the glorious faith that truth is worth discovering. It springs from the noblest attribute of the human spirit. But it is this same search for truth that has brought our civilization to the brink of destruction; and we are confronted by the tragic irony that when we have been most successful in pushing out the boundaries of knowledge we have most endangered the possibility of human life on this planet. The pursuit of truth has at last led us to the tools by which we can ourselves become the destroyers of our own institutions and all the bright hopes of the race. In this situation what do we do—curb our science or cling to the pursuit of truth and run the risk of having our society torn to pieces?

It is on the basis of this dilemma that serious questions are forming in the public mind. Unless research is linked to a humane and constructive purpose should it not be subject to some kind of restraint? Can our scientists afford to be concerned solely with fact and not at all with value and purpose? Can they legitimately claim that their only aim is the advancement of knowledge regardless of its consequences? Is the layman justified in saying to the scientist: "We look to you to distinguish between that truth which furthers the well-being of mankind and that truth which threatens it"?

One of the scientists who played a leading role in the development of the atomic bomb said to the newspapermen: "A scientist cannot hold back progress because of fears of what the world will do with his discoveries." What he apparently implied was that science has no responsibility in the matter and that it will plunge ahead in the pursuit of truth even if the process leaves the world in dust and ashes.

Is that the final answer? Is there no other answer? Frankly, as a layman I do not know. Offhand, this disavowal of concern for the social consequences of science seems callous and irresponsible. But we may be facing a situation where no other answer is realistic or possible. To ask the scientist to foresee the use—the good or evil of the use—to which his results may be put is doubtless beyond the realm of the attainable. Almost any discovery can be used for either social or antisocial purposes. The German dye industry was not created to deal with either medicine or weapons of war; and yet out of that industry came our sulfa-drugs and mustard gas. When Einstein wrote his famous transformation equation in 1905 he was not thinking of the atomic bomb, but out of that equation came one of the principles upon which the bomb was based.

Willard Gibbs was a gentle spirit whose life was spent in his laboratory at Yale University and who never dreamed that his work in mathematical physics might have even a remote relationship to war; and yet it is safe to say that his ideas gave added power to the armaments of all nations in both World War I and World War II.

I suspect that the way out of the dilemma is not as simple as the questions now being asked seem to imply. The good and the evil that flow from scientific research are more often than not indistinguishable at the point of origin. Generally they are by-products, or they represent distortions of original purpose, none of which could have been foreseen when the initial discovery was made. We are driven back to a question of human motives and desires. Science has recently given us radar, jet propulsion and power sources of unprecedented magnitude. What does society want to do with them? It can use them constructively to increase the happiness of mankind, or it can employ them to tear the world to pieces. There is scarcely a scientific formula or a process or a commodity which cannot be used for war purposes, if that is what we elect to

do with it. In brief, the gifts of science can be used by evil men
to do evil even more obviously and dramatically than they can be
used by men of good will to do good.

I fear there is no easy way out of our dilemma. I would not
absolve the scientists from some measure of responsibility, for they
are men of superior training and insight and we are entitled to
look to them for help and leadership—more help and leadership,
I venture to add, than have thus far been given. However, I note
that a considerable number of the scientists who were connected
with the atomic bomb project have publicly expressed their appre-
hension of the consequences of their own creation. "All of us who
worked on the atomic bomb," said Dr. Allison of the University of
Chicago, "had a momentary feeling of elation when our experiment
met with success; but that feeling rapidly changed to a feeling of
horror, and a fervent desire that no more bombs would be
dropped."

Nevertheless in the long run I do not believe that we shall be
successful in making science the arbiter of its own discoveries.
Somehow or other society itself must assume that responsibility.
The towering enemy of mankind is not science but war. Science
merely reflects the social forces by which it is surrounded. When
there is peace, science is constructive; when there is war, science is
perverted to destructive ends. The weapons which science gives
us do not necessarily create war; they make war increasingly more
terrible until now it has brought us to the doorstep of doom.

Our main problem, therefore, is not to curb science but to stop
war—to substitute law for force and international government for
anarchy in the relations of one nation with another. That is a job
in which everybody must participate, including the scientists. But
the bomb on Hiroshima suddenly woke us up to the fact that we
have very little time. The hour is late and our work has scarcely
begun. Now we are face to face with this urgent question: "Can
education and tolerance and understanding and creative intelligence
run fast enough to keep us abreast with our own mounting capacity
to destroy?"

That is the question which we shall have to answer one way or
the other in this generation. Science must help us in the answer,
but the main decision lies within ourselves.

BIBLIOGRAPHY

Many readers, intrigued by the necessarily brief material in the papers contained in this book, will wish to do further reading. Each of the scientists who contributed to this volume has furnished references to other more extended articles, or to books which discuss the various topics. These references are listed in the following bibliography.

CHAPTER 2

THE FACE OF OUR CONTINENT

Bretz, J. Harlen. *Earth Sciences*. New York: John Wiley & Sons, Inc., 1940.

Davis, William Morris. *Physical Geography;* with the assistance of W. H. Snyder. Boston: Ginn & Company, 1898.

Fenneman, Nevin M. *Physiography of Eastern United States*. New York: McGraw-Hill Book Company, Inc., 1938.

———— *Physiography of Western United States*. New York: McGraw-Hill Book Company, Inc., 1931.

Lobeck, Armin K. *Geomorphology; an Introduction to the Study of Landscapes*. New York: McGraw-Hill Book Company, Inc., 1939.

Longwell, Chester R.; Knopf, Adolph; and Flint, R. F. *Outlines of Physical Geology*. 2nd ed; New York: John Wiley & Sons, Inc., 1941.

THE SCIENCE OF THE ATMOSPHERE

Brunt, David. *Weather Study*. New York: The Ronald Press Company, 1942.

Byers, Horace R. *General Meteorology*. (Published formerly under the title *Synoptic and Aeronautical Meteorology*.) New York and London: McGraw-Hill Book Company, Inc., 1944.

Cline, Isaac Monroe. *Storms, Floods and Sunshine; a Book of Memoirs*. New Orleans: Pelican Pub. Co., 1945.

Starr, Victor P. *Basic Principles of Weather Forecasting*. New York: Harper & Brothers, 1942.

Stewart, George R. *Storm*. New York: Random House, Inc., 1941.

Tannehill, Ivan Ray. *Hurricanes, Their Nature and History, Particularly Those of the West Indies and the Southern Coasts of the United States*. 6th ed; Princeton, N. J.: Princeton Univ. Press, 1945.

OCEANOGRAPHY

Herdman, Sir William A. *Founders of Oceanography and Their Work; an Introduction to the Science of the Sea*. London: Edward Arnold & Co., 1923.

Murray, Sir John, and Hjort, Johan. *The Depths of the Ocean; a General Account of the Modern Science of Oceanography, Based Largely on the Scientific Researches of the Norwegian Steamer Michael Sars, in the North Atlantic*. With contributions from A. Appellöf, H. H. Gran, and B. Helland-Hansen. London: Macmillan and Co., Ltd., 1912.

Sverdrup, Harald U., and Others. *The Oceans; Their Physics, Chemistry and General Biology*. New York: Prentice-Hall, Inc., 1942.

FORECASTING EARTHQUAKES

Heck, Nicholas Hunter. *Earthquakes.* Princeton, N. J.: Princeton Univ. Press, 1936.
Macelwane, James B., S. J. *When the Earth Quakes.* Milwaukee: Bruce Publishing Company, 1947.
Wood, Harry O., and Gutenberg, Beno. Earthquake Prediction. *Science,* 82:219-220, (September 6) 1935.

MINERALS IN RELATION TO WAR AND PEACE

Emeny, Brooks. *The Strategy of Raw Materials; a Study of America in Peace and War;* with the statistical assistance of J. Edward Ely. New York: The Macmillan Company, 1934.
Leith, Charles K.; Furness, J. W.; and Lewis, Cleona. *World Minerals and World Peace.* Washington: Brookings Institution, 1943.
Pehrson, Elmer W. Our Mineral Resources and Security. *Foreign Affairs,* 23:644-657, (July) 1945.

CHAPTER 3

THE EXPLORATION OF SPACE

Hubble, Edwin P. *Observational Approach to Cosmology.* London: Oxford University Press, 1937.
———— *The Realm of the Nebulae.* New Haven, Conn.: Yale Univ. Press, 1936.
Jeans, Sir James H. *The Universe Around Us.* London: Cambridge Univ. Press, 1930.
Shapley, Harlow. *Galaxies.* Philadelphia: The Blakiston Co., 1943.

THE 200-INCH CAMERA

Dimitroff, George Z., and Baker, J. G. *Telescopes and Accessories.* Philadelphia: The Blakiston Co., 1945.
Hale, George E. *Signals from the Stars.* New York: Charles Scribner's Sons, 1931.
———— The 200-Inch Telescope. *Scientific American,* 154:237-240, 293; (May) 1936.
Pendray, Edward. *Men, Mirrors, and Stars.* Rev. ed; New York: Harper & Brothers, 1946.
Woodbury, David O. *The Glass Giant of Palomar.* New York: Dodd, Mead & Company, Inc., 1939.

THE UTILITY OF METEORS

Baker, Robert H. *Astronomy; a Textbook for University and College Students.* 4th ed; New York: D. Van Nostrand Company, Inc., 1946.
Duncan, John C. *Astronomy; a Textbook.* 4th ed; New York; Harper & Brothers, 1946.
Olivier, Charles P. *Comets.* Baltimore: The Williams & Wilkins Company, 1930.
———— *Meteors.* Baltimore: The Williams & Wilkins Company, 1925.
Watson, Fletcher G. *Between the Planets.* Philadelphia: The Blakiston Co., 1941.

ARE THE PLANETS HABITABLE?

Jones, Sir Harold Spencer. *Life on Other Worlds.* New York: The Macmillan Company, 1940.
Russell, Henry N., and Others. *Astronomy; a Revision of Young's Manual of Astronomy;* Vol. 1, *The Solar System.* Rev. ed; Boston: Ginn & Company, 1945.
Whipple, Fred L. *Earth, Moon and Planets.* Philadelphia: The Blakiston Co., 1941.

CHAPTER 4

LIGHTWEIGHT METALS

Du Mond, T. C. Magnesium Alloys. *Materials and Methods,* 25:99-114, (May) 1947.

Edwards, Junius D.; Frary, F. C.; and Jeffries, Zay. *The Aluminum Industry.* 2 Vols. New York: McGraw-Hill Book Company, Inc., 1930.

TODAY'S GLASS

Hodkin, Frederick W., and Cousen, Arnold. *A Textbook of Glass Technology;* with a foreword by W. E. Turner. New York: D. Van Nostrand Company, Inc., 1925.

Phillips, Charles J. *Glass: The Miracle Maker; Its History, Technology and Applications.* New York: Pitman Pub. Corp., 1941.

Rogers, Frances, and Beard, Alice. *5000 Years of Glass.* Philadelphia: Frederick A. Stokes Company, 1937.

BOUNCING MOLECULES

Davis, Carroll C., and Blake, J. T. (editors). *The Chemistry and Technology of Rubber;* contributors: W. F. Busse and others. New York: Reinhold Publishing Corporation, 1937.

Wilson, Charles Morrow. *Trees & Test Tubes; the Story of Rubber.* New York: Henry Holt & Company, Inc., 1943.

Wolf, Howard, and Wolf, Ralph. *Rubber—a Story of Glory and Greed.* New York: Covici, Friede, Inc., 1936.

THE STORY OF 100-OCTANE GAS

Brown, Bruce K. The Petroleum Industry in 1945. *Chemical and Engineering News,* 24:330-333, (February) 1946.

Kettering, Charles F. A Tribute to Thomas Midgley, Jr. *Industrial and Engineering Chemistry,* 36: pp. preceding 1077, (December) 1944.

Scheumann, W. W. Octane Number, the Refiner's Will-O'-the-Wisp. *Oil and Gas Journal,* 38 (No. 47):14-15, 98-99; (April 4) 1940; also in *National Petroleum News,* 32 (No. 15):33-39, (April 10) 1940.

Wilson, Robert E. Fifteen Years of the Burton Process. *Industrial and Engineering Chemistry,* 20:1099-1101, (October) 1928.

COWS, MOVIES, AND COLOR PHOTOGRAPHY

Mees, C. E. Kenneth. *The Fundamentals of Photography.* 8th ed; Rochester, N.Y.: Eastman Kodak Co., 1938.

———*Photography.* 2nd ed. rev; New York: The Macmillan Company, 1942.

Neblette, Carroll B.; Brehm, F. W.; and Priest, E. L. *Elementary Photography for Club and Home Use.* 2nd rev. ed; New York: The Macmillan Company, 1942.

Roebuck, John R., and Staehle, Henry C. *Photography, Its Science and Practice.* New York: D. Appleton-Century Company, Inc., 1942.

CHAPTER 5

THE STORY OF THE ELECTRON MICROSCOPE

Burton, Eli F., and Kohl, W. H. *The Electron Microscope; an Introduction to Its Fundamental Principles and Applications.* 2nd ed; New York: Reinhold Publishing Corporation, 1946.

Hawley, Gessner G. *Seeing the Invisible; the Story of the Electron Microscope.* New York: Alfred A. Knopf, 1945.

Zworykin, Vladimir K., and Others. *Electron Optics and the Electron Microscope.* New York: John Wiley & Sons, Inc., 1945.

FINGERPRINTS IN MEDICINE

The Application of Infra-Red Spectra to Chemical Problems. *Transactions of the Faraday Society,* 41:171-297, (April-May) 1945.

Barnes, Robert Bowling. The Infrared Spectrometer and Its Application. In *Major Instruments of Science and Their Applications to Chemistry,* edited by Robert E. Burk and Oliver J. Grummitt (New York: Interscience Publishers, Inc., 1945), pp. 123-147.

———— and Others. *Infrared Spectroscopy; Industrial Applications and Bibliography.* New York: Reinhold Publishing Corporation, 1944.

THE SPECTROSCOPE—A MASTER KEY TO NEW MATERIALS

Eddington, Sir Arthur S. *The Nature of the Physical World.* New York: The Macmillan Company, 1928.

Gray, George W. *New World Picture.* Boston: Little, Brown & Company, 1936.

Harrison, George R. *Atoms in Action; the World of Creative Physics.* New York: William Morrow & Co., Inc., 1939.

Jeans, Sir James H. *The New Background of Science.* New York: The Macmillan Company, 1934.

DDT

Froelicher, Victor. The Story of DDT. *Soap and Sanitary Chemicals,* 20:115-119, 145; (July) 1944.

Leary, James C., and Others. *DDT and the Insect Problem.* New York: McGraw-Hill Book Company, Inc., 1946.

Roark, R. C., and McIndoo, N. E. *A Digest of the Literature on DDT through April 30, 1944.* U.S. Dept. of Agriculture Bureau of Entomology and Plant Quarantine, Series E-631:1-53, (December) 1944.

———— *A Second Digest of the Literature on DDT (May 1, 1944 to December 31, 1944). Ibid.,* Series E-687:1-73, (May) 1946.

Wheeler, Charles M. Control of Typhus in Italy 1943-1944 by Use of DDT. *American Journal of Public Health,* 36:119-129, (February) 1946.

Wigglesworth, V. B. DDT and the Balance of Nature. *Atlantic Monthly,* 176 (No. 6):107-113, (December) 1945.

THE STORY OF STREPTOMYCIN

Feldman, W. H., and Hinshaw, H. C. Effects of Streptomycin on Experimental Tuberculosis in Guinea Pigs: a Preliminary Report. *Proceedings of the Staff Meetings of the Mayo Clinic,* 19:593-599, (December) 1944.

Hinshaw, H. C., and Feldman, W. H. Streptomycin in Treatment of Clinical Tuberculosis: a Preliminary Report. *Proceedings of the Staff Meetings of the Mayo Clinic,* 20:313-318, (September) 1945.

Jones, Doris; Metzger, H. J.; Schatz, Albert; and Waksman, Selman A. Control of Gram-Negative Bacteria in Experimental Animals by Streptomycin. *Science,* 100:103-105, (August 4) 1944.

Schatz, Albert; Bugie, Elizabeth; and Waksman, Selman A. Streptomycin, a Substance Exhibiting Antibiotic Activity against Gram-Positive and Gram-Negative Bacteria. *Proceedings of the Society for Experimental Biology and Medicine,* 55:66-69, (January) 1944.

Waksman, Selman A. *Microbial Antagonisms and Antibiotic Substances.* 2nd ed; New York: Commonwealth Fund, Division of Publications, 1947.

CHAPTER 6

WITHIN THE ATOM

Frisch, Otto R. *Meet the Atoms; a Popular Guide to Modern Physics.* New York: A. A. Wyn, 1947.

Hecht, Selig. *Explaining the Atom.* New York: The Viking Press, Inc., 1947.

Mott, Nevill F. *Outline of Wave Mechanics.* London: Cambridge Univ. Press, 1930.

Rasetti, Franco. *Elements of Nuclear Physics.* New York: Prentice-Hall, Inc., 1936.

Richtmyer, Floyd K., and Kennard, E. H. *Introduction to Modern Physics.* 3rd ed; New York: McGraw-Hill Book Company, Inc., 1942.

THE ATOMIC NUCLEUS

Frisch, Otto R. *Meet the Atoms; a Popular Guide to Modern Physics.* New York: A. A. Wyn, 1947.

Heisenberg, Werner (editor). *Cosmic Radiation; Fifteen Lectures;* translated by T. H. Johnson. New York: Dover Publications, 1946.

Stranathan, James D. *The Particles of Modern Physics.* Philadelphia: The Blakiston Co., 1942.

A VIEW OF THE MOLECULAR WORLD

Frenkel, Yakov Ilich. *Kinetic Theory of Liquids.* London and New York: Oxford University Press, 1946.

Ruark, Arthur E., and Urey, Harold C. *Atoms, Molecules, and Quanta.* New York: McGraw-Hill Book Company, Inc., 1930.

Slater, John C. *Introduction to Chemical Physics.* New York: McGraw-Hill Book Company, Inc., 1939.

MOLECULAR ARCHITECTURE AND MEDICAL PROGRESS

Landsteiner, Karl. *The Specificity of Serological Reactions;* with a chapter on molecular structure and intermolecular forces, by Linus Pauling. 2nd rev. ed; Cambridge, Mass.: Harvard Univ. Press, 1945.

Loeb, Leo. *The Biological Basis of Individuality.* Springfield, Ill.: Charles C. Thomas, Publisher, 1944.

Pauling, Linus C. *The Nature of the Chemical Bond, and the Structure of Molecules and Crystals; an Introduction to Modern Structural Chemistry.* 2nd ed; Ithaca, N. Y.: Cornell Univ. Press, 1940.

ISOTOPES AND ATOMIC RESEARCH

Urey, Harold C. Methods and Objectives in the Separation of Isotopes. *Proceedings of the American Philosophical Society,* **90** (No. 1):30-35, (January) 1946.

—— Separation of Isotopes. *Physical Society* (of London). *Reports on Progress in Physics,* **6**:48-77, 1939.

THE ATOMIC AGE

Masters, Dexter, and Way, Katharine (editors) *One World or None;* foreword by Niels Bohr; introduction by Arthur H. Compton; contributors H. H. Arnold, Hans Bethe, E. U. Condon, and others. New York: Whittlesey House, McGraw-Hill Book Company, Inc., 1946.

Smyth, Henry De W. *Atomic Energy for Military Purposes; the Official Report on the Development of the Atomic Bomb under the Auspices of the United States Government, 1940-1945.* Princeton, N.J.: Princeton Univ. Press, 1945.

U.S. Dept. of State. Committee on Atomic Energy. *Report on the International Control of Atomic Energy.* New York: Doubleday & Company, Inc., 1946.

CHAPTER 7

EFFECTS OF HIGH PRESSURE

Bridgman, Percy W. Recent Work in the Field of High Pressures. *American Scientist*, 31:1-35, (January) 1943; also in *Reviews of Modern Physics*, 18:1-93, (January) 1946.

———— *The Physics of High Pressure.* London: George Bell & Sons, Ltd.; also New York: The Macmillan Company; ·1931.

———— Theoretically Interesting Aspects of High Pressure Phenomena. *Reviews of Modern Physics*, 7:1-33, (January) 1935.

POLARIZED LIGHT

Jenkins, Francis A., and White, H. E. *Fundamentals of Physical Optics.* New York: McGraw-Hill Book Company, Inc., 1937.

Land, Edwin H., and West, C. D. Dichroism and Dichroic Polarizers; Chapter 6 in *Colloid Chemistry*, Volume 6, edited by Jerome Alexander (New York: Reinhold Publishing Corporation, 1946), pp. 160-190.

Taylor, Lloyd W. *Physics, the Pioneer Science;* with the collaboration, in the chapters on modern physics, of Forrest Glenn Tucker. Boston: Houghton Mifflin Company, 1941.

Wood, Robert W. *Physical Optics.* 3rd ed; New York: The Macmillan Company, 1934.

SCIENCE AND STANDARDS

Condon, Edward U. National Bureau of Standards; section in *United States Department of Commerce; How It Serves You on Land and Sea, and in the Air*, compiled by Vincent Vasco (Washington: United States Government Printing Office, 1946), pp. 67-78.

National Bureau of Standards. Section in *Thirty-Fourth Annual Report of the Secretary of Commerce, 1946* (Washington: United States Government Printing Office, 1946), pp. xxi-xxvi, 169-211.

Standards, National Bureau of. Articles in the *Americana Annual, 1947; Encyclopaedia Britannica*, 14th edition; and *Britannica Book of the Year* (annual supplements).

PHYSICS AND ART

Helmholtz, Hermann L. F. von. On the Relation of Optics to Painting. In *Popular Lectures on Scientific Subjects*, 2nd Series. London: Longmans, Green & Co., Ltd., 1881.

Ives, Herbert E. Thomas Young and the Simplification of the Artist's Palette. *Proceedings of the Physical Society of London*, 46 (Part 1):16-34, (January) 1934.

Vinci, Leonardo da. *A Treatise on Painting;* translated from the Italian by John Francis Rigaud. With a life of Leonardo and an account of his works by John William Brown. Rev. ed; London: George Bell & Sons, 1877.

MATHEMATICS AND THE LAWS OF NATURE

Courant, Richard, and Robbins, Herbert E. *What Is Mathematics? an Elementary Approach to Ideas and Methods*. London and New York: Oxford University Press, 1941.

Eddington, Sir Arthur S. *New Pathways in Science*. New York: The Macmillan Company; also London: Cambridge Univ. Press; 1935.

Weyl, Hermann. *The Open World; Three Lectures on the Metaphysical Implications of Science;* translated with the assistance of Lulu Hofmann. New Haven, Conn.: Yale Univ. Press; also London: Oxford University Press; 1932.

CHAPTER 8

THE GOLDEN AGE OF BIOCHEMISTRY

Rosenberg, Hans R. *The Chemistry and Physiology of the Vitamins*. New York: Interscience Publishers, Inc., 1942.

Williams, Robert R., and Spies, Tom D. *Vitamin B₁ (Thiamin) and Its Use in Medicine*. New York: The Macmillan Company, 1938.

Williams, Robert R., and Williams, Roger J. Vitamins in the Future. *Science* 95:335-344, (April 3) 1942.

Williams, Roger J. *The Human Frontier; a New Pathway for Science toward a Better Understanding of Ourselves*. New York: Harcourt, Brace & Company, Inc., 1946.

——— *What to Do about Vitamins*. Norman, Okla.: Univ. of Okla. Press, 1945.

PROTEIN CHEMISTRY AND MEDICINE

Stiegletz, Julius (editor). *Chemistry in Medicine: a Cooperative Treatise Intended to Give Examples of Progress Made in Medicine with the Aid of Chemistry*. New York: Chemical Foundation, Inc., 1928.

du Vigneaud, Vincent. The Role which Insulin Has Played in Our Concept of Protein Hormones, and a Consideration of Certain Phases of the Chemistry of Insulin. *Cold Spring Harbor Symposia on Quantitative Biology*, 6:275-285, 1938.

——— Some Aspects of the Study of Insulin. *Journal of the Washington Academy of Sciences*, 27 (No. 9):365-373, (September) 1937.

BLOOD AND BLOOD DERIVATIVES

Cohn, Edwin J. Blood and Blood Derivatives. *American Scientist*, 33:61-83, (April) 1945. Reprinted in *Annual Report of the Smithsonian Institution, 1945* (Washington: United States Government Printing Office, 1946), pp. 413-440.

——— Blood Proteins and Their Therapeutic Value. *Science*, 101:51-56, (January 19) 1945.

——— The Separation of Blood into Fractions of Therapeutic Value. *Annals of Internal Medicine*, 26:341-352, (March) 1947. See also articles in the same volume, pp. 353-376, by Joseph Stokes, Jr.; George R. Minot and F. H. L. Taylor; and Charles A. Janeway.

——— and Others. Preparation and Properties of Serum and Plasma Proteins. Studies III and IV. *Journal of the American Chemical Society*, 62:3396-3400, (December) 1940; and 68:459-475, (March) 1946.

SOME ACIDS WHICH ARE NECESSARY FOR LIFE

McCoy, Richard H.; Meyer, Curtis E.; and Rose, William C. Feeding Experiments with Mixtures of Highly Purified Amino Acids. VIII. Isolation and Identification of a New Essential Amino Acid. *Journal of Biological Chemistry,* **112**: 283-302, (December) 1935.

Meyer, C. E., and Rose, W. C. The Spatial Configuration of α-amino, β-hydroxy-n-butyric Acid. *Journal of Biological Chemistry,* **115**:721-729, (October) 1936.

Rose, William C. The Nutritive Significance of the Amino Acids. *Physiological Reviews,* **18**:109-136, (January) 1938.

——— The Role of the Amino Acids in Human Nutrition. *Proceedings of the American Philosophical Society,* **91** (No. 1):112-116, (February) 1947.

THE QUICK AND THE DEAD

Loeb, Jacques. *The Organism as a Whole; from a Physicochemical Viewpoint.* New York: G. P. Putnam's Sons, 1916.

Northrop, John H.; Kunitz, M.; and Herriott, R. M. *Crystalline Enzymes.* Rev. ed. to be published December, 1947, by the Columbia Univ. Press, New York.

AT THE TWILIGHT ZONE OF LIFE

Rockefeller Institute for Medical Research. *Virus Diseases,* by members of the Institute: Thomas M. Rivers, and others. Ithaca, N.Y.: Cornell Univ. Press, 1943.

Smith, Kenneth M. *The Virus, Life's Enemy.* New York: The MacMillan Company, 1940.

Stanley, Wendell M. Chemical Properties of Viruses. In *Annual Report of the Smithsonian Institution, 1942* (Washington: United States Government Printing Office, 1943), pp. 261-272.

——— Recent Advances in the Study of Viruses. In *Science in Progress; First Series;* edited by George A. Baitsell (New Haven, Conn.: Yale Univ. Press, 1939), pp. 78-111. In the same volume, see also: New Views in Virus Disease Research, by L. O. Kunkel, pp. 112-132.

——— Viruses. In *Currents in Biochemical Research,* edited by David E. Green (New York: Interscience Publishers, Inc., 1946), pp. 13-23.

VIRUSES—MASTER PARASITES

Burnet, Frank M. *Virus as Organism; Evolutionary and Ecological Aspects of Some Human Virus Diseases.* Cambridge, Mass.: Harvard Univ. Press, 1945.

Gordon, John E., and Others. *Virus and Rickettsial Diseases, with Especial Consideration of Their Public Health Significance; a Symposium Held at the Harvard School of Public Health, June 12-17, 1939.* Cambridge, Mass.: Harvard Univ. Press, 1940.

Smith, Kenneth M. *The Virus, Life's Enemy.* New York: The Macmillan Company, 1940.

Smith, Theobald. *Parasitism and Disease.* Princeton, N. J.: Princeton Univ. Press, 1934.

Van Rooyen, Clennel E., and Rhodes, A. J. *Virus Diseases of Man;* with an introduction by T. J. Mackie. London: Oxford University Press, 1940.

THE TIME FACTOR IN CHEMISTRY

Glasstone, Samuel; Laidler, K. J.; and Eyring, Henry. *The Theory of Rate Processes; the Kinetics of Chemical Reactions, Viscosity, Diffusion and Electrochemical Phenomena.* New York: McGraw-Hill Book Company, Inc., 1941.

Hinshelwood, Cyril N. *The Kinetics of Chemical Change.* London: Oxford University Press, 1940.

Rabinowitch, Eugene I. *Photosynthesis and Related Processes;* Vol. 1, *Chemistry of Photosyntheses, Chemosynthesis and Related Processes in Vitro and in Vivo.* New York: Interscience Publishers, Inc., 1945.

CHAPTER 9

AMBASSADOR TO THE PENGUINS

Armstrong, Edward A. *The Way Birds Live*. London: Lindsay Drummond, Ltd., 1943.

Kirkman, Frederick B. B. *Bird Behaviour; a Contribution Based Chiefly on a Study of the Blackheaded Gull*. London and New York: Thomas Nelson & Sons, 1937.

Levick, G. Murray. *Antarctic Penguins; a Study of Their Social Habits*. New York: McBride, Nast & Co., 1914.

Murphy, Robert C. *Oceanic Birds of South America: a Study of Species of the Related Coasts and Seas, Including the American Quadrant of Antarctica, Based upon the Brewster-Sanford Collection in the American Museum of Natural History*. 2 Vols. New York: Am. Museum of Natural Hist., 1936.

Nice, Margaret M. The Behavior of the Song Sparrow and Other Passerines. *Transactions of the Linnaean Society of New York,* **6**:1-328, (September) 1943.

CHIMPANZEES AS SERVANTS OF SCIENCE

Hooton, Earnest A. *Man's Poor Relations*. Garden City, N. Y.: Doubleday, Doran & Company, Inc., 1942.

Köhler, Wolfgang. *The Mentality of Apes;* translated from the 2nd rev, ed. by Ella Winter. New York: Harcourt, Brace & Company, Inc., 1925.

Yerkes, Robert M. *Chimpanzees; a Laboratory Colony*. New Haven, Conn.: Yale Univ. Press, 1943.

—— and Yerkes, Ada W. *The Great Apes: a Study of Anthropoid Life*. New Haven, Conn.: Yale Univ. Press, 1929.

PLANT ROOTS AND HUMAN PROBLEMS

White, Philip R. Developmental Responses in Isolated Plant Tissue Systems. *Growth; 4th Symposium on Development and Growth;* supplement to Vol. **6**:55-71, (August) 1942.

—— Potentially Unlimited Growth of Excised Tomato Root Tips in a Liquid Medium. *Plant Physiology,* **9**:585-600, (July) 1934.

—— "Root-pressure"—an Unappreciated Force in Sap Movement. *American Journal of Botany,* **25**:223-227, (March) 1938. Reprinted in *Annual Report of the Smithsonian Institution, 1938* (Washington: United States Government Printing Office, 1939), pp. 489-497.

—— "Vegetable Staticks" or Evidence Concerning Cell Secretion, Root-Pressure, and Gas Diffusion in the Functioning and Morphogenesis of Excised Plant Tissues. *American Scientist,* **30**:119-136, (April) 1942.

BACTERIA—FRIENDS OR FOES

Prescott, Samuel C., and Proctor, B. E. *Food Technology*. New York: McGraw-Hill Book Company, Inc., 1937.

Russell, Sir Edward John. *Soil Conditions and Plant Growth*. 7th ed; New York: Longmans, Green & Company, Inc., 1937.

Tanner, Fred W. *The Microbiology of Foods*. 2nd ed; Champaign, Ill.: Garrard Press, 1944.

Waksman, Selman A. *Principles of Soil Microbiology*. 2nd ed. rev; Baltimore: The Williams & Wilkins Company, 1932.

—— and Starkey, R. L. *The Soil and the Microbe; an Introduction to the Study of the Microscopic Population of the Soil and Its Rôle in Soil Processes and Plant Growth*. New York: John Wiley & Sons, Inc., 1931.

FUNGI—FRIENDS AND FOES

Stakman, Elvin C. Genetic Variation in Plant Pathogens and Its Practical Importance. *Proceedings of the Institute of Medicine of Chicago,* 14:250-260, (November) 1942.

——— The Need for Research on the Genetics of Pathogenic Organisms. In *The Genetics of Pathogenic Organisms;* (American Association for the Advancement of Science *Occasional Publications* No. 12; Lancaster, Pa.: Science Press, 1940), pp. 9-17.

——— Plant Diseases Are Shifty Enemies. In *Science in Progress; Fifth Series;* edited by George A. Baitsell (New Haven, Conn.: Yale Univ. Press, 1947), pp. 235-278.

HYBRID CORN

Hayes, Herbert K., and Immer, F. R. *Methods of Plant Breeding.* New York: McGraw-Hill Book Company, Inc., 1942.

Jenkins, Merle T. Corn Improvement. In *U.S. Dept. of Agriculture Yearbook, 1936,* pp. 455-522.

Richey, Frederick D. The What and How of Hybrid Corn. *U.S. Dept. of Agriculture, Farmers' Bulletin No. 1744.* Washington: United States Government Printing Office, 1935.

Wallace, Henry A., and Bressman, E. N. *Corn and Corn Growing.* 4th rev. ed; New York: John Wiley & Sons, Inc., 1937.

LIVING LIGHT

Harvey, Edmund N. *Living Light.* Princeton, N.J.: Princeton Univ. Press, 1940.

——— *The Nature of Animal Light.* Philadelphia: J. B. Lippincott Company, 1920.

PLANTS HOLD THE BASIC PATENTS

Barton-Wright, Eustace C. *General Plant Physiology;* foreword by Sir F. Gowland Hopkins. London: Williams & Norgate, Ltd., 1937.

Mangham, Sydney. *Earth's Green Mantle; Plant Science for the General Reader;* foreword by Sir Arthur W. Hill. New York: The Macmillan Company, 1939.

Meyer, Bernard S., and Anderson, D. B. *Plant Physiology; a Textbook for Colleges and Universities.* New York: D. Van Nostrand Company, Inc., 1939.

Sinnott, Edmund W. *Botany: Principles and Problems.* 4th ed; New York: McGraw-Hill Book Company, Inc., 1946.

Yocum, Lawson E. *Plant Growth.* Lancaster, Pa.: Jaques Cattell Press, 1945.

CHAPTER 10

THE SCIENCE OF HEREDITY

Colin, Edward C. *Elements of Genetics; Mendel's Laws of Heredity with Special Application to Man.* 2nd ed; Philadelphia: The Blakiston Co., 1946.

Roberts, John A. Fraser. *An Introduction to Medical Genetics.* London: Oxford University Press, 1940.

Scheinfeld, Amram. *You and Heredity;* assisted in the genetic sections by Morton D. Schweitzer. New York: Frederick A. Stokes Company, 1939.

GENES, VITAMINS, AND NUTRITION

Beadle, George W. Genes and the Chemistry of the Organism. *American Scientist,* 34:31-53, 76; (January) 1946.

BIBLIOGRAPHY

Sinnott, Edmund W., and Dunn, L. C. *Principles of Genetics*. 3rd ed; New York: McGraw-Hill Book Company, Inc., 1939.

Snyder, Laurence H. *The Principles of Heredity*. 3rd ed; Boston: D. C. Heath & Company, 1946.

Living Cells in Action

Speidel, Carl Caskey. Adjustments of Nerve Endings. *Harvey Lectures*, Series 36:126-158, 1940-1941.

———— Living Cells in Action. In *Science in Progress; Fifth Series;* edited by George A. Baitsell (New Haven, Conn.: Yale Univ. Press, 1947), pp. 280-314.

———— Studies of Living Muscles. I. Growth, Injury and Repair of Striated Muscle, as Revealed by Prolonged Observations of Individual Fibers in Living Frog Tadpoles. *American Journal of Anatomy*, 62:179-235, (January) 1938.

———— Studies of Living Nerves. II. Activities of Ameboid Growth Cones, Sheath Cells, and Myelin Segments, as Revealed by Prolonged Observation of Individual Nerve Fibers in Frog Tadpoles. *American Journal of Anatomy*, 52:1-79, (January) 1933.

Growth

Clark, Wilfred E. Le Gros, and Medawar, P. B. (editors). *Essays on Growth and Form Presented to D'Arcy Wentworth Thompson*. London: Oxford University Press, 1945.

Thompson, D'Arcy Wentworth. *On Growth and Form*. New York: G. P. Putnam's Sons, 1917.

Wells, Herbert George; Huxley, Julian S.; and Wells, G. P. *The Science of Life*. Garden City, N. Y.: Doubleday, Doran & Company, Inc., 1938.

The Structural Basis of Life

Astbury, William T. The Forms of Biological Molecules. In *Essays on Growth and Form Presented to D'Arcy Wentworth Thompson*, edited by Wilfred E. Le Gros Clark and P. B. Medawar (London: Oxford University Press, 1945), pp. 309-355.

Loofbourow, John R. Borderland Problems in Biology and Physics. *Reviews of Modern Physics*, 12:267-358, (October) 1940.

Schmitt, Francis O. Structural Proteins of Cells and Tissues. *Advances in Protein Chemistry*, 1:25-68, 1944.

———— Ultrastructure and the Problem of Cellular Organization. *Harvey Lectures*, Series 40:249-268, 1944-1945.

Light on the Blood Capillaries

Flexner, Louis B.; Gellhorn, Alfred; and Merrell, Margaret. Studies on Rates of Exchange of Substances between the Blood and Extravascular Fluid. I. The Exchange of Water in the Guinea Pig. *Journal of Biological Chemistry*, 144: 35-40, (June) 1942.

Harvey, William. *Exercitatio Anatomica de Motu Cordis et Sanguinis in Animalibus* (*On the Movements of the Heart and Blood*), 1628, with English translation and annotations by Chauncey D. Leake. Tercentennial ed; Springfield, Ill.: Charles C. Thomas, Publisher, 1928.

Krogh, August. *The Anatomy and Physiology of Capillaries*. New Haven, Conn.: Yale Univ. Press, 1922.

Young, James. Malpighi's "De Pulmonibus" (About the Lungs), 1661, Epistles I and II, translated into English by James Young. *Proceedings of the Royal Society of Medicine*, 23:1-11, (November) 1929.

CHAPTER 11

THE HUMAN EYE

Hecht, Selig. Energy and Vision. *American Scientist,* **32**:159-177, (July) 1944.
——— Seeing in a Blackout. *Harper's Magazine,* **185**:160-164, (July) 1942.
Klüver, Heinrich (editor). *Visual Mechanisms;* Vol. 7 of *Biological Symposia; a Series of Volumes Devoted to Current Symposia in the Field of Biology,* edited by Jaques Cattell. Lancaster, Pa.: Jaques Cattell Press, 1942.
Walls, Gordon L. *The Vertebrate Eye and Its Adaptive Radiation.* (Cranbrook Institute of Science *Bulletin* No. 19; Bloomfield Hills, Mich.: Cranbrook Institute of Science, 1942), pp. 1-785.

HOW MUCH CAN WE SEE?

Helmholtz, Hermann L. F. von. *Treatise on Physiological Optics;* translated from the 3rd German edition; edited by James P. C. Southall. 3 Vols. Ithaca, N. Y.: Optical Society of America, 1924-25.
Polyak, Stephen. *The Retina; the Anatomy and the Histology of the Retina in Man, Ape, and Monkey, Including the Consideration of Visual Functions, the History of Physiological Optics, and the Histological Laboratory Technique.* Chicago: Univ. of Chicago Press, 1941.
Southall, James P. C. *Introduction to Physiological Optics.* London and New York: Oxford University Press, 1937.
Troland, Leonard T. *The Principles of Psychophysiology; a Survey of Modern Scientific Psychology;* Vol II, *Sensation.* New York: D. Van Nostrand Company, Inc., 1930.
Zoethout, William D. *Physiological Optics.* Chicago: Professional Press, Inc., 1935.

THE SCIENCE OF HEARING

Fletcher, Harvey. Auditory Patterns. *Reviews of Modern Physics,* **12**:47-65, (January) 1940.
——— A Space-Time Pattern Theory of Hearing. *Journal of the Acoustical Society of America,* 1 (No. 3):311-343, (April) 1930.
——— *Speech and Hearing;* with an introduction by H. D. Arnold. New York: D. Van Nostrand Company, Inc., 1929.
Stevens, Stanley S., and Davis, Hallowell. *Hearing; Its Psychology and Physiology.* New York: John Wiley & Sons, Inc., 1938.

THE MUSCLE MACHINERY

Fenn, W. O. General Survey of Contractile Tissues; and Muscles; Chapters 32 and 33 in *Physical Chemistry of Cells and Tissues,* edited by Rudolf Höber, and others. Philadelphia: The Blakiston Co., 1945.
Hill, Archibald V. *Living Machinery; Eight Lectures Delivered at the Lowell Institute, Boston, March 1927.* New York: Harcourt, Brace & Company, Inc., 1927.
Wilhelmi, Alfred E. Energy Transformations in Muscle; Chapter 3 in *Howell's Textbook of Physiology,* edited by John F. Fulton, and others (15th ed; Philadelphia and London: W. B. Saunders Company, 1946), pp. 56-95. In the same book, see also Chapters 1 and 2 by David P. C. Lloyd: Electrical Properties of Nerve and Muscle, pp. 7-31; and Functional Activity of Muscle, pp. 32-55.

OUR INTERNAL ENVIRONMENT

Gamble, James L. *Chemical Anatomy, Physiology and Pathology of Extra-Cellular Fluid; a Lecture Syllabus.* 5th ed; Cambridge, Mass.: Harvard Univ. Press, 1947.
—— Physiological Information Gained from Studies on the Life Raft Ration. *Harvey Lectures,* Series 42, 1946-1947. To be published early in 1948.
Peters, John P. *Body Water; the Exchange of Fluids in Man.* Sprinfield, Ill.: Charles C. Thomas, Publisher, 1935.

THE SCIENCE OF THE INDIVIDUAL

Draper, George, and Others. *Human Constitution in Clinical Medicine.* New York: (Paul B. Hoeber book) Harper & Brothers, 1944.
Hooton, Earnest A. *Young Man You Are Normal; Findings from a Study of Students.* New York: G. P. Putnam's Sons, 1945.
Sheldon, William H., and Stevens, S. S. *Varieties of Temperament; a Psychology of Constitutional Differences.* New York: Harper & Brothers, 1942.
Sheldon, William H.; Stevens, S. S.; and Tucker, W. B. *Varieties of Human Physique; an Introduction to Constitutional Psychology.* New York: Harper & Brothers, 1940.

CHAPTER 12

AGENTS OF INFECTIOUS DISEASE

De Kruif, Paul H. *Microbe Hunters.* New York: Harcourt, Brace & Company, Inc., 1926.
Rivers, Thomas M. (editor). *Filterable Viruses,* by Harold L. Amoss, and others. Baltimore: The Williams & Wilkins Company, 1928.
Rockefeller Institute for Medical Research. *Virus Diseases,* by members of the Institute: Thomas M. Rivers, and others. Ithaca, N. Y.: Cornell Univ. Press, 1943.
Smith, Theobald. *Parasitism and Disease.* Princeton, N. J.: Princeton Univ. Press, 1934.
Vallery-Radot, René. *The Life of Pasteur;* translated from the French by Mrs. R. L. Devonshire; with an introduction by Sir William Osler. Garden City, N. Y.: Doubleday, Page & Co., 1923; also Garden City Pub. Co., Inc., 1926.

EPIDEMICS

Anderson, Gaylord W., and Arnstein, Margaret G. *Communicable Disease Control; a Volume for the Health Officer and Public Health Nurse.* New York: The Macmillan Company, 1941.
New York Academy of Medicine. Committee on Public Health Relations. *Preventive Medicine in Modern Practice;* edited under the auspices of the Committee on Public Health Relations of the New York Academy of Medicine by James Alexander Miller, George Baehr, E. H. L. Corwin. 3rd ed; New York and London: (Paul B. Hoeber book) Harper & Brothers, 1942.
Smillie, Wilson G. *Preventive Medicine and Public Health.* New York: The Macmillan Company, 1946.
Stallybrass, Clare O. *The Principles of Epidemiology and the Process of Infection.* London: George Routledge & Sons, Ltd., 1931.
Zinsser, Hans, and Bayne-Jones, Stanhope. *A Textbook of Bacteriology; the Application of Bacteriology and Immunology to the Etiology, Diagnosis, Specific Therapy and Prevention of Infectious Diseases for Students and Practitioners of Medicine and Public Health.* (See especially Chapters I, XII, and XX.) 8th ed. rev; New York: D. Appleton-Century Company, Inc., 1939.

RESISTANCE TO DISEASE

Heidelberger, Michael. Quantitative Absolute Methods in the Study of Antigen-
Antibody Reactions. *Bacteriological Reviews,* 3:49-95, (June) 1939.

Marrack, John R. *The Chemistry of Antigens and Antibodies.* Rev. ed. in: Great
Britain Privy Council. Medical Research Council. *Special Report Series,* London
1938, No. 230. London: His Majesty's Stationery Office, 1938.

Perla, David, and Marmorston, Jessie. *Natural Resistance and Clinical Medicine.*
Boston: Little, Brown & Company, 1941.

Zinsser, Hans; Enders, J. F.; and Fothergill, L. D. *Immunity; Principles and
Application in Medicine and Public Health.* (See especially Section I.) New
York: The Macmillan Company, 1939.

ANEMIA

Heath, Clark W., and Patek, Arthur J., Jr. The Anemia of Iron Deficiency.
Medicine, 16:267-350, (September) 1937.

Minot, George R. Some Fundamental Clinical Aspects of Deficiencies. *Annals of
Internal Medicine,* 3:216-229, (September) 1929.

Minot, George R., and Murphy, William P. Treatment of Pernicious Anemia by
a Special Diet. *Journal of the American Medical Association,* 87 (No. 7):470-
476, (August 14) 1926.

Strauss, Maurice B. The Rôle of the Gastro-Intestinal Tract in Conditioning
Deficiency Disease. *Journal of the American Medical Association,* 103 (No. 1):
1-4, (July 7) 1934.

MEDICAL BENEFITS FROM ATOMIC ENERGY

Gamow, George. *Atomic Energy in Cosmic and Human Life; Fifty Years of
Radioactivity.* New York: The Macmillan Company, 1946.

Rittenberg, D., and Shemin, David. Isotope Technique in the Study of Inter-
mediary Metabolism; Chapter 17 in *Currents in Biochemical Research,* edited
by David E. Green. New York: Interscience Publishers, Inc., 1946.

Ruben, S.; Kamen, M. D.; and Hassid, W. Z. Photosynthesis with Radioactive
Carbon. II. Chemical Properties of the Intermediates. *Journal of the American
Chemical Society,* 62:3443-3450, (December) 1940.

ATOMIC ENERGY AND MEDICINE

Lawrence, J. H. The Use of Isotopes in Medical Research. *Journal of the American
Medical Association,* 134 (No. 3):219-225, (May 17) 1947.

Smyth, Henry De W. *Atomic Energy for Military Purposes; the Official Report
on the Development of the Atomic Bomb under the Auspices of the United
States Government, 1940-1945.* Princeton, N. J.: Princeton Univ. Press, 1945.

Warren, Stafford L. Antipersonnel Effects [of the Atom Bomb]. *Air Affairs,*
1:347-352, (March) 1947.

CHAPTER 13

THE NEW GEOGRAPHY

Bowman, Isaiah. *Geography in Relation to the Social Sciences* [and] *Geography
in the Schools of Europe* by Rose B. Clark. New York: Charles Scribner's Sons,
1934.

Light, Richard U. *Focus on Africa;* photographs by Mary Light, foreword by
Isaiah Bowman. New York: American Geographical Society of New York, 1941.

Taylor, Thomas Griffith. *Our Evolving Civilization; an Introduction to Geo-
pacifics.* Toronto: Univ. of Toronto Press, 1946.

THE CHANGING WORLD POPULATION

Carr-Saunders, Alexander M. *World Population; Past Growth and Present Trends.* London: Oxford University Press, 1936.

Notestein, Frank W., and Others. *The Future Population of Europe and the Soviet Union; Population Projections 1940-1970.* New York: Columbia Univ. Press, 1944.

Thompson, Warren S. *Plenty of People.* Lancaster, Pa.: Jaques Cattell Press, 1944.
—————— *Population and Peace in the Pacific.* Chicago: Univ. of Chicago Press, 1946.

(U.S.) National Resources Committee: Report of the Committee on Population Problems to the National Resources Committee, May 1938. *The Problems of a Changing Population.* Washington: United States Government Printing Office, 1938.

OUR NORTHERN NEIGHBOR—CHINA

Cressey, George B. *Asia's Lands and Peoples; a Geography of One-Third the Earth and Two-Thirds Its Peoples.* New York: Whittlesey House, McGraw-Hill Book Company, Inc., 1944.

Greenbie, Marjorie, and Greenbie, Sydney. *Gold of Ophir; or, The Lure That Made America.* Garden City, N. Y.: Doubleday, Page & Co., 1925.

Latourette, Kenneth S. *A Short History of the Far East.* New York: The Macmillan Company, 1946.

Powell, John B. Today on the China Coast. *National Geographic Magazine,* 87:217-238, (February) 1945.

ENERGY AND THE DEVELOPMENT OF CIVILIZATION

Childe, Vere Gordon. *Man Makes Himself.* London: C. A. Watts & Co., Ltd., 1941.

Morgan, Lewis H. *Ancient Society; or, Researches in the Line of Human Progress from Savagery through Barbarism to Civilization.* New York: Henry Holt & Company, Inc., 1877; subsequent printings by Henry Holt & Company or Charles H. Kerr & Company, Chicago.

Tylor, Sir Edward B. *Anthropology; an Introduction to the Study of Man and Civilization.* London and New York: Macmillan and Co., 1881; subsequent printings by Daniel Appleton & Co., New York.

White, Leslie A. Energy and the Evolution of Culture. *American Anthropologist,* 45:335-356, (July-September) 1943.

CHAPTER 14

SCIENCE AT THE FRONT

Baxter, James Phinney 3rd. *Scientists Against Time.* Boston: (an Atlantic Monthly Press book) Little, Brown & Company, 1946.

Thiesmeyer, Lincoln R., and Burchard, John E. (editors). *Combat Scientists.* To be published September, 1947, by Little, Brown & Company, Boston.

AVIATION MEDICINE

Armstrong, Harry G. *The Principles and Practice of Aviation Medicine.* Baltimore: The Williams & Wilkins Company, 1939; 2nd ed. William Wood & Company (Division of The Williams & Wilkins Company), 1943.

Baxter, James Phinney 3rd. *Scientists Against Time.* (See Chapter 24: Aviation Medicine.) Boston: (an Atlantic Monthly Press book) Little, Brown & Company, 1946.

Bronk, Detlev W. Human Problems in Military Aviation. *Proceedings of the American Philosophical Society,* **88** (No. 3):189-195, (September) 1944.
—— The Physical Structure and Biological Action of Nerve Cells, with Some References to the Problem of Human Flight. In *Science in Progress; Fourth Series;* edited by George A. Baitsell (New Haven, Conn.: Yale Univ. Press, 1945), pp. 49-74.

MICROWAVES

Radar, a Report on Science at War. Released by the Joint Board on Science Information Policy for: Office of Scientific Research and Development, War Dept. and Navy Dept. Washington: Office of War Information, 1945.

Ridenour, L. N. (editor). *Radar System Engineering. M.I.T. Radiation Laboratory Series,* No. 1. New York: McGraw-Hill Book Company, Inc., 1947.

Slater, John C. *Microwave Transmission.* New York: McGraw-Hill Book Company, Inc., 1942.

Numerous technical articles describing microwave circuits, antennas and other shortwave techniques will be found in various issues during the past two years of such journals as: *Proceedings of the Institute of Radio-Engineers, Inc.; Electronics; Bell System Technical Journal;* etc.

DIRECT-LIFT AIRCRAFT

Francis, Devon E. *The Story of the Helicopter.* New York: Coward-McCann, Inc., 1946.

Macauley, Clinton B. F. *The Helicopters Are Coming.* New York and London: Whittlesey House, McGraw-Hill Book Company, Inc., 1944.

Morris, Charles Lester. *Pioneering the Helicopter.* New York: McGraw-Hill Book Company, Inc., 1945.

MEDICAL RESEARCH DURING THE WAR

Andrus, Edwin C.; Keefer, Chester S.; Lockwood, John S.; Wearn, Joseph T.; Bronk, Detlev W.; and Winternitz, Milton C. *Advances in Military Medicine.* 2 Vols. To be published November, 1947, by Little, Brown & Company (an Atlantic Monthly Press book), Boston.

Baxter, James Phinney 3rd. *Scientists Against Time.* Boston: (an Atlantic Monthly Press book) Little, Brown & Company, 1946.

Fishbein, Morris (editor). *Doctors at War.* New York: E. P. Dutton & Co., Inc., 1945.

PROGRESS IN AVIATION

Magoun, Frederick Alexander, and Hodgins, Eric. *A History of Aircraft.* New York and London: Whittlesey House, McGraw-Hill Book Company, Inc., 1931.

Mingos, Howard (editor). *The Aircraft Year Book for 1945-46;* official publication of Aeronautical Chamber of Commerce of America, Inc. New York: Lanciar Pubs., Inc., 1945-46.

Thirty-Second Annual Report of the National Advisory Committee for Aeronautics, 1946. Administrative report. Washington: United States Government Printing Office, 1947.

CHAPTER 15

SCIENCE AND OUR NATION'S FUTURE

Baxter, James Phinney 3rd. *Scientists Against Time.* Boston: (an Atlantic Monthly Press book) Little, Brown & Company, 1946.

Bush, Vannevar. *Science, the Endless Frontier;* a Report to the President by Vannevar Bush, Director of the Office of Scientific Research and Development, July 1945. Washington: United States Government Printing Office, 1945.

Sarton, George. *The History of Science and the New Humanism.* New York: Henry Holt & Company, Inc., 1931.

UNFORESEEABLE RESULTS OF RESEARCH

Langmuir, Irving. Atomic Hydrogen as an Aid to Industrial Research. *Science,* 67:201-208, (February 24) 1928; also in *Industrial and Engineering Chemistry,* 20 (No. 3):332-336, (March) 1928.

———— Fundamental Research and Its Human Value. *Scientific Monthly,* 46:358-365, (April) 1938.

Personalities in Science: Dr. Irving Langmuir. *Scientific American,* 157:131, (September) 1937.

THE ROLE OF CHEMICAL RESEARCH

Chemurgy: Cure or Cause of Surpluses? *Fortune,* 29 (No. 6):182, (June) 1944.

Nylon, Development, Uses, Cost and Manufacture. *Fortune,* 22 (No. 1):56-60, 114-116; (July) 1940.

Plastics in 1940. *Fortune,* 22 (No. 4):89-96, 106-108; (October) 1940.

Slosson, Edwin E. *Creative Chemistry; Descriptive of Recent Achievements in the Chemical Industries;* new edition revised by Harrison E. Howe. New York: Century Company, 1930.

SCIENCE AND HISTORY

Conant, James B. *On Understanding Science; an Historical Approach.* New Haven, Conn.: Yale Univ. Press, 1947.

Crowther, James G. *The Social Relations of Science.* New York: The Macmillan Company, 1941.

Sigerist, Henry E. *Civilization and Disease.* Ithaca, N. Y.: Cornell Univ. Press, 1943.

———— *Medicine and Human Welfare.* New Haven, Conn.: Yale Univ. Press, 1941.

Stern, Bernhard J. *Society and Medical Progress.* Princeton, N. J.: Princeton Univ. Press, 1941.

A LAYMAN LOOKS AT SCIENCE

Brown, Harrison Scott. *Must Destruction Be Our Destiny? A Scientist Speaks as a Citizen.* New York: Simon & Schuster, Inc., 1946.

Cousins, Norman. *Modern Man Is Obsolete.* New York: The Viking Press, Inc., 1945.

Dorr, Harold M. (editor). *The Social Implications of Modern Science; a Symposium.* Philadelphia: American Academy of Political & Social Science, 1947.

Fosdick, Raymond B. *The Old Savage in the New Civilization.* Garden City, N. Y.: Doubleday, Doran & Company, Inc., 1928.